A LIKELY STORY

A LIKELY STORY

Guy Clapshaw

A Light-Hearted Account of RAF
National Service in the 1950s

Librario

Published by

Librario Publishing Ltd.

ISBN No: 1-904440-85-1

Copies can be ordered from retail
or via the internet at:
www.librario.com

or from:

Brough House
Milton Brodie
Kinloss
Moray
IV36 2UA
Tel / Fax: 01343 850617

Printed in Times.

Cover design and layout by Steven James
www.chimeracreations.co.uk

Printed and bound by
4edge Ltd, Hockley.

This is not precisely how it was,
but it's how I like to remember it . . .

Contents

Foreword

Martin Barraclough in the cockpit of a Spitfire.

There are three reasons why I am writing this introduction. The first is that the late Ernest Hemingway, that master yarn spinner and most ardent admirer of aviation, is no longer available; secondly, Guy, amazingly, stands in awe of me because I have flown a Spitfire whereas he hasn't! And lastly, but most strangely, he couldn't find anyone else to do the job!

Fellow New Zealander, the late Ray Hanna, one of the top half-dozen pilots of all time, recognised the power and romance of Hemingway's writing. But the extraordinary thing is that, although he filled his writings with his passion for flying, he was not himself a pilot! Just imagine what

Hemingway would have written if he also had the flying experience of Antoine St. Exupery, Ernest Gann or Beryl Markham. Enter Guy Clapshaw! Guy started from the opposite end of the spectrum. By all accounts he was almost illiterate at school (not unusual for a Carthusian!) but, with the common sense that imbues Carthusians, he eschewed an agricultural career on his father's Sussex farm, where artificial insemination and chemical pesticides were promising such an absorbing future, in favour of a career in aviation, using his National Service to his country to take advantage of one of the finest free flying training schemes ever devised, that of a Royal Air Force officer.

Now retired in New Zealand, and rebuilding – and flying - aircraft of similar vintage to himself, the aviator has gone back to his roots to produce the first of what will undoubtedly be a series of lifetime stories. They say that fact is stranger than fiction – well, not quite! But blend the two in a manner that keeps the reader permanently unsure of his position (the aviator's term for "lost") and you come up with a fund of anecdotes, experiences, dreams and (half) truths that have bought pilots more drinks than all the flying pay they ever earned. You may well recognise some of Guy's experiences – you will probably say to yourself – "I remember hearing that story somewhere". Well, this is where it really happened! Didn't it? Of course it did; it is after all, as Guy has titled it, *A Likely Story*. You may not believe some of his yarns but you cannot help but enjoy them. Stand by for take-off!

Martin Barraclough
November 22nd, 2006

Acknowledgements

My thanks to Robin Phipps, Squadron Leaders Alan Sheppard and Mike Barringer, Martin Barraclough, Mike Parry, Trev' (Kiwi) Green, Des Elliott, Group Captain Dick Howard and Les Hammond for their assistance in checking technical details in the manuscript.

I also thank all my friends who provided me with so many wonderful stories and photographs for inclusion in this book. They are too numerous to mention but include Barry Gordon, Gary Graham, Andy McLeod, Barney Ruffell, Bill Freeman, Mike Furniss, Ian Frow, Norby King, Dacre Watson, John Wegg, Jules Tapper, Dave Welch, Stan Smith, Mike Winter-Kaines, Jerry Chisum, Peter Grant, Ryan Southam, Graeme Gleeson, Clive Perry, Greg MacDonald, Reverend Richard Waugh, Brian Hirst, Russell Brodie, Brian Borland, Frederick Forsyth, Colin Smith and Dave Simpson, who all shared what I consider was the best job in the world.

And to my darling wife Colleen for not only making my life so wonderfully happy, but also for listening to all these stories over innumerable dinner tables without ever flinching!

Introduction

A good story improves with re-telling and I had always believed a good book could be written about the myriad characters and events in the flying profession, so in 1994 I set about recounting my own early experiences.

Because the book was autobiographical, I wrote only about the characters and events that I'd encountered in my early flying career, so a lot of other people's stories, that had been going the rounds since flying began, were omitted.

A Likely Story is an effort to remedy this omission by including some of those wonderful tales, in the belief that every good story contains some elements of fiction as well as truth, and leaving it to you, the reader, to decide what is fact and what is writer's licence.

While I witnessed many of these events personally, some were told to me in numerous cockpits, crew rooms, bars and restaurants, crew buses and dinner tables all over the World. It would take too long to list all the pilots, despatchers, engineers, navigators, flying instructors, stewardesses, friends and families of colleagues who contributed in various ways to helping me write their stories; I can only thank them.

Finally, I ask that if you do open this book and begin reading a story you've already heard, don't stop because I'd love to hear it a second time myself!

Guy Clapshaw
Auckland, New Zealand
August 17th, 2007

Chapter 1

A Taste of Liquorice

I remember my first sexual experience. I was on my own at the time.

I also remember my first aeroplane flight about the same time. It was after the end of World War Two, when I was nine years old and mad about aeroplanes, although I'd never flown in one. My parents arrived at my school sports day on a sunny June afternoon in 1946. Sports day was a pretty popular event in the school calendar, for afterwards we boarders were allowed home until Monday evening. Dad now added to my anticipated enjoyment by announcing we were flying to the Channel Islands next day.

Dad was a dairy farmer in the Sussex Weald. We had 103 pedigree Jersey cows plus miscellaneous heifers, dry cows and one rather time expired bull. We had enough land to be almost self-sufficient, needing only to buy fuel and oil for the farm, a few household groceries and veterinary attention for the cows.

Veterinary care was provided by Tom Tyrrell, the local vet, who specialized in the care of Jerseys. Day-to-day care of the herd was administered by the farm bailiff (manager) Frank Gravitt, a countryman in early middle age who had recently surprised everybody by abandoning his life of bachelorhood to marry a bright young village maiden almost forty years his junior.

The running of the farm was spoiled by only one thing; we desperately needed a new bull to invigorate fresh energy into the herd, for the present incumbent was not only past his prime, his daughters now needed mating.

During the war years, petrol rationing had restricted the transportation of cattle round the country. This fact, coupled with no artificial insemination and a shortage of pedigree Jersey bulls in Southern England, created a general lowering of quality in Jersey stock. We urgently needed a sire for our herd.

Now with the return of peace, Jersey farmers were scrambling furiously to buy quality bulls to reinvigorate the blood lines of their herds. Dad had thought one step ahead of his rivals by going straight to the source of all Jerseys – the Channel Islands. Which was the reason he and I plus six others including Mr Tyrrell the vet, Mum's brother Uncle Horace, Frank Gravitt and his young wife, were assembled outside the Beehive terminal building at Gatwick airport early on that Sunday morning in June, 1946. We were about to fly to the Channel Islands to buy a Jersey bull.

The de Havilland de H89a Rapide.

The aeroplane was a twin-engined de Havilland de H89a Rapide, seating eight passengers plus the pilot and radio operator. Although Messerschmitts and a Heinkel had crash-landed on the farm during the war, this was the first airworthy aircraft I'd had a chance to inspect and I examined it with awe and interest. G–AKOA belonged to Air Enterprises Limited, one of many small air charter companies that had sprung up at the end of the war, using cheap ex-military aircraft. The pilot/managing director was an ex-fighter pilot who'd last been to Jersey strapped in a single-seat Spitfire. His less peaceful task then had been strafing German troops and equipment on the island. Now, a year later, he was taking us to Jersey to buy Jersey's best bull. By aeroplane!

The outward flight was a mind-boggling experience for this nine-year-old future pilot, who had determinedly secured the front passenger seat beside the radio operator and behind the pilot. Engine start up, taxi, take off and the whole experience of flight was as fascinating to me then as space travel is to youngsters today.

Our business in Jersey took all day and when we climbed back aboard our de Havilland Rapide airliner, Dad was the owner of 'Vanity Victor', the island's premier stud bull. Victor would follow later by steam ship to Southampton and cattle truck to our farm.

Two weeks later, Victor arrived at the farm. A small crowd of interested spectators which included Tom Tyrrell, Frank Gravitt's young wife looking rather forlorn, neighbouring farmers and Mum and Dad, gathered to witness his arrival. The rear door of the cattle truck swung down and Frank led the sullen angry-looking bull from the dark interior. Slowly and purposefully, ten thousand pounds worth of bovine cheesecake was led out of the cattle truck, across the stockyard and into the bull pen. Once the glowering presence was safely locked away, the onlookers pressed against the bars of his pen to admire his physique. The vet commented on his short forelegs and massive shoulders, sure signs of a good stud bull. Dad and Frank noted the distinctive liver and white patch across his back, which would identify Victor's future progeny. The local farmers murmured among themselves admiringly; only Frank's young wife remained strangely silent, gazing pensively at the bull's pendant scrotal sac.

Short forelegs and massive shoulders, sure signs of a good stud bull.

Sensing her eyes upon him, Victor uttered an angry snort and turned to look at her angrily. His male phallus began to appear beneath his belly. The seventeen-year-old girl was mesmerized by the speed of the metamorphosis. Noting her interest, one of the neighbouring farmers made a rather off colour remark, which sent her scurrying back to her cottage in embarrassment.

They allowed Victor a week to recover from his gruelling journey before calling upon him to perform. Although ten thousand pounds is not an enormous amount to spend on a pedigree bull today, in 1946 it was a fortune, sufficient to buy a two hundred acre farm with buildings and a house. A good farm worker's wage was two pounds a week, so Vanity Victor represented two men's lifetime earnings. News of this massive investment soon spread and became a main topic of conversation among other farmers at lunch in the Station Hotel after Wednesday morning market day.

The big day for Victor finally came. I was considered too young to be present but managed to observe these events from a hiding place in the hay loft.

Frank led the bull from his pen by a pole attached to the ring in his nose. Frank's young wife, looking rather sullen, watched the proceedings from a gate. At the other end of the yard, Dad led the bride, a dewy eyed young heifer, from her bed chamber. Vanity Victor snorted bad temperedly and attempted to wrest the pole from Frank's grasp. Dad led the young heifer towards Victor but the bull seemed more interested in escaping from his captor than promulgating the Jersey breed. Tom Tyrrell and several other onlookers assisted Frank to calm the bull. Victor's intended bride slunk seductively past her groom, who rudely ignored her.

Despite repeated attempts to draw the bull's attention to the expectant heifer, Victor remained uninterested. Finally, while a short conference was being held to decide what to do next, Victor wrenched the pole from Frank's hand and charged – back to his bull pen! Sensing danger, everybody had scrambled for cover but came out again when they realized Victor's intent. With a terrified snort he disappeared into the safety and darkness of his pen. His ample hind quarters bumped against the door, which slammed shut behind him. The onlookers gazed at the closed door in amazement while through the bars of the pen, Victor's white eyes could be seen peering out anxiously.

A half hour of anxious discussion with the vet reassured Dad that the problem was temporary. Tom was adamant Vanity Victor hadn't fully recovered from the rigours of the sea crossing.

A week later, Frank and his young wife entered the bull's pen to take him to meet another bride. Victor allowed himself to be led out by the nose into the daylight and fresh air of the stockyard, but when he spied his intended mate, he attempted to wrestle himself free to gallop back to his pen.

Everybody was ready for this move and Victor was unsuccessful. He was persuaded to stand motionless while his intended bride paraded before him. The bull ignored her completely, even when her smooth flanks and delicate hindquarters brushed past his nose. As the ultimate insult, Victor dropped his giant head as she was led past a second time and began nibbling a small patch of weed.

Dad gazed at the vet in disbelief. Nobody noticed when the gate in the corner of the yard closed and Frank's young wife returned to their cottage, an expression of contempt written all over her face.

On Tom Tyrell's advice, Victor was given a further week's rest, with identical results. A fourth week brought no change to the state of affairs either.

After much earnest discussion with the vet and Frank, Dad began to fear his ten thousand pound investment was wasted. Frank could offer no helpful advice, indeed rumours had been circulating that he was suffering matrimonial problems himself. His general appearance certainly reflected this, for the usually immaculately turned out herdsman had now acquired a somewhat unkempt haggard appearance, with dark shadows of fatigue under his eyes.

The vet believed the problem might be hormonal imbalance and mentioned that a local pharmaceutical company was conducting research on the subject. Dad urged him to contact them, which he did.

The following Friday the vet arrived unexpectedly, clutching a small cardboard carton, from which he removed an eye dropper containing an amber coloured fluid. "Three drops, four times a day," he instructed. "The dosage is critical, too much or too little could have a completely different effect."

Dad and Frank listened attentively as the vet explained the drug was still in the experimental stage, so there was no guarantee of its effectiveness. After a short discussion they decided Victor's water bowl was the best place to administer the dose. Noting down the time carefully, Dad placed three drops of amber liquid in the bowl. Victor ambled over and noisily drained the vessel, which caused an automatic float valve to open and allow fresh water to replenish it. The dose was carefully administered four times every day, just as the vet had instructed, and Victor was given a further week's rest before resuming his marital duties.

Well, to cut a long story short, seven days later I observed a completely different Vanity Victor emerge from his pen. On seeing the young heifer, he raced eagerly towards her, dragging Frank with him, and almost knocked the young cow to the ground in his eagerness to mate with her.

And there the story of my first flight and sexual experience ends. The experimental drug did its job, Vanity Victor became the champion Jersey sire bull in the south of England and our herd became famous for its progeny. Dad was delighted that his massive cash investment had eventually paid off.

Tom Tyrrell must have been incredibly relieved for his veterinary reputation had been in danger. Even Frank Gravitt the bailiff seemed a different man now, the haggard expression and the dark patches of fatigue beneath his eyes had disappeared and he now strode jauntily round the farm in fresh pressed jodhpurs and hacking jacket. His young wife seemed much happier too and had become her former bright young self again.

Dad was the centre of attention at every Wednesday lunch time after-market session in the Station Hotel and was invariably asked to repeat this story. Frank and I were there when he first told it.

" . . . and in his first year of service, Vanity Victor sired two hundred and fifty heifers," Dad ended the story dramatically. Absolute amazement lit the faces of the assembled countrymen for they recognized that was money in the bank. You could have heard a pin drop in the usually noisy saloon bar as they digested this information.

Finally somebody broke the silence. 'What was the name of the drug?" they enquired. Dad admitted he hadn't noticed a name and turned to ask Frank Gravitt if he knew what it was.

A beaming Frank Gravitt shook his head. "The vet never told us what it was, guv'nor," he admitted. "But it tasted of Liquorice."

Chapter 2

Anybody for a Nice Cup of Tea?

I suspect my lifelong interest in aeroplanes was sparked by a rather exciting event that occurred one dark winter night during the Second World War, when the air battle over Southern England raged at night. Several Spitfires, Beaufighters and Mosquitoes had crash landed in the fields around us in the preceding weeks, as well as a number of German Junkers 88s, Messerschmitt 110 night fighters and Heinkel 111 bombers.

The event occurred on a cold February night in 1942. Enemy air activity had been particularly active over London and the sound of the city's anti-aircraft fire could be heard like distant thunder to the north. Just before midnight, an aircraft had skimmed over our roof before impacting into a distant field with the sound of tortured metal. About an hour later, there was a knock at the door.

"That'll be the Air Raid Prevention warden," Mum warned. "We must be showing a light. I'd better go and check the blackout curtains upstairs." Dad motioned her to sit down, reminding her that he was one of only two ARP wardens in the village and the other was attending an aircraft recognition course in Horsham. Uncle Horace opened the door and the light from the kitchen fell on the tall figure of a young man in flying kit outside with a dark bruise above one eye. He blinked in the unaccustomed glare before introducing himself.

"Ernst, oberleutnant, drei tausend, funf und funfzig," he said. We all looked at him in blank amazement then Dad asked him to repeat what he'd just said.

"Oh sorry, I forgot you don't speak German here," the flier explained. "First lieutenant Ernst, Luftwaffe serial number three oh five five."

Mum had returned from checking the upstairs blackout curtains and asked whether he was lost. "All the road signs have been turned round the wrong way," she explained confidentially. "Something to do with the war."

The pilot smiled rather ruefully. "Ich habe . . . er sorry, I have just come from London," he explained, stepping into the kitchen uninvited and drawing a Luger automatic pistol from a holster. Everybody reeled back one step as he advanced.

"Under the terms of the Geneva Convention, I wish to surrender," he informed Dad, holding the pistol by the barrel and offering it to him. We recoiled back another pace.

"He's a blooming Jerry come to surrender!" Uncle Horace suddenly exclaimed. Dad looked at the pistol nervously. "What do you want me to do with that?" he enquired. The German shrugged.

"Under the terms of the Geneva Convention, I must give up all arms and munitions when surrendering," he replied. Dad still looked doubtful.

"It isn't loaded, is it?" Mum enquired anxiously.

"Jawohl, natürlich . . . er, yes, of course it bloody well is," the German replied.

"Better put it up on the shelf above the door then," Dad suggested. "The children won't be able to reach it and it'll be safe there till morning." The German stood on tiptoe to place the gun in its hiding place and having completed his task, returned to continue standing awkwardly to attention in the centre of the kitchen. Everybody felt very ill at ease, especially Uncle Horace, who made two attempts at conversation.

"Quite mild for the time of year," he remarked. "Although the radio says we could have snow later in the week." The German looked at him puzzled and repeated his name, rank and number.

"Is this your first visit to England?" Uncle enquired a minute or two later.

"Nein!" This time the pilot relaxed a little to explain he'd studied political science at Balliol College, Oxford before the war. "And I went to school at Cranleigh before that," he added.

"That's not far from here!" Dad exclaimed. The enemy aviator nodded affirmatively.

"Jah, I know. I was looking for the old place when one of your night fighters got me."

"Looking for your old school, were you? Oh, that's rather nice, isn't it?" Mum murmured.

"Jah, I'd saved a couple of 50 kilo incendiary bombs to drop on the Quad," the German explained. "I hated it there; the prefects were always making fun of my German accent." His voice had become slightly hysterical as he told her this.

We digested this piece of information while he remained at attention. After a while, Dad picked up the phone to call the local village policeman. He tapped the cradle several times before announcing the phone was out of order. "Something must have broken the lines again, probably a crashed aircraft," he explained to our uninvited guest, who continued to embarrass us with his insistence on standing.

"Would you like to take your life jacket and boots off?" Mum ventured. Although he was perspiring heavily under the weight of the bulky garments, the German clicked his heels and declined.

Dad and Uncle Horace debated what to do with their uninvited guest.

"We can't get through to the police and I'm not going to use the last of the petrol coupons to take him down to the police station," I heard Dad whisper.

"Whaddabout the bicycle?"

"The lights don't work. He'd get arrested."

"That's what he wants."

"Supposing he can't ride a bicycle?"

"Couldn't he walk?"

"Course not, he doesn't know the way."

"We could draw him a map . . . "

"Don't be silly, he might use it to walk back to Germany and then we'd all be hung for treason – collaborating with the enemy and that sort of thing." Everybody felt terribly embarrassed as we tried to ignore the uniformed figure standing stiffly to attention in our midst. The German flier had lapsed into sullen silence after hearing the decision not to drive him to the police station.

"We'll have to keep you here till morning," Dad explained to him in a raised voice. "You can sleep in the armchair in the lounge." The German haughtily ignored the suggestion.

It would have been a long night if Mum hadn't come to the rescue.

"Are you quite sure you wouldn't like to take some of those hot things off?" she gestured at his kapok life jacket, fleece lined boots and leather flying jacket as she placed a battered copper kettle on the stove. The aviator shook his sweat-beaded head.

"Ernst, First Lieutenant, three oh five five," he intoned monotonously.

"You can hang them on the peg behind the door," Mum suggested persuasively. "They'll still be there in the morning, I promise." The German wavered for a moment. "The village policeman cycles past at eight o'clock," she continued. "You can surrender to him and he'll give you a lift to the police station on his crossbar."

Uncle Horace had retrieved the Luger automatic pistol from its hiding place and offered it back to the German. "You'll be perfectly warm in the lounge," he assured him. "We can get you a blanket." The German ignored him and continued to remain rigidly at attention, determined not to break the strict protocol of surrender. Uncle Horace sighed resignedly and gingerly placed the gun back on the shelf.

Sensing that events were getting nowhere, Mum went for the jugular. The kettle came to the boil as she suggested, "You could have a nice cup of tea before retiring." She began spooning tea into the pot.

The German turned and his gaze fell on the tea packet. He licked his lips greedily. "Is that real English tea from Ceylon?" his voice trembled as he spoke.

"Yes, English Breakfast, it's our favourite." She poured boiling water into the pot. "And there's Oxford marmalade if you'd like toast with it . . . " The German never wavered. He was beginning to break under the threat of intense pleasure. Reaching up on the shelf, he retrieved his Luger from its hiding place and placed it back in its holster. "Two sugars and plenty of milk," he requested croakily, removing his bulky flying gear, hanging it behind the door and joining us at the kitchen table.

Since the events of that night, I have never been able to believe the medical evidence of the harmful effects of drinking tea.

A Heinkel 111 Bomber shot down!

Chapter 3

They Shoot Horses, Don't They?

There was a pronounced social pecking order in the village of Warnham where we lived, based on a formula of prestige and wealth. Nobody ever analyzed the exact qualification for top position, which was held by Captain Corah, a Midlands textile manufacturer who had been decorated as an infantry officer in the First World War before embarking on a highly successful career in peacetime business. Subsequently he had sacrificed one of his three sons to RAF Bomber Command, another had served with distinction flying Mosquitoes in the in the Pathfinder Force and the youngest was awarded a Military Cross for service in Greece.

Second in social order was the local estate agent, 'Piggy' Hodgson, an expensively educated Old Etonian and president of the cricket club, Crawley and Horsham Hunt, Young Conservatives' Association and the Bridge Club. Unlike the Corahs, Piggy Hodgson had been exempted from military service apparently because of fragile health. The Hodgsons lived in an impressive manor house on a hill looking down on the village and surrounding farms. What they lacked in popularity and prestige they made up for in wealth.

Third in social standing was the local vet, Tom Tyrrell, who narrowly beat the Reverend Fairbrother for third ranking.

Tom Tyrrell had qualified as a veterinary surgeon at Trinity College, Dublin in July, 1929. Wartime service had kept him in southern England, where he had married and chosen to settle down to practise after the war.

His Irish pragmatism enabled him to handle a variety of difficult situations: when an elderly spinster's only life companion, her yellow and green budgerigar, died of cardiac arrest during treatment, Tom quietly replaced it with an identical bird. When the elderly owner complained her 'Billie' didn't talk any longer, Tom convinced her that this was as a result of the recent treatment and the problem would eventually correct itself, which it did when the new bird learned to talk.

We had an excellent insight into Tom's modus operandi when he visited our farm to conduct regular tuberculin tests on the cows. A flat fee of a penny a mile for transportation was added to Tom's bill for professional services, whether the visit was to attend to one animal or ten. On the occasions when only one cow needed attention, Dad would look around for other infirm animals.

"The dairy cat seems a bit off colour," he once observed. "Spends all her time sleeping beside the boiler and hasn't caught a mouse for months." Tom quickly examined the feline and diagnosed worms as the cause of the problem. On other occasions the farm dogs, our chickens, the bailiff's ferrets, my brother's pet pony and even our goldfish received free consultations.

Problems arose when nothing else required veterinary attention. Dad would wrack his brain for some way to avail himself of one or more free consultations. Inspiration came to him during a midweek tuberculin test. At the end of the procedure, Tom began packing up his veterinary equipment.

"Any other problems, Edgar?" he enquired.

"Conjunctivitis," Dad replied immediately. Tom paused in his packing to remove an animal ophthalmoscope from its case and asked to be taken to the patient.

"Conjunctivitis in my right eye," Dad explained. "I've noticed it's been very sore and bloodshot recently. Probably nothing serious but I thought perhaps you might have something to help clear . . . "

"Edgar, I'm a veterinary surgeon, not a doctor," Tom interrupted, hastily packing away his equipment.

"Yes, I know but the principle's the same . . . "

"Edgar, I'm not licensed to practise medicine," he insisted. "And if I were to be caught doing so, I could incur all sorts of penalties." He had finished stowing away the last piece of equipment and shut his case with a purposeful click to signify the end of the discussion.

Ten days then two weeks later, similar performances were repeated, and each time the vet pointed out that he was an animal veterinarian, not trained to diagnose and treat human maladies.

It was a month before Tom was called out again, this time to attend a heifer with a suspected broken leg. The animal had broken through a gap in a wire fence and slipped into a deep culvert. By the time the vet and his young female assistant had arrived, the animal had sunk ten feet below the level of the bank.

Two dairymen helped Dad lower Tom by rope down to a position beside the still animal. The vet checked for vital signs and announced the animal was unconscious but still breathing. He signaled to be hoisted back to the surface.

"Pulse and breathing are very weak," he pronounced as he unpacked a humane killer from the trunk of his car. "There are usually multiple compound fractures in these cases, sometimes even a broken back. The animal will probably be paralyzed; I'll carry out a couple more checks but I suspect it'll be quicker and more humane to dispatch her."

"You mean shoot her?" Dad reacted alarmedly. A heifer was a future revenue earner in our herd and this one could be expected to provide milk and income for the next eight to ten years. The prospect of losing such a source of revenue was grave.

"More than likely," Tom admitted detachedly as he loaded the gun. "The pain and distress caused by pulling her out would probably result in the animal's death anyway. It would be kinder and easier to spare her such suffering . . . "

"Couldn't we try one attempt at pulling her out with ropes?" Dad implored. Reluctantly the vet agreed and the dairymen climbed cautiously down the slippery banks of the culvert and succeeded in securing a sling hoist round the middle of the still animal. She began to struggle and kick violently when they tied a second line to the horns.

"Hmm, that would tend to indicate there are no broken bones," Tom ruminated aloud as Dad and the others pulled the lines tight. Almost imperceptibly at first, the animal began to emerge from its trapped position. Ten minutes later she surprised everybody by struggling up the last few feet of the bank unassisted, shaking herself free of the lines and charging back through the gap in the fence to join the other heifers in the field.

Tom began unloading the pistol while the others watched the happy heifer prancing around in the field.

"I'll be on my way then, Edgar," the vet announced. "Unless there's anything else requiring my attention. Is there anything else, Edgar?"

"Er no, Tom, thanks for coming out at such short notice," Dad replied, watching the vet replace the short barrelled pistol into its wooden box. "Oh except that . . . "

"What is it then?" the vet paused momentarily.

"That conjunctivitis . . . " Dad began hesitantly. "Much improved but still giving a bit of trouble."

"Which animal was that?" Tom enquired curiously. Dad admitted none of the farm animals had suffered from eye disease but reminded the vet they had discussed it between themselves on an earlier visit. To everybody's surprise, Tom said he did remember and listened attentively as Dad listed the symptoms.

"And you say its worst when you first wake up in the morning?" the vet signalled to his assistant to cease packing away the tools and instruments. Taking a small torch, he shone it into Dad's eyes.

"Yes, definitely worse in the morning," the patient confirmed delightedly. "Although dry dusty conditions also tend to aggravate the symptoms." Tom wrote something on the bottom of a discarded carton and gestured to his young assistant to throw a halter round Dad's neck. He reached into the back of his vehicle and retrieved a large bovine thermometer and a drench syringe. The assistant tightened the halter as Tom approached Dad.

"You don't think it's anything serious, do you?" Concern began to creep into Dad's voice as he watched Tom unpack more equipment, first a large plastic sheet, a variety of scalpels and retractors, artery forceps, then a face mask, rubber gloves and finally a bone saw. "Its only conjunctivitis," the patient added weakly.

Tom said nothing as he finished his note taking and began assembling various pieces of complicated veterinary equipment.

"What do you think it is then?" Dad enquired alarmedly. Syringes, scalpels and bone saws implied some sort of surgery. Tom seemed deeply concerned as he consulted quietly with his assistant.

"I don't really know," Tom finally admitted. "As I've told you on many previous occasions, I'm a vet, not a doctor." Behind him the assistant had begun removing an animal stretcher from the car.

"But you must have some idea!"

"Oh yes, I've got a very good idea," Tom assured him confidently as he opened a wooden box. "But only from a veterinary standpoint of course." The assistant suddenly tightened the halter uncomfortably tight.

"Well, from a veterinary standpoint, what would you do if I was a large animal like say a horse?"

Tom removed the humane pistol from the wooden box and inserted a bullet into the breech. Leaving the weapon broken open in the safe position, he advanced on Dad.

"If you were a horse, Edgar," he pronounced slowly but with great emphasis. "I'd shoot you."

After that experience, Dad never bothered Tom with personal medical problems again.

Chapter 4

Education

After the experience with the tea drinking German bomber pilot, I had begun to read books and magazine articles on various aeronautical subjects. A series of easily understood articles in 'Aeromodeler' magazine by the Reverend R. F. Calhoun explained technical terms like torque, incidence, dihedral, aspect ratio, angle of attack and wing wash out to a small group of us and we became prolific builders and fliers of model aircraft.

When I reached thirteen and a half, I was sent to Charterhouse, a famous English public school that was proud to number writers, politicians, musicians, scientists, physicians, lawyers and other gentlemanly occupations among the ranks of Old Carthusians. It also produced the first British test pilot to exceed the speed of sound – John Derry.

My house master, Mr Arrowsmith, usually referred to behind his back as 'The Arrow', was an Old Carthusian out of the original mould. A past member of the Charterhouse First XI and Classics scholar par excellence, he managed to avoid the real world of science. I once heard him tell a group of new boys' parents that 'if a fellow reads Classics and plays cricket, I maintain he'll turn out all right.' Inevitably The Arrow and I rarely saw eye to eye; he thought I was a pleasure-seeking individual never interested in settling down to study the Classics, and I frankly never worried about him and his antiquated theories.

World War Two had only been over five years then and most of the teaching staff had distinguished war records. A plaque in the school chapel listed the names of the many Old Carthusians who had lost their lives in that conflict.

Charterhouse.

The school cadet force paraded every Tuesday afternoon, lest another foe threaten Great Britain again. I joined the Royal Air Force section of the Combined Cadet Corps and spent many enjoyable afternoons launching and occasionally flying the primary glider, and the link trainer. Once every term we went away on Field Day when we visited an operational RAF station and were taken for flights in Avro Ansons or Meteor T.7 jet fighters. My first glimpse of Heaven was the dispersal at RAF Tangmere when we were introduced to and allowed to talk to the pilots of 601 Squadron as they stood around in their flying kit and Mae West life jackets between sorties. There was nothing I craved more than to become a part of that scene. A small group of us were destined to join the peacetime Air Force – Tony Boyle, Cranwell sword of honour winner, Anthony Phipps, Dave Malloch, Tony Gaitskell and I.

The Cadet Corps further fuelled our enthusiasm and often a small band of us would cycle 30 miles to the Royal Aircraft Establishment at Farnborough to spend a Wednesday sports afternoon watching the British Aircraft industry's latest aircraft taking off and landing. One of our members built a bulky battery-powered portable radio which he fastened to the carrier rack of his bike so we could listen to the voices of the test pilots in the circuit. We soon learned to recognize Neville Duke in the Hawker Hunter, Roly Falk in the Avro Vulcan, Mike Lithgow in the Supermarine Swift and our favorite Old Carthusian, John Derry in the de Havilland 110 fighter.

Other plane spotters parked outside the perimeter fence could be forgiven for thinking we were close friends of these famous aviators, for frequently one of us would suddenly announce "Here comes Neville in the Hunter" and another might add "Roly's just called up over Hindhead to say he's joining downwind."

One Corps Day afternoon, an aerodynamicist from the Royal Aircraft Establishment (RAE) at Farnborough came to lecture and bring us up to date on some of the latest British designs under development at the RAE. The British aircraft industry was at the cutting edge of aeronautical technology in the 1950s and aircraft like the de Havilland Comet jetliner, the Vickers Viscount prop-jet, the world's first jet night fighter the Venom, the Avro Vulcan delta shaped bomber, the supersonic Hawker Hunter and Supermarine Swift fighters, the giant 100 seat Bristol Brabazon airliner, the 150 passenger Saunders Roe flying boat and the Fairey Rotodyne helicopter were only a few of the innovative designs currently under development.

The knowledge gained in this lecture prompted us aeromodellers to try various ways of improving the performance of the Frog and Keil Kraft kits that we built from balsa, tissue and wire. First we tried boundary layer fences midway along each wing, which seemed to have no effect, then we modified the aerofoil sections with varying results. Adding end plates or winglets to the tips improved both the climb and the glide angle of our rubber powered models, increasing flight times significantly. Then a syndicate of three of us sent away to Aeromodeler magazine and built their plan of a free flight model, which we powered with a tiny Mills .75 diesel engine, which one of our number had bought with a whole term's pocket money.

During the construction, we incorporated our best performance enhancing modifications into the design and after a few successful power-off hand launches, started up the engine and launched the plane into the sky. Our aerodynamic theories worked a treat, for the model climbed like a homesick angel until the motor ran out of fuel and it transitioned into a long flat glide before catching a thermal and flying away on its maiden flight!

One day our dearest wish was granted when the headmaster announced John Derry was coming to visit his old school to inspect progress on the new science block. When it was announced the famous test pilot would be having lunch in our house, Bodeites, I determined nothing was going to prevent me talking to him.

On the day of his arrival, anybody interested in meeting the legendary test pilot was instructed to come to the housemaster's study at 11 a.m. Only about five other boys went, three of them sixth form Classics scholars, and I was surprised to find that John Derry was a quiet rather modest person when I was introduced to him. He listened politely as conversation ranged around various matters connected with the school then two of us asked him about his current test project, the de H 110, which de Havillands hoped to sell to the RAF as their next front line fighter. He seemed to suddenly come alive when the conversation got onto aerodynamics, and listened attentively when we expounded a few of our pet theories on the use of winglets to reduce wing tip vortices, and the benefits of boundary layer control. The test pilot explained some of the manufacturing problems in achieving boundary layer control but seemed intrigued at our suggestion to use winglets to reduce induced drag. He mentioned they had been unable to explain the increase in performance of their Venom fighter when wing tip tanks were fitted. He made a note of our names and said he'd get back to us on this subject after he'd talked to the de Havilland design office.

All too suddenly it was time for lunch and John Derry was seated far away at the housemaster's table, where he listened to long discussions on Latin construe, Greek mythology and medieval history. After lunch he was whisked away to the science block site before departing to resume his experimental test flying duties at Hatfield.

A day later, two of us were summoned before The Arrow, who vented his displeasure at us for monopolizing yesterday's guest's short time in the house.

It is interesting to note that most of today's high performance jet aircraft use winglets to improve performance, for three years later when one of my aero modelling companions submitted an imaginative end of term thesis on the subject, his form master marked him down severely, adding the curt remark in blue pencil "All highly improbable. Don't you think somebody would have thought of this already?"

Two weeks after John Derry's visit to Charterhouse, we received a phone call from a Mr Richards in de Havilland's flight test department, enquiring whether any of us would care to come over to Hatfield to repeat some of the theories we'd expounded to their test pilot. It was now the end of the Cricket Quarter (summer term), School Certificate exams were under way and everybody tiptoed everywhere to avoid disturbing the examination candidates. It wasn't a good time to ask 'The Arrow' permission to leave school for a day, especially if he learned it was to monopolize more of Mr

Derry's time. Better to wait for the summer holidays to start, when we would be free to travel to Hatfield. I phoned the caller back and told him we'd contact him after term had ended.

I remembered reading somebody's opinion that the ideal committee must not have more than one member when I tried to arrange a mutually convenient date for us to visit the de Havilland factory. Family holidays, overseas trips, weddings, birthdays and other matters continually frustrated us throughout August. Finally we agreed on a date in mid-September and I phoned Mr Richards.

Three days later, a thick envelope arrived bearing a Hatfield - Herts, postmark. It contained five complimentary passes to the Society of British Aircraft Constructors' (SBAC) air display in four weeks time, together with a note confirming our appointment for the 14 September.

The annual SBAC air display was one of the highlights of the air show season and ran for a week, the first four days being reserved for members of the aircraft industry. It was here that orders for new aircraft were placed by various air forces and airlines. The remaining three days were an opportunity for British aircraft manufacturers to show off their latest products in front of the public. Our tickets were for the first public day, Friday.

Everything was perfect on that day: the British weather behaved itself, the variety of aircraft ranged from the tiny four-seat Auster Aiglet through to the supersonic Hawker Hunter, but our favourite and our star of the show was the de Havilland, 110 flown by an Old Carthusian – John Derry.

By the time we left Farnborough after a wonderful day watching the latest high performance aeroplanes demonstrating their capabilities, even our insatiable appetites for flying had been temporarily satisfied.

We spent most of the next day discussing the merits and shortcomings of the various aircraft we'd seen. Everybody was unanimous the de Havilland 110 would beat the Hunter and the Swift in the battle to become the RAF's next front line fighter. Furthermore, every airline would rush to order their Comet jetliner, which cruised above the worst of the weather 200 mph faster than piston engined airliners. De Havilland was the name on everybody's lips.

Around about teatime, conversation had drifted on to our forthcoming visit to Hatfield, when one of the neighbouring farmers dropped in to talk to Dad.

"Bad news from the Farnborough air show, eh?" he called out to us conversationally. We enquired what he meant.

"Haven't you heard? There's been a crash; an aircraft flew into the crowd." Our first reaction was disbelief; test pilots were the crème de la crème of the flying community, only the very best were accepted for the Empire Test Pilot's School and it was inconceivable that one of them would misjudge a manoeuvre and crash. A news flash had just started as we turned on the radio. The BBC announcer's sombre voice informed listeners that a jet aircraft had disintegrated in flight at today's Farnborough Air show, showering debris onto the crowd. The crew and several people in the crowd were reported to have been killed; further details could be heard on the news at 6 o'clock.

"Wonder which one it was?" somebody voiced everybody's thoughts. I thought of the voices we'd listened to on our cycle trips to Farnborough. Roly Falk, Neville Duke, Mike Lithgow, Mutt Summers; I hoped it wasn't one of them.

"Probably a bomber or airliner if all the crew were killed."

"Crikey, yeah, hope it wasn't the Comet."

The first news item at 6 o'clock had an account of the accident. Nervousness turned to dread when we learned it was a military jet that had crashed.

"Let's hope it wasn't Neville Duke," somebody hoped. I thought of the dozens of times I'd seen the Hunter taking off and climbing out over our school.

"Naagh, it wouldn't be him, the Hunter only has one pilot."

"So does the Swift but it could have been Bill Waterton in the Javelin."

"Crikey, yes, the Javelin has a crew of two. Hope it wasn't Bill."

"It could have been the Canberra, they carry three."

The BBC announcer continued with details of the accident. A military jet had broken up while pulling out of a supersonic dive. We looked at each other alarmedly, the odds were narrowing. Only three aircraft were capable of going supersonic – the Hawker Hunter, the Supermarine Swift and the de Havilland 110. The announcer then confirmed our worst fears by revealing the aircraft had been the de H. 110.

The pilot was John Derry.

Chapter 5

Aircrew Selection

I drifted through my first years at Charterhouse rather undistinguishedly and lazily. I enjoyed maths, physics and English because I found them quite easy and knew I'd need them if I wanted to join a fighter squadron. French was also pretty simple but Latin, history and chemistry required more effort than I was prepared to put in. I wouldn't need the last three subjects to fly a jet fighter so there seemed no point in working hard at them.

Especially when in the sky outside the classroom, Neville Duke was pushing Hawker's Hunter through the sound barrier almost daily. The British aircraft industry led the world in aeronautical supremacy in the early fifties, with the first jet engine, the first jet aircraft, the world's first jetliner, the first jet fighter and the first jet aircraft to land on a carrier. These and many other achievements were attributed to British scientists and inventors.

Rather too suddenly, about the time of my sixteenth birthday, School Certificate exams reared their unwelcome heads. Until now I had been totally unconcerned about them since I didn't intend progressing to university prior to entering a profession. Virtually everybody managed to pass School Certificate without too much of a problem so I didn't worry about it – until I read an advertisement in *The Times* for young men between the ages of eighteen and twenty-six to join the RAF as pilots on short service commissions. 'Candidates should be in good health, single, have uncorrected vision and have passed School Certificate in five subjects including Mathematics and English'.

Five subjects? Hmm. I counted those I could be reasonably certain of passing: English? – Yes, everybody passed. Mathematics? – No problem but I'd better start working a little harder. Latin? – No chance, I detested the subject. History? – similar to Latin, I wasn't interested. Geography? – Dunno, probably not, likewise chemistry. Physics? – Well I did quite enjoy the subject and my end of term report indicated I was expected to pass. Biology? – Not terribly interested in the reproductive processes of amoeba or paramecium but was able to struggle through the tests OK, so I could probably expect to pass School Cert. in English, maths, physics and maybe biology.

Four subjects! I needed five to be accepted as a pilot by the RAF and exams were now less than eight weeks away. After several days' soul searching, I decided to concentrate my academic efforts on five subjects – English, maths, physics, history and biology. There was insufficient time to go through the whole syllabus so I concentrated on past papers. Physics invariably had two or more questions on the energy theorems so I learned them off by heart and could trace their derivations. History seemed to concentrate on certain topics at regular intervals – The Hundred Years War, Benjamin Disraeli, Henry V and other boring subjects from the past. Biology posed little problem, it was simply a question of reading and remembering the subject material for the exam.

To cut a long story short, I crammed furiously and succeeded in passing the five subjects. Inexplicably I also passed geography and French but failed Latin miserably. Frankly, I couldn't have cared less if 'Gallia omnis in tres partes divisa est' (All France is divided into three parts). If Air Vice-Marshals Keith Park or Leigh-Mallory had written in Latin 900 years later that southern England of Fighter Command was divided into two groups, I might have been more interested but Caesar's Gallic Wars were strictly for historians.

I applied to the Royal Air Force for a cadet flying scholarship, which would entitle me to learn to fly at Government expense at a civil flying school. I was told to report to the RAF Aircrew Selection Centre at Horchurch for medical and other tests, where I spent four very full days of examinations, interviews, aptitude tests, debates, extensive medical examinations and other evaluations. We aircrew candidates were accommodated in Nissen huts, about thirty to each hut, and as each day passed, numbers of applicants packed their bags and returned to the safety of civilian life after having been diagnosed as colour blind, high tone deaf or unsuitable to fly for some other medical reason.

On the fourth day I began to worry about failing a small part of the selection procedure myself, after being asked by a highly decorated squadron leader whether I would fly as a navigator if selected. I thought long and hard about my reply while staring intently at my inquisitor's half wing (navigator's brevet). Some inner instinct told me this was a crucial part of the testing. I had got through the medical assessments OK, had enjoyed the various debates, seemed to have had no problems with the physical tests and thought the interviews had gone OK until this one. Now I was in a quandary for the inquisitor was himself a navigator, apparently of some distinction to judge from the medal ribbons on his chest. To tell him I wouldn't accept a job as a navigator could indicate I wasn't sufficiently dedicated to flying for the RAF. On the other hand, I knew the Air Force had difficulties in recruiting sufficient navigators. The real truth was I'd have been delighted to fly as anything – navigator, bomb aimer, flight engineer or rear gunner, but my keenest ambition was to be a pilot. If I admitted to him I wouldn't accept an offer of navigator, he might reject me as being 'insufficiently motivated for aircrew duties'. On the other hand, if I said I'd accept, I might jeopardize my chances of becoming a pilot.

My gaze had been directed to his navigator's brevet and Pathfinder clasp as these thoughts raced through my mind. Acting on premonition, I looked him straight in the eyes.

"Navigator is a very important position aboard an aircraft," I heard myself say. "But I hope to fly single-seat fighters." He smiled understandingly and wrote something on a form in front of him.

After lunch, we assembled to learn the results of our assessments. Already fifty per cent had been rejected on medical grounds. Of the remaining fifty per cent, half were offered jobs as Air Electronics Officers (AEOs), wireless operators or radar observers.

Most of the remainder were offered navigator. Only two of us, out of eighty initial applicants, were offered pilot.

Chapter 6

Flying Scholar

Although the Air Force had assessed me as suitable for pilot training, I was still below the minimum age. The purpose of the tests had been to assess whether I was suitable for a Cadet Force Flying Scholarship.

I returned to Charterhouse at the end of April and two days after my seventeenth birthday a month later, received a letter from the Air Council, advising me I'd been awarded a Flying Scholarship to enable me to gain my Private Pilot's Licence at a civilian flying club. I was told to contact the Airways Aero Club at Croydon to arrange a suitable time to start learning to fly.

After what seemed an interminable wait for the summer holidays to arrive, I phoned the chief flying instructor (CFI) and arranged to meet him on Friday. Dad lent me the car and I set off for Croydon about 9 a.m.

Croydon had been the major air terminal for European air travel into and out of London in the 1930s. Now because of its small size and inability to extend its runways into surrounding suburbia, it mainly catered for small feeder airlines, private aircraft and flying clubs.

I approached the aerodrome from the south, driving up Purley Rise. As I topped Purley Hill on a beautifully sunny August morning, I beheld a scene that has become indelibly imprinted in my mind. A large freshly mown grass airfield was playing host to swarms of brightly coloured light aircraft landing and taking off. There were yellow Tiger Moths, silver Austers, bright red Percival Gulls and cream colored miles Hawks.

Round the airfield perimeter, row upon row of surplus military aircraft awaited the scrap merchant or conversion to civilian use.

Aerial view of Croydon Airport.

It is a view that has remained with me ever since and it reinforced my desire to make flying my career.

The Airways Aero Club premises were on the first floor of the old terminal building. There I met the club manager, who noted down my personal details for their records before showing me round the club, emphasizing that I must wear my Cadet Corps uniform throughout my training and I was not permitted to use the bar.

He seemed rather surprised when I explained I'd hoped to start flying that day. Excusing himself briefly, he disappeared into the timekeeper's office, reappearing a few minutes later to tell me there was a spare lesson at one o'clock. "One of the BOAC navigators phoned in and cancelled his lesson, so we've got an instructor for you," he explained. "You'll be learning on Tiger Moths. We keep the Austers for club members." I quickly collected my flying kit and waited for the instructor to appear.

Squadron Leader Len Brinsden, DFC, had achieved a distinguished war record as a Lancaster pilot and later as a member of the élite Pathfinder force. He was an outstanding pilot, who was now reduced to aero club instructing. He entered the club lounge and enquired which person was Clapshaw.

"That's me, Sir," I informed him excitedly, extending my right hand, which he ignored as he turned on his heel.

"Let's go and fly then, if we have to," he suggested irritably, leading the way down the staircase towards a silver Tiger Moth parked on the grass. My excitement was almost uncontrollable as I approached my baptism of the air, but Brinsden was oblivious of my exuberance.

"If there's one thing I hate, it's bloody Tiger Moths," he announced more to himself than to anybody in particular. "Nasty, draughty, noisy, smelly little Tiger Moths." He shuddered at the thought of the forthcoming flight in his least favourite aeroplane. I remained discreetly silent.

I strapped myself in while he did the walk-around check.

"Can't you do anything right?" he enquired irritably when he saw me having problems with the unfamiliar Sutton harness. I apologized, explaining this was my first time in a small plane. He muttered bad-temperedly as he untangled the mess of straps.

"Don't let me have to explain that to you again," he commanded as he fastened my harness.

"Sorry Sir but this was the first time I've . . . "

"And don't bloody well argue. It's bad enough having to fly in one of these beastly machines, without having you making pathetic excuses . . . "

Feeling rather subdued, I sat in the rear cockpit while Brinsden strapped himself into the front. A mechanic waited expectantly by the propellor.

"Fuel on, throttle closed, mixture fully rich, switches off," the instructor called. My excitement returned; this was just like in the movies.

The mechanic approached the propellor. "Switches off, sucking in, Sir," he called, turning the propellor over several times. "Throttle set, contact!" he challenged, holding the propellor on compression.

Brinsden flipped the front switch and confirmed "Switches on".

"Contact!" The mechanic pulled the propellor blade through top dead centre and the Gypsy Major engine burst into life. The smile on my face must have been ear to ear. The mechanic removed the wheel chocks and walked to the port wing tip. Seeing my enormous smile, he gave me an encouraging wave and headed back to the hangar.

Brinsden didn't speak until we were at a thousand feet in the circuit. "Done any flying before?" he bellowed into the intercom.

"A little, Sir," I admitted, looking at his angry reflection in a mirror attached to the centre section struts.

"All right then, you've got control, just follow the circuit direction round." I grasped the control column firmly and concentrated on keeping the Tiger Moth straight and level. As we approached the end of the downwind leg, I banked left to bring us onto base leg.

"Look round before you turn!" Brinsden's voice bellowed in my ear pieces and the face in the mirror turned an angry shade of red.

"Sorry Sir." We were now coming up to the runway extended centre line. Concentrating very hard, I banked again to turn onto final approach.

"Did you look round that time?" the same voice demanded. I could see the angry red face in the mirror had turned even darker.

"Er no, sorry Sir, I forgot . . . "

"Well bloody well do as you're told next time!" the angry red face screamed. "Here, I've got it, take yer blasted hands and feet off the controls." The rest of the flight continued much the same as those first five ghastly minutes. Brinsden was a screamer, one of those who tried to teach by fear rather than persuasion. At the end of the forty-five-minute lesson, he parked in the same position on the grass and cut the switches. Without a word, he got out of the cockpit and walked back to the clubhouse, leaving a miserable-feeling cadet to fight his way out of the unfamiliar Sutton harness. Once free of the aircraft, I hurried after him.

" . . . bloody horrible little Tiger Moths, ugh!" he muttered to himself, oblivious of my presence. We mounted the steps to the clubhouse and he headed straight to the instructors' room, slamming the door behind him. I was left facing the closed door. After waiting half an hour for him to reappear, I concluded my first flying lesson was now over so enquired in the timekeeper's office whether it was all right to go home now.

"Had your lesson, have you?" the manager enquired brightly. I admitted I had.

"Tell Marianne when you'd like to fly next and we'll see you then," he suggested cheerily, indicating towards an extremely attractive young girl of about nineteen.

"What about 10 o'clock Monday morning?" she suggested sweetly. "They like to keep the weekends clear for club members." Indecision engulfed me for my first flying lesson had been absolutely ghastly and I wasn't sure I wanted to learn to fly if it meant being shouted at by Squadron Leader Brinsden, DFC, for thirty miserable hours. The club manager made the decision for me.

"That'll be fine, put him down for ten on Monday and again on Tuesday," he instructed Marianne. "We'll see you after the weekend then," he dismissed me with a smile.

The drive home was long and thoughtful, spoiled by my disappointment at discovering learning to fly could be so unpleasant. Mum and Dad asked how the first lesson had gone and were surprised when I told them I hadn't enjoyed it.

"Were you airsick or something?" Dad enquired. "Don't worry, that's not unusual on a first flight, you'll get over it." I assured them airsickness wasn't the problem and ended up telling them about the horrible first flight with Brinsden. Dad was really upset.

"What a pity after all these years," he muttered half to himself. "I can understand how you feel." We sat together in gloomy silence and considered the matter until finally Mum spoke. "Give it another try on Monday," she suggested. "Maybe the instructor wasn't feeling too good. He'll feel better after the weekend and if you still don't enjoy it after the second lesson, you can give it up." I agreed to follow her advice and spent the weekend trying to forget the whole horrible experience.

Monday morning came and I caught the train to East Croydon, contemplating the unpleasant experience awaiting me, unaware that salvation had arrived.

"Your instructor's here," Marianne greeted me with a beautiful smile as I entered the times office. I wrinkled my nose in distaste. "What's the matter, he's very nice," she protested. My miserable glance told her we disagreed on the matter. "Everybody likes him," she insisted. "I'm sure you'll like Mr Ward too. He's having a cuppa in the cafeteria . . . oh no he's not, here he is now."

I suddenly took a very active interest in what Marianne was saying. Who was this Mr Ward that everybody liked? I'd flown with squadron leader Brinsden on Friday, wasn't he my instructor?

A dark haired young man in his late twenties smiled as he approached me.

"Guy Clapshaw?" he enquired interestedly and I admitted I was.

"I'm Glyn Ward, your instructor," he explained. "I've been away on holiday and only got back last night. Which house are you in at

Charterhouse?" He was looking at the 'Charterhouse Cadet Corps' patches on my shoulders.

"Bodeites, Sir."

"Really? I was in Gownboys. I left in 1945." He asked several questions about our school before turning to the subject of learning to fly. He explained the flying training syllabus consisted of fifteen hours of dual instruction and the same amount of solo.

"At the end of that, you'll get your Private Pilot's Licence and be able to take your friends on flights," he concluded. I nodded my interest. Glyn briefed me on what my next lesson would consist of, so that I would know what I was about to learn, and how to do it. These briefings were a part of every flight with Glyn.

The next twenty-nine hours of my Flying Scholarship were pure delight, renewing once again my enthusiasm for flying. Under Glyn's instruction, I went solo in eight hours and obtained my PPL at the end of the course. He was the archetypal perfect instructor: calm, patient, polite, understanding, able to impart knowledge and interested in people and the job. I never heard him raise his voice or become angry for he had a far more subtle way of conveying his message. He once asked me where our farm was and when I told him, suggested I plan a cross-country to Portsmouth via home.

Taking off after lunch, we reached Horsham in seven minutes. I pointed out the farm, intending to alter course for Portsmouth but Glyn announced he had control and descended towards the front paddock. Flying across the farm, he pulled up into a dumb-bell turn and returned to fly across it once more. As we cleared the farm buildings, I saw Frank Gravitt and one or two of the farm hands waving.

We continued our cross-country via Portsmouth and landed back at Croydon an hour and a half later. As I filled in the flight times, Glyn suggested we go for a cup of tea in the cafeteria.

Over a cup of tea I conversed excitedly about the flight, telling him how much I'd enjoyed flying low over the farm. He became serious and looked me straight in the eyes. "I thought it better that we do it together," he explained kindly. "Then you'll never be tempted to try it alone – will you?" I understood the message loud and clear. Glyn was an excellent judge of character and perhaps because of this was also an excellent instructor.

Croydon airport was one of the earliest English international airports and conveniently close to the A23 London to Brighton road.

Before the Second World War, as well as being the operating base for Imperial Airway's London to Paris service using Handley Page HP-42 Hannibal and Heracles airliners, it had also been the departure point for many of the world's record breakers – Amy Johnson, Jean Batten, Jim Mollison, Kingsford-Smith, A. E. Clouston and Charles Lindberg.

On the tarmac at Croydon Airport.

During the Second World War, several RAF fighter squadrons operated out of Croydon during the Battle of Britain and subsequently.

Post-war its short grass runways relegated it to second place to Northolt and Heathrow, so when I reported there, only a few smaller feeder airlines like Olley Air Services, Morton's and Trans-Air operated a miscellany of de Havilland Doves, Herons, Rapides, Airspeed Consuls and DC-3 Dakotas to the Channel Islands, le Touquet and other close continental destinations.

The largest aircraft operating out of Croydon were Trans-Air's fleet of DC-3s, which never seemed to fly. This was because they were only used on night freight runs conveying English newspapers to ex-patriot readers in France, Germany and the Channel Islands.

The control tower and surrounding buildings were examples of contemporary Edwardian architecture of their time, and although outdated by the modern standards of the 1950s, when modern navigational aids like the 'Beam', non-directional beacons (NDBs) and Very High Frequency (VHF) communications made flying easier, it continued to man its antiquated navigational aids like the airport rotating beacon, Aldis lamp and cathode ray direction finding.

The 1950s were also the beginning of the end for the multi-crew concept, where the cockpit complement of a BOAC Solent Flying boat or an Argonaut four-engined airliner totalled five or more specialist aircrew – the captain, one or more co-pilots, a flight engineer, a navigator and a wireless operator. Soon the wireless operators were phased out and eventually navigators and flight engineers would follow them into redundancy.

The control tower at Croydon had both short range VHF communication plus the less intelligible but longer range High Frequency (HF), which when reception was bad, used Morse code for communication. Sadly, HF was seldom used in the mid-fifties but the radio operators remained at their Morse keys, waiting for the increasingly rare occasions when an aircraft transmitted 'QDM' for a magnetic bearing to the airfield.

These technical innovations impressed me immensely, although the Tiger Moths I flew were not equipped with any form of communication between the aircraft and ground stations. I particularly enjoyed visiting the Met office to listen to the duty weather forecaster tell the Morton's or Olley Air Services crews what the weather would be on their forthcoming flight to Hanover, Jersey or wherever their destination lay. To ensure they didn't forget his words of wisdom, the duty forecaster would hand them a folder containing a cross section of the anticipated en route weather, which he had drawn by hand. A red line denoted the height of the en route freezing level and the various cloud types expected to be encountered would also be drawn – wispy long lines for Cirrus, cauliflower shapes for Cumulus, flat mattress-like layers for Stratus and anvil-shaped clouds to indicate Cumulo-Nimbus clouds, the pilot's worst enemy for they meant low visibility, turbulence, ice and lightning, with cloud tops too high for any aircraft to surmount.

The control tower also fascinated me, especially its Cathode Ray Direction Finding (CRDF) which enabled radio equipped aircraft to call up for a course to steer to the airfield.

But in my seventeen-year-old's opinion, the most impressive item of equipment was in the men's wash room, where instead of paper towels to dry your hands, there was an electrical hand drier which directed warm air onto your hands for 30 or 40 seconds after pressing a button. Directions for its use were engraved on the machine and urged users to 'notice how much smoother your hands feel after using the Bendix electrical hand drier, patent pending.'

This convinced me that as long as Croydon used state of the art devices like the Bendix patented electrical hand drier, our tiny airport with its grass runways, Edwardian architecture and antiquated navigational aids would never be eclipsed by more modern airports!

The Airways Aero Club's fleet of aircraft consisted of several types of aeroplanes – Auster Aiglet trainers, a twin-engined Airspeed Consul, and two Tiger Moths which had been specially bought for training us Flying Scholarship cadets. Every evening, when flying had stopped for the day, the aircraft were pushed into a large hangar which 25 years earlier had housed Imperial Airway's HP-42 'Hannibal' and 'Heracles' airliners, used on the London to Paris run.

Croydon from the air.

Nowadays the hangar housed the club aircraft plus a few private machines, including the Miles Gemini flown by Group Captain Douglas Bader, the legendary World War Two flying ace who had returned to command a wing of Spitfire squadrons after losing both legs in a peacetime air crash. Whenever he appeared at Croydon, he was always surrounded by a swarm of admiring fans, which must have been tedious for him at times.

My only contacts with him were very occasional, once when I tried to engage him in conversation in the hangar and a second rather unfortunate time when he caught me on the wing of his aircraft peering into the cockpit. .His abrupt order to "Buzz off, can't you!" and subsequent derisory remarks to his companions about "grubby little kids interfering with his aeroplane" put me in awe of the great man.

Croydon airport was unusual in having grass runways but the manoeuvring area in front of the terminal building and hangars was sealed tarmac. Rapides, Proctors, Consuls and Transair DC-3s parked on this tarmac area to embark and disembark their passengers. It never occurred to me to wonder why our Tiger Moths were always parked a considerable distance away on the grass.

My flying training progressed satisfactorily and by the end of August I had soloed and accumulated twelve hours dual and seven hours solo. I was approaching that dangerous stage of overconfidence when you start to realize how pleasant flying is and think you're getting quite good at it. Late one summer's evening I received a lesson in how unforgiving any aircraft can be if you don't heed its limitations.

Most of the flying club staff had gone home at 5 p.m. when Glyn, my instructor, told me he was sending me off on an hour's solo practice. "Fly over to the low flying area and practise a few forced landings then come back here and practise your glide approaches," he instructed. "Then when you're finished, taxi slowly back towards the hangar until you get to the edge of the tarmac then wait. A mechanic will come over to hold your wing tip to help you taxi to the hangar."

I had no inkling that in less than an hour's time I would become involved in an incident of my own making that might result in the destruction of six or more aircraft, a hangar fire and possibly the deaths of several innocent people.

It was a beautiful August evening and I was ecstatic at the prospect of enjoying an hour's flying before returning home for dinner. Quickly gathering up my flying equipment, I hurried past Consuls and Rapides parked on the 200 yards of tarmac leading towards my aircraft. The duty mechanic in the hangar saw me and came over to swing the propellor.

I still remember that flight, for flying conditions were perfect. A light breeze of less than five knots blew down the runway, temperature was in the low twenties and the only clouds were a few thin wisps of cirrus far away to the west.

An hour later, having landed back from the detail, I taxied to the edge of the grass area and kept the engine running, waiting for the duty mechanic to come over and hold the wing tip while I taxied across the tarmac to the hangar.

I should have mentioned that the Tiger Moth's undercarriage consists of two main wheels slightly aft of the leading edger of the lower wing, and a metal skid at the tail which acts like a brake by providing enough friction to slow the aircraft to a stop when the throttle is closed. This tail skid also swung left or right with the rudder to assist the aircraft to turn. The system worked well on grass but nobody had told me it was totally ineffective on a hard smooth surface like tarmac.

After three or more minutes it became obvious nobody had seen me so I decided to taxi to the hangars unassisted. Opening the throttle cautiously, I bumped up onto the tarmac area and headed towards the hangar full of Proctors, Consuls, Rapides and Douglas Bader's Gemini.

It was unfortunate I had never noticed the slight down incline in the tarmac area leading towards the hangar, because it now caused my Tiger's taxiing speed to build up rather alarmingly.

Pulling firmly back on the throttle only confirmed it was already fully closed so I decided the best way to reduce speed was to fishtail left and right. This was when I learned the tail skid was useless for steering on tarmac!

Douglas Bader's Gemini loomed large in my field of vision as I accelerated down the slope towards the hangar full of highly inflammable wooden aircraft. Panic-stricken, I reviewed my options which seemed limited to either opening up to full power to raise the tail to perform a ground loop away from certain collision and probable death by cremation in the hangar, or to cut the engine, jump over the side and grab the Tiger by its tail to stop it. My favoured option was the first: open the throttle in an attempt to ground loop but I was now alarmingly close to the hangar and the thought of Douglas Bader's wrath if I slammed into his aircraft at full power deterred me momentarily. Now only the second option remained so I cut the switches and began fumbling with my harness prior to jumping over the side. Unfortunately aircraft harnesses are designed to keep you *in* the cockpit so this took quite a time while the Tiger careened towards the hangar full of highly inflammable wood and fabric aircraft. Even when free of the straps I found the door latches difficult to unfasten then one foot caught in the rudder pedals as I tried to abandon the aircraft.

Perhaps the Gods of Aviation had been watching all this with benevolent amusement, for when the aircraft was within thirty feet of the hangar entrance, it crossed a drain and the tarmac began to slope upwards, causing the aircraft to slow down. I hadn't noticed this in my preoccupation with abandoning the aircraft and had jumped to the ground just as the aircraft stopped, less than ten centimetres from the nose of Douglas Bader's Gemini.

"Oh so you managed on your own," the duty mechanic stubbed out a cigarette as he emerged from the tea room to survey the scene.

"Well, no, actually I jolly near crash . . . " I began indignantly, but he had lifted the tail and was busily manoeuvring the aeroplane into the hangar.

"Right then, now we can all go home," he announced.

Derelict aircraft at Croydon.

When I wasn't flying, I loved to prowl among the lines of surplus military aircraft strewn around the airfield. The most numerous type was the familiar Tiger Moth, used for ab initio pilot training. There were several hundred of these machines lying around the airfield in various states of repair ranging from brand new to old hulks.

I dreamed of buying a Tiger and taking it home to restore to flying condition, so I could continue flying after I'd got my PPL. Most of the aircraft had had their wings removed and stored in hangars and I spent many happy hours examining the various component parts of Tiger Moths to see how they fitted together. It must have been rather irritating for the mechanics to have a small boy, albeit dressed in a Cadet Corps uniform, grubbing among their aircraft wrecks.

One morning Les Bolton, another instructor, came up to me after I'd landed from an hour's solo and motioned me into a club armchair.

"I've been speaking to Johnny Longmore in the cafeteria," he explained quietly. "He saw you poking around his Tigers and wondered what you were up to . . . " I explained I hoped somehow to be able to buy my own aircraft once I'd got my PPL. Les Bolton managed to hide a faint smile.

"Aircraft are cheap to buy but expensive to maintain," he warned me. "Anyway, I'll tell Johnny you're not up to any harm." I thanked Les and he departed on a training flight with one of his students.

Next morning, Glyn collared me as I arrived at the club. "Morning Guy, Mr Longmore of Vendair would like a word with you some time today." I nodded my understanding and Glyn briefed me for the morning's flying.

I returned from an hour's forced landing practice and remembered the message to call Johnny Longmore. Dumping my flying kit in the locker, I walked round the perimeter track to the Vendair hangar. I found Johnny in a corner office and introduced myself.

Derelict Tiger Moths at Croydon in 1954.

He led me into a hangar stacked wall to wall with Tiger Moths, hundreds of them, up-ended on their noses to make more space available. Their wings had been removed and placed in padded racks. I gazed in wonder at so many aircraft in one hangar; there was scarcely room to stand.

"Bit crowded, eh?" Johnny chuckled. "We need a bit more room, there's nowhere to work and it'll take us ten years to sell this lot." I continued to gaze in wonder at this Aladdin's cave. "Les Bolton said you're looking for an aircraft to buy," he went on. I nodded as he continued, for I hadn't recovered from the sight of so many beautiful aircraft in one hangar – all brand new. "If you want a good aircraft, I've got just the one for you." He led me towards a bright yellow fuselage while he spoke. "PG-640, built at Hatfield in June, 1945. I bought her a year later at a War Surplus auction for seventeen pounds, ten shillings (about $25)." He produced an aircraft logbook as he spoke. "Total flying time, five hours and ten minutes, of which two were the delivery flight down here. If you want her, she's yours for what I paid for her, seventeen pounds, ten."

I couldn't believe my luck! A brand new Tiger sold for three hundred pounds or more. This one only needed reassembling and registering, two tasks I felt supremely confident to do.

"I haven't got seventeen pounds ten shillings on me," I explained. "Could I come back tomorrow and pay you?"

Johnny nodded understandingly. "She'll still be here tomorrow or six months from now. If you want her, she's all yours."

I returned home that night feeling as if I had wings on my heels. I couldn't wait to tell Dad of my incredible piece of luck. "A brand new aircraft for seventeen pounds, ten," I enthused. "We can keep her in the barn beside Vanity Victor and I'll teach you all to fly."

Dad was rather sceptical. "Who's going to assemble it?" he enquired doubtfully. I assured him it would be no problem to a few aero modeler friends and myself. He looked even more sceptical after this bit of good news.

"Aircraft are rather specialized," he ventured. "The wings have to be set at the correct incidence, dihedral angle is important, flying wires have to be tensioned, engine serviced regularly, controls correctly connected . . . anyway, where did you find seventeen pounds, ten?"

I patiently explained I only had thirty shillings, carefully saved from the travel allowance the Air Force paid me between home and the airport. I now needed a temporary loan of sixteen pounds to buy Tiger Moth PG-640. Dad shook his head regretfully.

"I'd be signing your death warrant if I let you buy that plane and assemble it yourself," he explained. I argued, pleaded, cajoled and almost threatened him but he was adamant. He would not lend me the money.

Two days later, on a beautiful sunny Monday August morning, I returned very crestfallen to Johnny Longmore. He was waiting for me in front of his hangar and pointed towards a fully assembled Tiger Moth sparkling in the morning sunlight.

The fully assembled Tiger Moth.

"The boys put her together for you over the weekend," he explained and I realized it was my Tiger he was talking about. "They reckoned it was about time we got something flying again round here."

I gazed regretfully at the gorgeous yellow biplane. The identification letters PG-640 stood out on the sparkling yellow fuselage. The mechanics had checked her over, run the engine and issued a ferry permit to allow me to fly her away to her new home.

I struggled to choke back tears as I regretfully explained to Johnny I couldn't raise the money. He smiled sympathetically. "Planes and women need a lot of upkeep," he commiserated. "You've got to accommodate them, feed them, service them regularly and keep 'em in top condition. Leave it for a few years until you can better afford it." He patted me encouragingly on the back and I murmured how sorry I was at not being able to buy his aircraft.

I walked sadly past PG-640, my Tiger, on the way back to the Airways Aero Club. The yellow biplane sat outside the hangar during the remaining weeks of my summer school holidays, for there was no room for it inside. Gradually the effects of sun, wind and rain took their toll. The once glossy doped fabric lost its sheen and faded. Paint began to flake away on the top surfaces; the cockpit seats filled with water and one night a sharp frost cracked the glass in the windscreens. Every time I taxied out to the runway past the Vendair hangar, I had to look away from where my Tiger lay dying.

What would my Tiger Moth be worth today? Well, in original condition probably over a hundred and fifty thousand pounds sterling ($225,000) but I wouldn't be here.

The engine would probably have failed at some critical time of flight, due to my amateurish servicing or use of farm petrol, causing me to crash and probably die. Maybe something else critical would have failed due to incorrect assembly or insufficient maintenance.

I didn't appreciate it at the time, but Dad saved my life when he refused to lend me sixteen pounds.

We still laugh at it!

I obtained my Private Pilot's Licence (PPL) in September before returning to my last year at Charterhouse. Once again examinations loomed on the horizon, this time A Levels, to enable one to progress to university to study for a profession.

Studying was even harder after having learned to fly. During dull moments in lectures my mind would drift away thinking of aircraft I'd seen or flown. To make matters worse, Hawker Aircraft's airfield was only a few miles away at Dunsfold and they were competing against Supermarine and de Havilland to sell their P-1067, now named the 'Hunter', to the RAF as their next front-line day-fighter. The pre-production prototype needed more testing before it could go supersonic and almost every day their chief test pilot, Neville Duke, would fly over our school at the start of yet another test flight, while I studied. A boring physics lecture would often be interrupted by the sound of the Hunter pre-production prototype pulling out of a near supersonic dive.

Meanwhile, the rival Vickers Supermarine team were pushing their Swift development as fast as it could reasonably go.

My final year at school started with the 'Arrow' calling me into his study to discuss my choice of future career. We discussed my interests and academic record then he asked me what I would like to study at university. When I informed him I had no desire to spend another three years studying, he looked at me curiously.

"What on earth do you want to be then, Guy?" he demanded challengingly.

"A pilot, sir."

"A what?" Open-mouthed astonishment smothered his face.

"Pilot, Sir. I want to join the Air Force and become a pilot, preferably a fighter pilot."

"Did you say pilot, Guy?" he enquired incredulously.

"Yes, sir."

The 'Arrow' gazed at me in amazement. "That's no occupation for a gentleman," he chided. "Pilot? I don't know any pilots, why on earth do you want to be a pilot?" He stared long and hard at me, willing me to change my mind under his wilting gaze.

We remained there for maybe thirty seconds although it seemed like thirty minutes, and I was beginning to think it might be better to choose a nice safe career in law or banking when the house was suddenly struck by a terrific impact. Plaster flakes fell from the ceiling, cups rattled in saucers and window panes shook from the terrific bang. We both rushed outside to see what the problem was, and found a sizeable crowd of other boys and masters squinting up into the clear October sky.

High overhead, a beautifully streamlined winged shape was pulling out of a dive. Wing tip vortices traced its flight path as it recovered level flight.

"Looked like one of those guided missiles to me," a Classics master informed everybody authoritatively.

"Naagh, you wouldn't see it after it exploded," somebody countered.

"That's the Hawker Hunter!" I informed everybody. "Neville Duke's finally gone supersonic in the pre-production prototype." We discussed this moment in aeronautical history. The RAF's first production supersonic fighter had broken the sound barrier. We stood around and talked about it for another hour.

I never did go back to tell the 'Arrow' why I wanted to be a pilot.

Chapter 7

Experience is What You Still Have When You've Lost Almost Everything Else!

The Flying Scholarship experience confirmed my desire to pursue a flying career but to do that, I needed more flying experience. As I was still below the minimum age for acceptance into the Air Force, I would have to maintain my flying proficiency at a civil flying club, which cost the monumental sum of three pounds (about $4.50) for an hour's flying.

Many of my school friends had never flown and were keen to go up in a light aircraft, so I offered flights to anybody who would share the cost. My first fare paying passenger had the added advantage of owning a Vespa motor scooter, which solved our transportation problem rather nicely, so one Saturday morning two 17-year-old schoolboys fronted up to the Airways Aero Club and asked to borrow one of their Tiger Moths for an hour's flying.

Bad news greeted us. "Now that you're no longer on a flying scholarship, there's a joining fee of thirty shillings to pay plus the annual subscription of three pounds before you can fly the club aircraft," the club manager informed me.

"But that's more than an hour's flying!" I protested. He shrugged and suggested I become a social member, which only cost ten shillings.

"But you can't fly," he added unhelpfully. "It's for members' wives and girl friends who want to use the club's social facilities." He gestured towards the bar as he spoke. I thanked him and informed my school friend of the sad news. It was a Saturday morning with perfect flying weather. All around the airfield, others were preparing to go flying in Tiger Moths, Austers, Chipmunks, Miles Hawks, Percival Gulls and a machine that I didn't recognize. I approached it curiously for a closer look.

"D'ye know what it is, young feller?" Somebody in a fighter pilot's sheepskin jacket approached me as I was examining the wing struts.

"Well . . . it looks like a Tiger with the lower wing missing . . ." I ventured rather lamely, for I had thought aircraft recognition was one of my strong points until now. The fellow in the sheepskin jacket guffawed with laughter at my response.

"Lotta chaps think that," he reassured me. "Actually it's a Hirtenberg.

"A what?" I demanded.

"Hirtenberg, a wartime German experimental aircraft designed to investigate slow flight. It was brought to Farnborough at the end of the war and became part of the Enemy Aircraft Flight along with various Messerschmitts, Heinkels, Dorniers and other strange bits and pieces," he explained. "Lovely machine, anybody can fly her. All the paper work's in German but she handles just like a Tiger Moth. We picked her up at a Ministry of Supply disposal auction 'bout a year ago . . . "

"Who's we?" I enquired.

"The Experimental Flying Group," he explained. "There's about thirty of us with PPLs who want to keep flying but can't afford club rates so we all share the cost of operating this little beauty. We pay thirty shillings an hour and that covers everything, there are no hidden charges like joining fees, subscriptions and all that sort of rubbish."

"Could I fly her?" I enquired eagerly. "I've just got my PPL?"

"Course you can. You'd need to do a quick dual check with me but that wouldn't be a problem, just a quick circuit."

"Could we do that now?"

"Well yeah. I suppose so," he admitted, looking around. "Nobody else seems to want her for the next hour."

I told my school friend to wait by the hangar while I did the required check flight. The instructor helped me into the rear cockpit and pointed out a few important controls and instruments. "Throttle's on your left, just like a Tiger, oh and the airspeed indicator's in kilometres and the altimeter's in metres but that's no problem, we climb and descend at 90, and three hundred metres is near enough to the circuit height of a thousand feet," he explained. "Ignore all those German signs and don't worry about the other funny instruments 'cos none of us know what some of them are." I looked around the cockpit at the bewildering array of strange dials and unintelligible notices while my instructor chocked the wheels and positioned himself in front of the propellor.

"Ready to go?" he called and I nodded.

"Switches off, fuel on?" he called.

"Dunno, which is on?" I replied.

"Oh sorry, Ein is On and Aus is Off."

"OK switches off, fuel on," I chanted. He pulled the propellor through several revolutions before calling "Throttle set?"

"Throttle set."

"Contact!"

"Contact!" the engine stuttered and stopped on the first swing but caught next time. He removed the chocks and I closed the throttle while he clambered into the front cockpit. Following his instructions, I taxied out and performed a full circuit and landing. The Hirtenberg was delightful to fly and handled just like a Tiger Moth, in fact my landing was smoother than many I'd done in Tigers.

"Very nice, OK old chap, I've got her," my instructor shouted over his shoulder before we'd even rolled to a halt. He fast taxied back to the hangar and beckoned my friend to come over.

"OK, she's all yours," he shouted in my left ear once my passenger was secured in the front seat. "Take her away and try a few manoeuvres and get used to how she handles – try a few turns, gliding, slow flight then come back and try a couple of circuits once you feel confident enough." He waved me away and I taxied out to the grass runway.

After take-off, I headed south towards the practice area, climbing to a thousand metres on the way. My passenger was ecstatic at being in a small plane for the first time and asked me to perform some aerobatics. This posed a problem because I'd never learned aerobatics before, only spins and stalls, so I leveled out and closed the throttle prior to trying a stall. It proved to be very gentle, similar to a Tiger Moth's, which unfortunately didn't satisfy my passenger, who announced he felt entitled to something a little more exhilarating for his thirty shillings. Not wishing to upset my very first fare paying passenger, I closed the throttle again and announced I would now demonstrate a spin to the left.

He loved it, letting out a Red Indian type whoop when the aircraft surprised us by abruptly flicking inverted before entering a fully developed spin. I allowed it to do three turns before initiating recovery action and encountered some difficulty applying full opposite rudder against the air loads during the recovery, which took a lot longer than the trusty Tiger Moth. Then I nearly pulled back too hard because the aircraft almost snapped into a spin in the opposite direction during recovery, and we were below the height of the nearby Surrey Downs by the time I'd pulled out from the ensuing dive. The German altimeter had wound down to less than two hundred by this time.

Hirtenberg G-AGAK which was subsequently crashed at
Butser Hill, Petersfield, Hants, a few years later.

I decided this was enough aerobatics for one day and set course with
trembling hands back to Croydon, above the protestations of my
passenger, who demanded more aerobatics for his money. After a cautious
circuit and landing, I parked outside the Experimental Flying Group's
hangar, stopped the engine and waited for my body to stop trembling. The
same instructor chocked the wheels as I cut the switches. "How d'yer like
her?" he enquired pleasantly.

"Fantastic!" my passenger was bubbling over with enthusiasm. "We did
a spiral dive and a zoom. I loved it!"

"Actually it was a spin," I reassured the instructor. "I took her up to a
thousand metres, tried a stall then did a spin to the left." I sensed I had said
something of great interest, for several members of the Experimental
Flying Group hurried over and stared at me with undisguised curiosity. The
sheepskin clad instructor asked quite a few questions about the spin and
became very attentive when I mentioned the excessive rudder loads and the

tendency to snap in the opposite direction. Several other Experimental Flying Group members broke away from the small crowd of on-lookers and asked more questions while others crowded closer to hear my answers.

"Why is everybody so interested in my flight?" I enquired, stepping down from the cockpit after ten minutes of interrogation.

"Just building up information for the other members," the sheepskin jacket reassured me, pointing to a conspicuous sign in the centre of the instrument with red letters annunciating *Spinnen Verboten!*

"We think that means 'Spinning Prohibited'" he confided conspiratorially. "So as you're the first person to ever spin the Hirtenberg, we're all very interested to hear how she handled."

The post-war British government required every able-bodied young man to serve two years 'National Service' in the Navy, Army or Air Force on reaching the age of eighteen.

Hundreds of thousands of young men had been trained as aircrew during the Second World War and I suspect nobody had filled in the appropriate form advising the relevant department of the Air Ministry that the war was over and the requirement for large numbers of pilots, navigators and other aircrew categories no longer existed.

Probably because of this, some National Servicemen were trained as RAF and Fleet Air Arm pilots during their two years military service. It took 21 months to train a pilot and at the end of this time, they were expected to join one of the Auxiliary Squadrons and fly with them at weekends.

Almost everybody regarded this compulsory military service as not only a waste of two years but also a financial penalty, and endeavoured to find ways of avoiding it.

My first experience of this was when the 'Arrow' enquired whether I'd applied for deferment. "Deferment from what, Sir?" I enquired innocently.

He explained that as I was nearing my 18th birthday, I could expect to be called up for National Service unless I found a reason to defer my call up date. A university degree course was one way of achieving this. Simultaneously, several other ways were offered to me, the most memorable being an eminent doctor who specialized in certifying young men as unfit for military service.

I was regarded with disbelief and horror when I explained I desperately wanted to join the RAF to learn to fly military aircraft.

My last term at school ended in July and I went home to enjoy two or more months' holiday while waiting to hear from the Royal Air Force.

It was mid-August when the official letter from Air Ministry House arrived, containing a rail warrant and instructions to report for duty in four weeks time.

Dad was busy with hay making when the date came round, so uncle Horace, Mum's brother, drove me to Horsham station. As we drove through the picturesque Sussex countryside, he reminisced about his war service with No.617 Dam Busters Squadron as a corporal (stores). His war service was coming to an end as we pulled up outside Horsham station.

"The Central Band of the Royal Air Force played the 'Dam Busters March' as we ended our careers in the service of our country," he informed me proudly. "See if you can do the same. Good Luck!"

We shook hands and I rather rashly promised him I would.

Chapter 8

A Shortage of Tall Fellows

No hot-blooded potential fighter pilot would get very excited about RAF Cardington, for its only connections with flying were the pre-war airship hangars, which now only sheltered old cars and young courting couples from the weather and prying eyes. Dismal lines of wooden huts housed the thousands of personnel engaged in the administrative work connected with new recruits, for Cardington in the late 1950s was the centre through which every Air Force entrant passed, whether they be pilots, cooks, bottle washers or anything in between.

Shortly after arriving there as an AC2 trainee pilot, I was documented, indoctrinated, vaccinated and accommodated. Then a large squad of us new entrants was herded to the camp barber for the coup de grace, an Air Force haircut which left us with skulls shorn so closely that our ears protruded from our heads and gave us the appearance of Volkswagen cars with the doors open.

Any sense of smug satisfaction any of us might have felt at being selected as pilots was shattered when we paraded alphabetically for our first roll call. The three recruits to my left (Alcock, Barringer and Bull) and others to my immediate right (Dorrett, Forsyth, Furniss, Geach, Green, Howard, Parry and Phipps) were pilots, whereas Quinn, Roberts, Sanders and other names running alphabetically through to Turner were navigators. Air Electronics Officers seemed to run from U to W, leaving Yates, York, Young, Yapton and Zimmerman as air signalers.

This led me to the conclusion that too many aircrew candidates had proved suitable for pilot training, forcing some anonymous clerk in Air Ministry to have to cull the numbers to ensure the correct balance of aircrew categories was maintained.

Before being marched to the airmen's mess for our first meal, the elderly corporal in charge of us had to form our group up into three orderly ranks, with the tallest to the front and left and the shortest to the rear and right of the squad.

To do this, we first had to form up in one long line with the tallest at one end and the shortest at the other. Unfortunately for our corporal, our tallest member was six feet eight inches in height, considerably more than the next in line, who was a mere six feet! This caused the corporal great dismay, for the sudden disparity in height made his squad look rather untidy when compared to all the others. Orderly appearance is a vital aspect of service life and he began to look at the rest of the squad, hoping to find several others ranging in height from six foot seven inches down through six foot six inches, five inches, four etc.

Regrettably he couldn't understand there just weren't any such people present, and kept searching fruitlessly. After wasting more than an hour, daylight was beginning to fade and the dining mess was about to close when the duty sergeant came over to enquire why our group were still on the darkened parade ground when the rest of the station were finishing their evening meal. The corporal explained the problem rather uniquely.

"There's a shortage of tall fellahs, sarge," he explained.

Eventually we were introduced to Air Force food – also bromide tea, which took more than thirty-five years to have any effect on any of us!

At the end of the first day, I found myself in a long barrack block hut with thirty-nine other young men from every part of the UK and its territories.

South Africans conversed heatedly with New Zealanders, Liverpudlians played Manxmen at cards while others of us discussed the thunderbolt that had just dropped at our feet: the National Service pilot training scheme, the very reason for us being in the Air Force, had been stopped! No more National Servicemen would be trained as pilots; in future, only those prepared to sign on in the regular Air Force would be accepted for aircrew training.

This was a bombshell to those of us who had interrupted careers to train as aircrew during our two years. Now we would probably waste two precious years in some menial job as administrative orderlies or cleaners, before returning to civilian life.

A grey cloud of despondency hung over our barracks that cold November evening at the end of my first day in Her Majesty's Royal Air Force.

The corporal in charge of us was a rotund and bald individual by the name of Bollock. I estimated his age at forty and he had been in the Air Force since before World War Two, which to us eighteen-year-olds was literally a lifetime.

Corporal Bollock (that really was his name!) lived in a small bedroom-cum-office at one end of our block. Occasionally he would appear from his sanctum sanctorum to ensnare a required number of volunteers for some job.

For example: "Anybody here know anything about driving steam trains?"

Steam trains? Now that sounded an interesting diversion from the boredom of barrack life and if we couldn't be pilots, well locomotive driver would be an interesting occupation for a couple of years. When several of us raised our hands in interest, Corporal Bollock smirked and produced a coal scuttle from behind his back.

"Fine, go and get me some coal for my fire!"

In this and many other ways he inveigled us into doing jobs we wouldn't otherwise have volunteered for.

"Anybody here know anything about riding?"

Riding? Now here was a unique opportunity, maybe there were some horses needing to be exercised every morning. That would be infinitely better than early morning drill or PT. I raised my hand. "Fine, see if you can fix the saddle on my bike!" Another trap!

So within a few hours of joining the junior service, I had learned the first rule of survival – never volunteer – which was the reason that four others and myself, bemoaning our bad luck in missing out on the National Service pilot trailing scheme, avoided Corporal Bollock's gaze when he emerged from his office and approached us.

"You lot, get your kit packed and report outside in five minutes. Do it quiet now, we don't want everybody to see you going." I tried to sneak away from the group but he saw me.

"You too. They need six. Now get moving, I want to see you all outside in five minutes." Not knowing what lay in store for us, I attempted to argue with him. It was a bitterly cold November night outside, pouring with rain, and at least the barrack block was warm, dry and reasonably cheerful.

He turned his back on me and retreated to his office, slamming the door with a bang to signify he had given an order, there was to be no discussion about it. I looked at the closed door and decided it would probably be better to obey. Hurriedly packing up my very new kitbag, I joined the five others on the road outside, straining to hear Corporal Bollock's voice above the noise of wind and rain.

It was Singer who asked what we were all thinking. "Where are we going, corp.?"

Corporal Bollock struggled to make himself heard above the forces of nature. "Officer train . . . truck'll be along from the MT[1] section . . . railway

---

1. Motor Transport.

station . . . Kirton in Lindsey . . . " a particularly strong gust of wind drowned most of his speech and Singer asked him to repeat it.

"Kirton in Lindsey, in Lincolnshire, next course starts there on Monday."

"What course, why are we going on a course?" we wanted to know.

"ITS. Initial Training School. You're all aircrew candidates, aren't you? Well, they need six more officer cadets to complete the next course, so you were the ones I chose. All right, here's the truck now. Get aboard, look lively . . . "

Aboard the truck taking us to the railway station, I had time to reflect on this incredible quirk of fate. Minutes before, I had been committed to staying in the Air Force as a dogsbody for two years because the pilot training scheme had stopped. Now suddenly the powers that be had decided in their magnanimity they needed six more pilots and had left the selection to a lonely corporal at Cardington.

Had I been elsewhere in the barrack block that evening, maybe in the latrines, I would have missed out on a Heaven-sent opportunity to train as a pilot, which would have been a pity, because ahead of me lay twenty-four months of unique experience – humour, tragedy, excitement, boredom and other life ingredients blended together to make two unforgettable years of my life.

In the railway carriage taking us to Kirton Lindsey, we introduced ourselves. Mike Parry was twenty-two and had just completed his law degree at Oxford. He was now completing his National Service before being called to the bar. Richard Howard was six feet eight inches and had come straight from school; because of his height, he was promptly christened 'Big Dick' to distinguish him from Richard Jones, who was five feet four inches tall and christened 'Little Dick'. The youngest member of our group was David Brown the eldest son of a prominent motor manufacturer, and the last member of our party was Singer, a pale-faced quantity surveyor from Leeds.

We arrived at Kirton in Lindsey after an all-night train journey across England, and were told we would start number ninety-seven aircrew course the following Monday. In the meantime, our instructions were to unpack our gear, sort ourselves out, have breakfast then report outside at 0900 hours for Sunday Church Parade.

There were people from more parts of the world than there had been at Cardington. Canadians, Australians, New Zealanders, Africans, Indians and a few Middle Eastern countries were all represented, so that one of the first and most important tasks was to sort the various religions into their own groups. I found myself classified as Church of England while others were classified as either Roman Catholics or Jews. In the Air Force's eyes there were only three religions: C of E, Roman Catholic or Jewish. A protest by one that "I'm not Jewish, corporal!" received the reply "Sorry, Sir. I only saw your top 'alf."

After giving our names to the NCO[2] in charge of us, we 'Church of Englands' were marched down to the Kirton in Lindsey village church for Sunday morning service, leaving behind a puzzled motley crew of Jewish Arabs and Roman Catholic Moslems.

As we neared the church, I noticed a sharp-eyed young corporal positioned in the entrance portico removing the hat of every officer cadet, for that was what we were now, and mutter something to each owner. As I entered the church, I felt the cap tugged from my head and the corporal's cockney voice admonished me to "Take yer 'at orf in the Lord's 'ouse, cunt!"

The next day, Monday, the officer training part of the course started. This was to consist of twelve weeks of lectures on most subjects that a young

---

2. NCOs were non-commissioned officers with ranks ranging through corporal, sergeant, flight sergeant and warrant officer. They performed various tasks on behalf of an officer.

Air Force officer needed to know – aerodynamics, mathematics, service writing, Air Force law, general duties, current events, navigation, weapons firing and much else. At the end of the course, the graduates would be posted to an elementary flying training school to start flying. There were also navigators and air electronics officers doing the same course but after graduation they would be posted to specialized navigation or electronics courses.

Chapter 9

I'm in the Nude
for Love

A medical examination and inoculations came before we started lectures. A medical orderly ushered us into a long room, where he instructed us to remove all our clothing and await the medical officer, who would be along shortly. Before anybody could remove one piece of clothing, a stunningly beautiful blonde female flying officer doctor appeared in the room.

"Good morning, Sir," the orderly saluted her. "The men are ready for your examination." She returned the salute and instructed him to send the first recruit into her office. Consulting the alphabetical list of our names on his clip board, he called out the first.

"Alcock, strip orf and report to the medical officer, now!" he ordered. Nobody moved then one of our number shuffled nervously when the order was repeated.

"Alcock, on the word 'Go' you will take one step forward march. Go!"

Somebody shuffled forward and admitted to being Alcock.

"Right then, strip off and report to the medical officer," the orderly beckoned towards the small office.

"But . . . " Alcock had turned purple with embarrassment. Impatient at being kept waiting, the medical officer reappeared in the doorway to see what the delay was.

"Right then, off with your clothing and into my office," she instructed. Alcock had become incoherent with embarrassment at the thought of exposing himself before a female. Eventually after some persuasion he removed everything but his underpants. The medical officer motioned for him to follow her into her office, which he did reluctantly.

Leaving the door open, she checked his blood pressure, reflexes, scars and balance before instructing him to remove his last item of clothing.

"But can't I . . . " he clutched the last garment tightly to his body while trying to think of a way to avoid inevitable embarrassment.

"Now I need to check for hernias and haemorrhoids," the MO explained patiently. "So pants off please." The patient gazed at her paralyzed with embarrassment, physically and mentally unable to bare himself before her.

When gentle persuasion by the MO had no effect, she pointed out that failure to be medically examined would bar him from starting the course. This last bit of information caused further indecision in his mind but still he clung to his dignity.

The situation must have occurred before because a subtle nod from her was a signal for the medical orderly to come up behind the patient and swiftly remove the offending garment with the speed and dexterity of a poacher skinning a rabbit. The problem was over in a second and Alcock stood before the doctor totally nude.

"There now," she murmured reassuringly as she eyed him with professional detachment. "All that trouble over a silly little thing like that."

The twelve week Initial Training Course consisted of lectures and many hours on the parade ground, learning rifle drill. Our evenings were spent preparing kit for the next day's inspection – polishing brasses, blancoing webbing and boning boots until they shone like patent leather. Then next day the rain would melt the blanco, tarnish the brasses and crack the highly polished leather.

After finishing our kit every evening, there was still two or three hours of study to be done re-reading the day's lecture notes on chains of command, how aircraft instruments work ("Right, gentlemen, today we're going to learn about compasses. Now what are the desirable characteristics of the perfect compass, eh? That's right, Sir, accuracy, aperiodicity, sensitivity, and horizontal stability, just like the perfect girl friend, eh Sir?"), how aircraft flew or sometimes didn't ("And as the angle of attack of the wing increases still further, the lift increases until suddenly at around eighteen degrees the airflow breaks away and the wing stalls and bingo, your aircraft's dropping out of the sky like an empty gin bottle. Now are there any questions on stalling, gentlemen?")

Throughout the twelve weeks, most of us were extended to the limits of our intellectual ability and I now realize this was the Air Force's way of weeding out the unsuitable early on in their training. The only time we could relax was during Saturday morning's padré's hour, when we could catch up on lost sleep by dozing off. Even this was fraught with hazard if the officer cadet next to you nudged you awake and whispered "He's just asked you a question." You would then stand up and attempt to answer a question you hadn't heard. The question hadn't been asked either and much amusement resulted from the ensuing confusion.

The obvious misfits never made it to the end of the course. Falling behind academically, they concentrated harder on their evening studies so that their kit cleaning suffered. This would result in them being charged next morning with having dirty kit on parade and being made to attend defaulters' parade in the evening, just when they needed to study. It was heartbreaking to see fellow officer cadets fall by the wayside in this manner and it was even harder to accept the fact that if we sacrificed our precious time to help them, we in turn would probably become casualties of the system. I sat beside a young Scotsman in lectures who had left school at sixteen to support his mother while attending night school to reach the required educational standard for entry into the Air Force. Now after many years of toil, he had achieved his ambition but was obviously not able to reach the required academic standard. Initially I devoted considerable time to coaching him in mathematics and other subjects but then found myself falling behind. To my distress, I had to stop helping him and concentrate harder on getting through the course myself.

Eventually final exams came and I was relieved to find that I was one of about seventy-five per cent who passed. Of those who failed, some were put back on a later course and given a second chance, while others were failed completely and either released from the Air Force or posted to some unit to complete their national service in non-commissioned roles. Regrettably my Scottish friend was in the latter category and it says a lot for his strength of character that his enthusiasm for flying was not diminished by this considerable set back and he went on to learn to fly privately, eventually becoming a jet captain with British Caledonian Airways.

At the end of the course we were taught weapons firing, which was a pleasant change from the academic grind and the drill square.

After learning about the Smith and Wesson .38 revolver, the .303 rifle, the Bren gun and the Sten in the class room, we were now about to use them for real. Things proceeded as planned until we got to the Sten light machine gun. The Sten is a rudimentary looking weapon, consisting of a crude metal-framed stock to which is clipped the barrel. The magazine containing the bullets is attached to the left of the barrel. It was inevitable that malfunctions would occur in something so crude – the Sten was notorious for jamming. When this happened on the range, our instructions were to keep the gun pointed at the target and advise the range officer our gun had jammed. He would then come up behind us, take the weapon from us and render it safe. Unfortunately for us, Singer was the first person to have a gun jam. He turned round to the back of the range butts where the rest of us were waiting, pointed the weapon at us and announced "Look Sir, my gun's jammed!"

Suddenly the weapon cleared itself and sprayed a hail of bullets at us; fortunately the weapon's recoil directed them over our heads into the corrugated iron roof but despite this, I have never seen fifteen people hit the ground quite as quickly as we did that day!

We also learned deflection shooting, where we had to aim ahead of a frangible clay target shot from a launcher. For this we used a shotgun. The purpose of this exercise was to teach us future fighter pilots to aim ahead of a moving target such as another aircraft, which would be twisting and turning ahead to evade us.

One member of our course had been a gamekeeper before joining the Air Force. He was a third generation gamekeeper (although since the recent publication of 'Lady Chatterley's Lover' he preferred to describe himself as an estate manager) and had handled all sorts of guns; consequently he was an unusually fine shot, being both fast and accurate. When his turn came to fire, he loosed off a round as soon as the clay target appeared, hitting it squarely in the middle every time. His technique however was at variance with what the Air Force wanted to teach us, whereas the rest of us, who had little or no experience with firearms, used the weapons in the approved Air Force manner, and usually missed the target. The reaction of the sergeant in charge was rather amusing; he praised those of us who were doing it the approved Air Force way (and rarely hitting the target) but scolded our crack shot game keeper, who had hit the target every time, telling him: "No, no, Sir, you're doing it all wrong. Here, let me show you."

He would then demonstrate the Air Force technique, scoring half as many hits as his student who was 'doing it all wrong'.

Weapons Training included a visit was to the medical Section to learn about the damage venereal disease could inflict on various parts of the body. The Medical Office (MO) first showed a graphic film so realistic in its portrayal that one or two members fainted and had to be carried outside to revive in the fresh air.

The film finished, the lights came on, and the MO stood before us and began listing ways to avoid contracting the various types of Sexually Transmitted Disease (STDs).

"Infection is spread by sexual contact so the best advice I can give you is to choose your partners carefully," he began. "Avoid those known to be promiscuous." The expression on every face told him none of us were likely to heed this advice so he approached the subject from a different angle.

"If you choose to ignore that advice, then I recommend the use of a prophylactic," he turned to delve into a cardboard packet, removing a small packet as he spoke. "Yes, I'm talking about our good old friend, the French Letter, the Durex, Johnny or what our American friends call the Condom." Several of his audience giggled as he opened the package and removed a rubber sheath. "Using one of these is probably the second best way of avoiding a dose of the clap," he held it aloft to add emphasis to his words.

The audience's scepticism could almost be felt. The MO realized he wasn't getting his message through. "It's a matter of health and survival," he focused his attention on one of our number in the front row, who quickly looked away.

"A few simple precautions could prevent the irreparable damage to your body and central nervous system you've just seen in the film," he protested. "Surely you can appreciate that?" When nobody responded, he tried a different argument. Addressing the same person in the front row, he beckoned him to stand before him.

"Would you want to ruin your life and career for a few minutes' pleasure when you can so easily avoid it?" he demanded. The subject of his inquisition looked highly embarrassed and mumbled something about diminishing the pleasure.

"You're aircrew, aren't you?" the doctor enquired. "What category?"

"Navigator, Sir,"

"Would you want your flying career to be ended because you didn't use a condom?"

"No, Sir, but it's not as simple as that . . . " his victim started to protest.

"Nonsense!" the MO roared, unrolling the rubber sheath over his right middle finger. "It couldn't be simpler; look, you say you're going to be a navigator. Would you jump out of your aircraft without a parachute?"

"No, Sir, but . . . "

"But what?" the MO waved his rubber sheathed finger threateningly in the other's face . . .

"I wouldn't jump out with a condom either," his victim pleaded.

The lecture seemed to have a partial effect however; even the most ardent were deterred from their pursuit of bare female flesh for a few days, or at least until the following weekend.

The final part of weapons training was grenade throwing. It was here that I witnessed an incredibly brave selfless act, albeit in amusing circumstances and all for nothing. It happened like this.

We learned grenade throwing in groups of six, in a brick bunker far away from people or buildings. The corporal in charge explained he would first demonstrate the correct technique, then each of us we would have a turn. The live grenades were contained in a closed stout wooden box and only taken out when required. A quantity of practice dummy grenades lay jumbled together in another similar box. The corporal took one of these dummies, removed the pin, counted to three then arced his arm skyward to simulate throwing it, but instead of releasing it, he retained his hold to save having to retrieve it from the mud later. When he had finished his demonstration, he dropped the grenade back into the box and pointed at Singer.

"All right then, that's all there is to it, gentlemen. Now you, Sir, come and see if you can do the same thing." He opened the box containing the live grenades while somebody else handed Singer a grenade.

Singer carefully removed the pin, counted to three, described an arc with his arm then threw the grenade back into the box! Every one of us realized simultaneously that unless we departed the bunker immediately, we would be blown apart and probably killed. Everybody rushed the exit together and got stuck in it for a few vital seconds.

Realizing the danger to us, the corporal in charge reacted immediately by throwing himself on the grenade which had bounced out of the box into the mud, in the hope that his body would shield the worst of the blast and provide us with some small chance of survival.

Only after I had covered a hundred yards in record breaking time did I look round. There had been no explosion and the corporal was picking himself up out of the mud with a rueful expression on his face.

It transpired that whoever had handed Singer the grenade had selected a dummy, being under the impression that we were going to throw practice grenades first. The corporal thought a live grenade had been thrown back into the box and had unhesitatingly thrown himself upon it to save our lives. His reward for such a brave act was laughter from us and derisory remarks about his muddy appearance from the senior NCOs later.

While we waited for the day of our passing out parade to receive our probationary commissions and begin wearing the thin blue line denoting our rank as pilot officers, the Air Force occupied us in a variety of ways.

The most important of these was practice passing out parades, which usually occupied every week-day morning. The cadet parade commander was a spotty faced, difficult-to-understand Yorkshireman, who when he had to shout across the parade ground, often into the teeth of a strong wind, became completely unintelligible. To make matters worse, he tended to stutter when nervous. On the first practice parade, the tension of the occasion got to him. We marched onto the parade square, passed the saluting base and continued off the other side. As we trudged through flower beds, hedges and across lawns, I realized our parade commander was experiencing difficulty in getting out the command to halt.

We could hear the drill instructor admonishing him to "Halt the parade there, Sir. Come on, Sir, tell the parade to halt, come on, Sir, come on . . . " Meanwhile, we were wading through the last of the flower beds towards the bomb dump. Still the instructor exhorted the parade commander to "Halt them there, Sir, just there, come on, Sir, tell the parade to halt." The poor Yorkshireman struggled to utter the one word as we passed the 'Danger, No Entry' signs around the bomb dump. Finally the drill instructor's patience gave out, he lost his temper and screamed at the parade commander "Say something to 'em fer Chrissake, Sir, even if it's only goodbye!"

Eventually we learned to decipher the Yorkshire man's commands and he gained sufficient confidence to overcome his stutter.

When we weren't practising passing out parades in the morning or drinking in the evening, the Air Force arranged other activities for us, which on one occasion was a flight in a Hastings parachute-dropping aircraft. All the internal furnishings had been removed for parachute operations and for some of the would-be aircrew, this was not only their first flight but also their first time close to an aircraft.

As the large passenger door was swung open and we looked inside the aircraft for the first time, one of our number exclaimed "Blimey, it's 'ollow."

After the passing out parade, as acting pilot officers we moved from the rather spartan barrack blocks into the Officers' Mess, where we could wait in comfort for orders posting us to an Elementary Flying Training School (EFTS). Meanwhile, the navigators went to Canada for their training and the Air Electronics Officers went to Norfolk for theirs.

While waiting for our posting orders we enjoyed some quite fantastic parties in the Mess, when large quantities of alcohol were consumed. Our instructors from the course joined wholeheartedly in the revelries, for their part in our metamorphosis as aircrew was now over. After about a week of waiting for a posting, just as I thought my liver was about to pack up, our orders came. We were to report to Number Six EFTS Ternhill for flying training.

Now we were about to start the activity for which we'd all joined the Air Force – flying!

Chapter 10

Ready, Fire, Aim

We travelled to Ternhill by British Railways early in March.

Five of the course were ex-apprentices who'd joined the RAF as boy entrants at 16 and over the next three years had learned most of the tricks of service life, one of which was how to get something for next to nothing. When the rest of us obtained our tickets to Ternhill in the usual way at the ticket office, four of the 'Famous Five' ex-boy entrants waited outside the station until the train arrived then hurried past the ticket office and boarded. Only their leader had bought a ticket.

An hour later, half way between Sheffield and Stoke on Trent, we were woken from a light doze by a uniformed British Railways ticket inspector. He clipped our tickets and we waited rather jubilantly for him to catch the four boy entrants, who had hurriedly moved towards the end of the carriage when he first appeared. From our seats we had observed the five of them squeeze into the train's lavatory compartment at the end of the carriage.

The inspector, on seeing the locked door, knocked once and called "Ticket please." The lock unbolted, the door opened fractionally and a single ticket was passed to the inspector, who clipped it and returned it to the owner's waiting hand.

When he was a safe distance further along the train, the Famous Five emerged triumphantly from their hiding place and chided us for wasting money on so many tickets. Rather grudgingly, we admitted they had beaten the system and we'd be doing the same thing next time we travelled by rail. They found this incredibly amusing and winked conspiratorially at each other when we announced our intention.

Number Six Elementary Flying Training School was in Shropshire, 15 miles North of Shrewsbury and a similar distance from the Welsh border. It had first been laid out as an airfield in the 1930s to train members of the Auxiliary Air Force on Gypsy Moths and Hawker Hinds. Because of its location in relatively flat countryside, it was considered an ideal site for an airfield, although some of the more dilettante weekend warriors in the auxiliary squadrons had commented unfavourably on its distance from the social and artistic delights of London.

Upon outbreak of war in 1939, the airfield became an operational conversion unit, equipped with Miles Masters, Hurricanes, Spitfires and Ansons. The culvert at the western boundary of the airfield persistently claimed aircraft which over-ran the runway and during one week in 1944, managed to damage more Spitfires than the Luftwaffe. When we arrived, the operational conversion unit's badge with the motto 'Ready, Aim, Fire' was still displayed at the guardroom, where late night pranksters often rearranged the letters to 'Ready, Fire, Aim.

The station's main claim to fame was the three Victoria Cross winners numbered among its wartime students. The staff rarely lost an opportunity to remind visitors of this fact but they never told of the dark wartime night when the pilot of a top secret Focke-Wulfe 190 German fighter mistook the Mersey for the English Channel and landed at Ternhill, thinking it was his home airfield. Taxiing to a position in front of the control tower in sleet and rain, he was abused by an irate orderly officer, who having mistaken his aircraft for an American P-47 Thunderbolt fighter, climbed up on the wing and told him he couldn't park there. The German pilot was given a map of Northern England, shown his position on it and told to push off to the nearby American Air Force base. He took off and presumably made it home to his base, for nothing more was heard of him. It was later estimated that the capture of an intact Focke-Wulfe could have assisted the allied war effort immensely, possibly shortening the war by several months.

After the war, the station remained a flying training school, initially with Tiger Moths then Percival Prentices until by the time we arrived, these had been superceded by Percival Provosts.

Due to overcrowding in the mess and because we were the junior course on the station, we were initially accommodated in what was termed the officers' mess annexe, a line of temporary huts erected adjacent to the east wing. There we were looked after by two batmen who made our beds, cleaned our rooms, polished the buttons on our number one uniforms and generally helped to make our lives more pleasant. After the almost perpetual blancoing, pressing, polishing and grooming we'd had to perform at Kirton in Lindsey, it was a wonderful change.

The batmen kept two nondescript mongrel dogs who, when they weren't sleeping on one of our beds, leaving behind dog hairs and fleas for the bed's rightful owner, were often seen copulating on the lawn outside the mess dining room. All attempts at cooling their ardor had failed and eventually the sight of theses two canine lovers enjoying themselves together hardly raised an eyebrow.

Early on the first morning, the batmen woke each of us with an incredibly strong cup of tea, which proved undrinkable.

Before starting our flying training we had to be issued with flying equipment, so after breakfast we assembled outside the Mess and marched down to 'Stores' to be issued with flying clothing before meeting our instructors in 'Flights'.

The sergeant in charge gave instructions on the use of each item of equipment, which included a parachute, in a rather unusual way. As each piece of equipment was pushed across a wide counter towards us, he recited a strange litany of disjointed English.

"Gloves, two, Cape Leather, aircrew for the use of, sign 'ere, Sir." holding out a form for signature. Hearing "Boot, one, left, aircrew, ditto one right ditto for the use of," made some of us wonder how he spoke to his wife when off duty. Maybe "Morning, one, good, one, dear, ours, for the enjoyment of" or something similar.

When the time came to issue us with parachutes, aircrew for the egress of, he stressed the importance of lifting and carrying them only by the correct carrying handle, not the silver 'D' ring used to deploy it in flight.

"Your parachute could be your lifeline in the event of fire or in-flight structural failure," he explained. "But never attempt to use it below a height of less than a thousand feet above the ground. Remember to first unfasten your Sutton harness, exit over the side and count to three before pulling the 'D' ring to open the 'chute." He also reeled off other information on how and when to use it.

Inevitably somebody asked what to do if the parachute failed to open.

"Then you'll be the first to reach the ground, won't you, sir?" he replied.

"But surely . . . " somebody blustered, fearful of the awful consequences of the parachute canopy failing to open in time.

"Just bring it back 'ere and we'll give you anuvver one," he reassured his inquisitor.

Having drawn our flying equipment, we then proceeded to 'Flights', the name given to the collection of wartime wooden huts provided for student pilots and their instructors to relax in between flights. Our 'flight' hut consisted of a flight commander's office, instructors' crew room, pupils' crew room, several briefing rooms and a locker area to store our flying kit in. Here we were introduced to our instructors by the squadron commander, squadron leader D. Arm, who as well as being in charge of our 'B' flight course, commanded another 'A' flight. At the start of the course, we numbered thirty students.

I began to notice a relaxation in discipline compared to Kirton in Lindsey, where as officer cadets, we had been expected to march everywhere, salute just about everything, and always stand to attention when addressing an officer, NCO or member of a senior course. Here, as APOs (Acting Pilot Officers), things were more relaxed and the atmosphere in the Officers' Mess with its bar, dining room and barber's shop was more like a gentleman's London club.

Our instructors consisted of fifty per cent NCO pilots (sergeant pilots, flight sergeant, or warrant officer pilots) and fifty per cent commissioned (flying officers or flight lieutenants).

Our flight commander, Flight Lieutenant Henry Bilek, would have more to do with the day to day administration of our course than the squadron commander. Henry was a short, bald, rather amiable looking roly poly figure of a man, rather reminiscent of Arthur Lowe's Captain Mainwaring character in the *Dad's Army* TV series. Henry was Polish and probably because of this had several other Polish and Czechoslovak instructors under his command, all with impossible to pronounce names like Grzybowski, Knczetchni etc. His amiable appearance belied his true nature, for when the Germans overran his homeland at the start of the war, he and several other Polish Air Force officers hid themselves aboard a Heinkel 111 bomber and silently killed each crew member as they climbed aboard. They then flew the aircraft to England, crash-landed on Newmarket race course and joined the RAF.

Post-war they had remained in the RAF and now, more than ten years later, were approaching the end of their active Air Force flying careers. For some, the job of ab initio flying instructor was a grace and favor position before being pensioned off to air traffic control or some other department where their experience would suit them admirably for their new task.

The number of decorations worn by the instructors was impressive, with Distinguished Flying Crosses, Distinguished Flying Medals, Pathfinder Clasps, and the occasional Distinguished Service Order (second only to the Victoria Cross) in evidence. All this reminded us that the Second World War had only ended eleven years ago and we were in the post-war Air Force.

Although Henry Bilek and his instructors appeared ancient to us eighteen-year-olds, their flying ability was superb, which was one of the reasons they were instructing *ab initio* pilots. Later on in the course, it was brought home to me just how good Henry was.

All the Polish and Czech instructors still spoke with heavy accents, although English had been their main language for fifteen years. To make it even more difficult to understand them, they had picked up most of the British swear words and colloquialisms currently in use, so an instruction to go to lunch would be phrased as "You fockers can bogger off to zer ploddy mess now."

These eccentricities only added lightness to the already colorful circle of pupils and instructors at Ternhill. It was once said that 'England is the paradise of individuality, heresy, anomalies, hobbies and humor.' Well, with the exception of heresy, I think that statement describes the members of the Ternhill Officers' Mess rather well. Looking at a photograph of the course taken shortly after our arrival, I see an aerodynamicist, economist, beachcomber, Irish peer, undergraduate historian, accountant, bloodstock dealer, vet, farmer, barrister, bookmaker as well as others like myself who'd joined the Air Force from school. Some of the fellows possessed incredible wit and initiative, which enlivened dull lectures. Most of the ground school staff were quickly christened with titles appropriate to their physical appearance or role in the teaching hierarchy. The meteorologist was a florid faced civilian who appeared every morning with a massive hangover acquired in the mess the night before. He would move and communicate with great difficulty until lunch time, when coincidentally the bar opened. His nickname became 'Deep Depression Dan'. Two of the drill instructors were once heard to tell an APO he was 'walking like a flower pot man, Sir' and thereafter never lived down the titles of 'Bill and Ben, flower pot men', the name of a children's afternoon television programme. The electronics instructor, flight lieutenant Duckett, earned his nickname the day an electrical experiment went very wrong and a condenser jolted him with a high voltage shock. His curt remark as he dropped the whole apparatus earned him the nickname 'Fuckit-Duckett'.

Often a particularly boring lecture would be enlivened by a caricature of the lecturer or a witty note passed surreptitiously round the class. One hot summer afternoon we were listening to a rather dull lecture on navigation. The lecturer was describing the function and operation of the drift sight, an instrument that told the navigator what effect wind was having on the aircraft's flight path. It was a bulky piece of equipment, with an eye piece through which the navigator squinted at the earth below. To acquaint us with its use, the instructor passed it round the class. As each student held the eye piece to his eye, he uttered a hearty chuckle and passed it on to the next student. When the drift sight came to me, I found the reason for their merriment: glued onto the glass graticule inside the instrument was a neatly written message, reading "Smile if you had sex last night". That drift sight had probably been in use for ten or fifteen years and maybe is still being passed through the hands of trainee pilots somewhere!

Another lecturer, a north-countryman, frequently started every sentence with the phrase 'in actual fact'. The bookmaker on our course cashed in on this habit by running a sweepstake on how many times the phrase would be repeated in one lecture. I recall the event particularly clearly because I held the 'high field' and to my delight, won the sweep. The exact number of 'actual facts' was a staggering 135 in forty-five minutes! In later sweepstakes, punters holding the high numbers endeavored to increase the number of 'actual facts' by asking questions. Sometimes these questions would irritate the trained scientific mind of the lecturer and he would lose his temper, exclaiming 'Yer wanter kip yer big maouth shoot and not shaw yer awn bloody ignorance!' but most of the time he was delighted at the close attention our course paid to his lectures and was once heard to confide to another ground school instructor that our number ninety-seven course listened to his every word. He was right of course for we were counting the number of 'actual facts'.

Events like these enlivened an already very pleasant way of life.

After meeting our instructors, each pupil was taken for a forty-five minute familiarization flight, which we put down in our new log books as 'Air Experience'. This was the first of many enjoyable sorties I shared with Flight Lieutenant Ian Wilson, my instructor over the next nine months.

Before accompanying Ian out to the aircraft, I put on the conspicuously new flying overalls, white doeskin gloves, leather boots, and scarf. Picking up the bulky parachute pack in the approved manner, I then carried the rest of my flying kit out to the waiting aircraft. Once in the cockpit, Ian showed me how to pull on the inner helmet, put on the bone dome protective outer helmet (called a 'brain bucket' by the Americans), connect the oxygen mask and microphone and pull down the sun visor atop the outer helmet. When attired in all this equipment, virtually every piece of bare skin was obscured, giving one the appearance of a robot.

This was the first time I had seen the cockpit of the Percival Provost basic trainer on which we were about to learn to fly. Compared to the Tiger Moth it looked incredibly complicated and I initially despaired of ever learning the positions and functions of so many controls, levers and instruments. The cockpit was dominated by a large purposeful looking control column, on which two buttons and a brake lever were positioned. Beyond the control column, which we were told never to refer to as 'the stick', the rudder pedals lay beneath an instrument panel crammed with dials – altimeter, turn and slip, rate of climb and descent, air speed, another strange looking dial with a small aeroplane superimposed on it which I recognized as the artificial horizon, directional gyro, fuel contents gauge, cylinder head temperature, oil pressure; you name it and it was probably there. To ensure absolute confusion in the novice pilot's brain, there were also the many controls to remember and learn to operate. Each was distinctly labeled: *propellor RPM High/Low, Ram Air Selector, up for Filter, Booster Pump, Fuel ON/OFF cock, Battery Master Switch, canopy jettison Pull in Emergency, radio, gyros, electrics, pneumatics.* Everything seemed so different from the Tiger Moths I'd flown with the Air Cadets at school. Ian my instructor sensed my confusion and did everything he could to set my mind at rest.

The Provost trainer looked sufficiently like a Focke-Wulfe or Zero to satisfy us.

The weather was typical for March: dull, overcast with a cloud base around 4,000 feet. After the 45 minute famil' flight I was completely sold on flying: the Provost had a large radial engine in front, enclosed cockpit, and looked sufficiently like a Focke-Wulfe 190 or Japanese Zero to satisfy us fledgling aviators until we could graduate to jets in less than a year's time.

A Double Diamond Works Wonders

After settling down in the mess annexe and starting our flying training, the only thing remaining was a bit of social life.

Initially the thrill of flying a relatively high powered[1] powered aircraft was our sole topic of conversation, especially when the time for first solos drew near, but after a while we began to find the weekends and summer evenings were not as exciting as we would have liked. In typical APO fashion, we set about doing something to rectify the situation.

The first necessity was a means of transport to enable us to reach the fleshpots of the surrounding towns. The obvious solution was to buy one of the 'course chariots' from a graduating course. The current selection on offer was a choice between a very large stately looking Daimler, named 'Lady Chatterley's Lover', and another equally impressive but slightly less roadworthy Austin tourer, with the licence number 'PP 1'. The Austin was considerably cheaper than the Daimler, so we bought it for fifteen pounds ($US 22) and christened her the "Pheasant Plucker' because of the license plate letters 'PP'. Five other members of our

---

1. The Provost's engine developed 550 horse power, considerably more than the trusty old Tiger's 130.

course, Kiwi Green a New Zealander, Phipps, Lord Jim the blood stock dealer, Mlig and Alcock pooled their funds and bought 'Lady Chatterley's Lover' for an undisclosed sum.

Both vehicles were inclined to break down occasionally and the members of the Daimler syndicate were often referred to as 'Lady Chatterley's Shovers' and our Pheasant Plucker syndicate also acquired a nickname . . .

We had been cautioned by the Pheasant Plucker's previous owners that our vehicle was not in current roadworthy condition. Closer inspection of her innards revealed the engine needed new main bearings, a relatively easy but laborious task to carry out. Otherwise, apart from a thick layer of grime, the old girl was in acceptable condition, bearing in mind the price we had paid for her, so three of us took on the task of returning the Pheasant Plucker to running order.

The "Pheasant Plucker" and other course chariots.

We spent a hot Saturday afternoon beneath our vehicle, draining the oil, removing the fifty or more bolts holding the crankcase pan in position and performing the other tasks associated with the installation of new bearings. The Pheasant Plucker had sat on flat tyres in an empty site behind the mess for several weeks, so we set about doing the repairs in situ. The hot sun beating down on the metal parts made working underneath very hot work, and soon the sweat was rolling off us.

Halfway through the afternoon, when we had got to a particularly difficult part of the repair work, we heard voices along the road. The owners of the voices were obviously not aware of our presence underneath the dilapidated old car for they continued talking in confidential tones. From our position beneath the car, we could see they were three members of a senior course and they were carrying a heavy wooden crate.

"Here's a bonny spot," a Scottish voice was heard to say above the noise of clinking bottles in the crate. Sounds of puffing and grunting were an indication of the physical effort required to heft a full crate of beer up a bank and into a clump of tall grass.

"Great, we'll leave it here and tonight when the party's well under way, we can come out for a quick refill . . . Be a damn sight quicker than queuing at the bar."

"And a damn sight cheaper," the Scotsman added as they camouflaged the crate with dried grass and leaves. Only when this task was done and their voices had faded away into the distance did one of us dare to speak.

"I wonder what they were hiding? Better go and have a look," 'Big Dick' Howard suggested. We were glad of an excuse to stop work for it had been incredibly hot under the car and perspiration was pouring in rivulets from our bodies. We scrambled out from beneath the vehicle and hunted around in the long grass for the hidden treasure.

'Little Dick' Jones was the first to find it. Holding an ice-cold half-pint bottle of Double Diamond beer aloft in each hand, he formally claimed the goods in our name. The others agreed with me when I remarked how hot and uncomfortable it had been beneath the Pheasant Plucker and after a short unsuccessful wrestle with our consciences, we unscrewed the caps from three bottles and poured the ice cold golden brown nectar down our parched throats. Only after all the bottles were empty did we discuss the morality of our actions. "They probably wouldn't have found them out here after dark," Big Dick suggested.

"Anyway, APOs aren't allowed to consume alcohol except in the proscribed places," I quoted from our law lectures at Kirton in Lindsey. Little Dick didn't say anything; he was imagining the rightful owners' wrath when they discovered the theft. If they discovered we had been in the immediate area when they deposited their loot, we would be the prime suspects in their enquiries. Little Dick stood up, belched, unfastened his fly buttons and refilled the bottle. Replacing the screw stopper, he placed the warm bottle back in its crate.

To our discredit, Big Dick and I did the same thing before returning to work on the Pheasant Plucker.

By five o'clock we had her running. I checked the oil pressure and generator charge and pronounced the engine OK. Little Dick borrowed a tyre pump from the Motor Transport (MT) section and an hour later three grimy but very proud APOs parked the old car in front of the officers' mess before going inside to shower and change for the night's revelries.

Discussion with the other shareholders in the Pheasant Plucker syndicate decided the vehicle should not be used by more than three owners at a time if they wished female companions to escort them, to prevent everybody being crushed in together. It was also decided democratically that we three who had got the car running again should be the first to use her.

The Pheasant Plucker was now in relatively good condition apart from a battery that wouldn't hold a charge and lights that had a disconcerting habit of going out on sharp bends. The previous owners had craftily covered several holes with carpet where the rear passenger compartment floor had rusted away, but once you knew where they were, entry and exit from the vehicle was relatively simple. A loan of a garden hose soon cleaned off the worst of the grime and we felt rather proud of ourselves as we headed towards the bright lights of Shrewsbury.

By 9 p.m. we were comfortably settled in a pleasant pub at the end of the main street, chatting up three local girls from the teachers' training college. Everything was going well as the hands of the clock behind the bar approached closing time. Little Dick had already latched onto the elder of the three girls and they disappeared off in her car as the landlord called for "Last Orders Please!"

Gathering up our glasses, I gave Big Dick the wink; now was the time to make our play. While I ordered a last round of drinks, he suggested to our lady friends they might like us to drive them home.

"That's very nice but we can take the bus," I heard one reply.

"I think I can hear it coomin' now," her companion stood up to leave but was dissuaded by Big Dick, who pointed out that a car was more comfortable and convenient.

"Are you sure it's not too far?" they enquired concernedly. "We can still take the bus."

"Nonsense, we'll run you home in style," I called out reassuringly as their bus departed in a haze of thick exhaust smoke.

It took several minutes to get served at the crowded bar and when I arrived back at our table I found Dick looking very pale. He'd been drinking at a fast rate during the evening, and taking into account the two pints we'd had during the afternoon, he must have had close to twelve pints of strong bitter. I made a mental note to do the driving when we got outside.

Dick was talking to me. 'They live in Nantwich." he repeated. "That's nearly thirty or forty miles away!"

"Can't they take a bus or something?"

"They were going to until you called out and said we'd run them home in style."

I groaned inwardly as I did a quick mental calculation: assuming the Pheasant Plucker could average fifteen miles to the gallon at long range cruise, it would require slightly less than three gallons to get the girls home, plus one more to get us back to the mess. The fuel gauge indicated half full, so if it was correct, we had just enough fuel to get there and back provided we drove conservatively.

I smiled at both girls. "Fine, well, when you're ready, we'll get going." They fussed and twittered for a bit then picked up their handbags and we headed for the car park. Big Dick was now very much under the weather, weaving from side to side as he walked. As he climbed in the back, his feet went through the holes in the floor but he eventually extricated himself with some difficulty. The other girl sat in front with me.

I turned the ignition key and a barely discernible glow from the light told me I'd have to hand crank the motor. I turned to Dick in the back seat but he was drunkenly forcing his attentions upon his companion. Getting out of the driver's seat, I cranked the engine until it started on the fourth attempt.

The drive to Nantwich was quite exciting. Ignoring the noises in the back of Dick attempting amorous advances then falling asleep halfway through them, I began holding hands with the other girl but whenever I began exploring further, the Pheasant Plucker's lights would suddenly fail on a bend. I then needed both hands to juggle the light switches to get them working again before we crashed into a hedge or stone wall.

The road became bumpier as we approached Nantwich and the car lurched rather alarmingly at times. This lurching motion must have upset Big Dick's stomach, because he suddenly sat up straight and commanded me to "Stop the car, I'm going to be sick."

I applied maximum braking and stopped as fast as a 1936 Austin tourer can stop; Dick had already opened the rear door and as we slowed to a stop, he lurched towards the verge, grabbed a small tree and began emitting sounds of retching and vomiting. We waited in the car while he finished his technicolour yawn and climbed back into the rear compartment, this time managing to avoid the holes in the floor.

We had travelled less than a hundred yards when the girl in the back spoke "That's me moom's 'ouse on the corner," she informed me. I parked outside a neat semi-detached house with a stone path leading between concrete gnomes and pink flamingos to the front door.

Big Dick seemed to have now recovered completely after his recent spew. Punching me playfully on the shoulder, he told me to "Wait here, I might be gone quite a while." He then hurried up the garden path after his companion, who was already halfway to the safety of her mother's front door.

Although I didn't purposely watch to see how things went , I couldn't help noticing they didn't go quite as he'd predicted when he told me he might be 'quite a while'. Within a minute his girl friend had disappeared into the house and Dick was back. As he opened the door, the interior light came on dimly, revealing traces of vomit around his mouth and sweaty face.

"The little minx," he muttered indignantly. "She didn't even want to kiss me goodnight."

Early the next morning, after dropping the other girl home, we reached the mess on what must have only been the fumes in the tank. The oil pressure warning light had begun to flicker intermittently after leaving Nantwich and I realized we were going to have to fix the problem next afternoon. But first I was going to catch up on some sleep.

After a Sunday lunchtime session in the mess bar, where the success or otherwise of various individuals' Saturday night activities were discussed, we had a light lunch then returned to the Pheasant Plucker. Once again we parked her on the same empty site at the back, since it would be inconvenient as well as hazardous to work on her in the busy car park.

Initial examination confirmed our fears; the drive back from Nantwich had damaged the bearings again. There was no other choice but to drain the crankcase and fit new ones. Taking a spanner and a deep breath each, Big Dick and I disappeared beneath the car to remove the bolts while Little Dick drained the oil.

We made good progress and were soon deeply engrossed in our tasks. So engrossed in fact that we didn't hear footsteps coming along the road until they were almost upon us. Little Dick was the first to spy three pairs of legs kicking the grass by the road side. He nudged me and I whispered a warning to Big Dick.

"Whassamatter?"

"Shhh, I think our beer drinking friends from yesterday have returned. Don't make a sound . . . " He did exactly as he was told; the three of us lay beneath the car listening to the three recent arrivals.

"It was about here we left it, I'm absolutely sure. Dunno why we couldn't find it last night," the first voice stated.

"Ye don't think somebody stole it, do ye?" the Scotsman enquired anxiously. A third voice much closer to where we lay concealed, dispelled their anxiety.

"Naagh, here it is, beside the broken down old car. Wonder why we couldn't find it last night?"

The other two came over and helped lift the crate from the grassy clump. As if on a given signal, each reached in and lifted out a bottle. The nearest one spoke. "Ah well, pity we didn't find it last night but now we can have a nice Sunday afternoon glass of piss." Murmurs of approval from the others followed as three bottle tops fell to the ground. The first took a long swig from his bottle.

"Bloody beer's flat!" he announced indignantly. The second finished swigging, his face puckered in a thoughtful frown. "Still, it's beer ennit?"

It was the Scotsman who put into words what we already knew. After taking a swig from his bottle, he looked thoughtful for a moment before holding it up to the light and announcing very authoritatively, "Some bastard's pissed in this."

How we managed to laugh silently beneath the Pheasant Plucker I don't know for if the whole motor car had dropped and crushed us, we would have died still laughing.

Chapter 11

First Solos

As spring turned to early summer, the more adept pilots began going solo. The first member of our course to go solo was also the youngest – David Brown, who seemed to have no problem in assimilating everything he was taught. He soloed in less than six hours and I suspect he could have gone in less for afterwards I heard his instructor apologizing that he hadn't sent him off earlier. "But regulations required me to demonstrate spins and stalls to you first, which took another hour."

David was a total aviation enthusiast who, like several of us, had gained a Cadet Force Flying Scholarship enabling him to get his private Pilot's Licence. His only ambition in life was to fly, which he did well.

It usually took between eight and ten hours for an average pupil pilot to reach solo standard. Initially we would be taught the effects of controls then to fly straight and level, then turning before learning climbing and descending. Spins and stalls also figured somewhere in the syllabus, to warn us of the dangers of getting too slow, as laid down in the aerodynamical First Commandment – 'Watch thy airspeed, lest the ground come up and smite thee!'

I recall my first session of spinning and stalling very clearly for everybody has a fear of the unknown or the unnatural. Some are terrified of water, others of height. My fear was unusual manoeuvres in aircraft, especially flying upside down.

There had only been one occasion when I'd been inverted in an aircraft intentionally and that had been in an open cockpit Tiger Moth as a member of the school cadet force. I had kept my eyes tightly shut throughout the whole manoeuvre, from the moment the pilot had suggested "let's try a loop" until the noise of the wind in the wires had diminished to gale force again and the voice tried to convince me "that wasn't too bad, was it?" It could probably have been said that I wasn't qualified to say whether or not I liked unusual attitudes because I'd only experienced one – with my eyes closed.

My instructor started the stalling and spinning detail with a few mild stalls, talking as he closed the throttle, the engine note died to a rumble, the nose began to rise above the horizon, the airspeed dropped lower and lower, the airframe began trembling and shaking, then abruptly the nose dropped and we were descending very fast towards the ground. Ian applied down elevator and power, and as the speed built up, he raised the nose onto the horizon again.

He performed the next stall with flaps down and even I noticed the speed was ten or fifteen knots slower than the stall in the 'clean' configuration – that is to say with the flaps 'Up'.

After a third stall, Ian looked at me closely. "Feeling OK? Not going to be sick or anything, are you?" I assured him I felt fine, just wonderful. Me be sick, whatever gave him that idea? If only my stomach would settle down from that last stall . . .

"OK, now let's try a spin. Here we go again," Ian's reassuring voice was speaking again as he reduced power. The air speed crept back, eighty knots, seventy-five, still decreasing, vibration's starting now, that's the stall warning. Suddenly the left wing dropped abruptly and the aircraft rolled over onto its back before plunging into a vertical corkscrew dive towards the ground. I found myself holding onto the edge of the coaming in front of me, thinking "Fer Chrissake, why can't the pit of my stomach keep up with the rest of me?"

As the earth continued rotating in front of me, I became aware of my instructor's reassuring voice again. "The spin's now fully developed, three, four, five turns, OK recovering now, stick centrally forward and full opposite rudder . . . "

Outside the windscreen, the spiral had stopped and we were now pulling out of the steep dive. The engine noise resumed its normal in-flight roar as the nose came back to the horizon.

"OK, I'll climb up again and we'll do another one. Don't forget the correct recovery sequence, stick centrally forward THEN full opposite rudder then centralize the rudder when the rotation ceases. Still feeling OK?"

After a few more spins and stalls, I became accustomed to any attitude the aircraft adopted and eventually, thanks to Ian's patience and enthusiasm, I came to love aerobatics.

After the spinning and stalling exercises we began doing innumerable circuits and landings to prepare me for my first solo flight. I flew my first solo in the middle of March 1957 at High Ercall, a satellite airfield to Ternhill used exclusively for pupil pilots' circuits and landings. We had been doing circuits for thirty minutes and I noticed Ian seemed to be talking less and less. Finally, as we reached the end of one landing roll, he indicated he had control and taxied back towards the black and white chequered caravan beside the touchdown point of the duty runway.

"Feel all right about going solo, Guy?" was my first indication of the event to follow. I muttered something appropriate as Ian unfastened his straps and climbed out onto the wing, still wearing his parachute and bone dome. He secured the seat straps before banging on my bone dome and giving me the thumbs-up sign.

"Just one circuit and landing, make it a good one, I'll be watching, then taxi back here and pick me up and we'll go back to Ternhill." I returned his thumbs up sign and opened the throttle, unintentionally blowing him off the wing.

Nobody who loves flying can forget their first solo. The weather was chilly and damp, with a high overcast. The wind was down the runway and I had no problem keeping the aircraft straight as I opened the throttle and accelerated down the runway. Once airborne, I experienced the enormous thrill that comes with an event like this.

I turned left at 500 feet onto the crosswind leg and when the hands of the altimeter indicated 1,000 feet, leveled the nose. Continuing on to downwind leg, I called "Downwind" and carried out the downwind checks. Fifteen seconds after passing abeam the downwind end of the runway, I turned left again onto base leg. The rounded nose of the Provost trainer dipped below the horizon as I closed the throttle and began the descent to land. Gliding down at ninety knots with the flaps in the first position, I turned left onto finals as the wing tip came towards the edge of the runway.

"Romeo Foxtrot, finals."

"Romeo Foxtrot cleared to land." I selected full flap, the aircraft ballooned slightly then settled faster towards the runway. Suddenly I was over the 'piano keys', the white painted marks at the threshold, throttle completely closed, easing back on the control column, raising the nose a little higher, holding the wheels off, feeling for the runway, off, off, nose higher then the wheels touched, the tailwheel sank to the ground and suddenly my first solo was over.

Ian was waiting for me beside the 'Chequers' caravan as I taxied in. "Go all right? Looked OK from here . . . " The broad grin on my face told more than a thousand words. He strapped himself in and flew us back to Ternhill.

I witnessed my first aircraft crash at Ternhill and it couldn't have been in more comfortable surroundings.

Our course had been divided up into two sections, so that on a normal working day one half would spend the morning in ground school while the other went flying. Then at lunch time the situation would reverse. Next day, those who had attended morning ground school previously would change to the afternoon session and vice versa.

I had returned to the mess for an early lunch before going down to 'Flights' for the afternoon's flying. I was standing at one of the anteroom windows, sipping an after-lunch cup of coffee. Gazing across the sports field towards the aerodrome, I watched a Provost take off from the grass runway heading towards the mess. It contained Phipps, a member of our course, and his instructor.

One of the practice emergencies taught to students was a 'Fanstop', meaning engine failure after take off. Usually the instructor would close the throttle; simultaneously uttering the one order "Practice Fanstop" and the pupil was then expected to go through the correct procedure and convert his excess speed to height, trim for a glide of ninety knots and select an area to land in. Any time remaining would be spent trying to find the reason for the engine failing and getting it re-started if possible. In a real "Fanstop", if the engine couldn't be started in the short time available, the pilot was committed to the forced landing and should turn off the fuel and ignition to minimize the risk of fire. Naturally the fuel and ignition were not switched off in a practice Fanstop. When the instructor was confident his pupil would have got the aircraft down onto the most suitable piece of land, he would apply power and overshoot.

Naturally, before a pupil could be expected to do this, his instructor would demonstrate one to him. On an impulse, Phipps' instructor decided to demonstrate a Fanstop that day. Closing the throttle abruptly, he announced "Fanstop" and proceeded to reel off the emergency check list items, ending with "Fuel and Ignition Switches Off".

Phipps didn't realize this was a practice manoeuvre, and turned off his switches! When the instructor decided the time had come to overshoot, he pushed forward the throttle and heard the sound most hated by pilots of single-engined aircraft – silence!

In the second or so remaining before ground contact, he flared the aircraft for touch down, smashed through a fence, ripped off the main undercarriage and careened across the sports field, finally coming to a stop in a flower bed outside the anteroom. The aircraft was a twisted piece of metal but the cockpit section was relatively intact. We watched as the canopy was jettisoned and pupil and instructor struggled to free themselves from their straps. We raced the fifteen yards to where the crashed aircraft lay, expecting to find two injured pilots inside.

The scene that greeted us was not what we expected. The instructor was beating Phipps on the bone dome, crying out accusingly, "Switches, you turned the bloody switches off on me!"

Poor Phipps. This had been his first practice Fanstop demonstration and there was really no way he could have known it wasn't for real. When his instructor had called "Switches Off", he'd turned them off.

From then on he became known as 'Switches Phipps'.

At this stage of our training, pupils began falling by the wayside, or to use the phrase current at the time, to be 'chopped'.

A strange blend of attributes is required to fly an aircraft. The would-be pilot requires intellectual ability to be able to understand the function and operation of the parts of his machine; he must also be able to recall many facts and numbers such as maximum take-off weight, limiting speeds, cockpit checks, temperatures, pressures, be able to perform navigational calculations and manage fuel systems, while flying his aircraft safely and accurately.

We had several brilliant academicians on our course; surprisingly, some of them were the first to be chopped.

There was Alcock, who has already featured in an earlier tale. He was an aerodynamicist from Bristol (Brunel) university, who passed all his ground school exams with ease, but couldn't get an aircraft near the ground without terrifying his instructor, spectators on the ground and himself! When it became obvious his training wasn't progressing fast enough, he was passed to another instructor, in the hope he would learn better from a different person.

No such luck, he showed no signs of improvement so was passed to the flight commander for a chop flight. Amiable Henry Bilek, who made flying look so simple, could see no hope of Alcock ever learning to fly, so passed him on to the squadron commander, who echoed his opinion. Finally Alcock was up for the final chop flight with the Wing Commander Flying, a man with a reputation for passing practically nobody.

I arrived at flights in the late morning to witness Alcock's chop flight, having been in ground school until 12.30.

The mental pressures on a pupil pilot at this time are considerable; fellow students either avoid him with embarrassment or mutter their sympathy. The instructor conducting the chop flight must do everything possible to put the victim at ease without actually helping him fly the aeroplane. At the same time he must allow him to make mistakes and only take over when it is fully apparent that the pupil is not going to correct them himself.

Alcock was on final approach to the southerly runway running past our flight hut. It was a pleasantly warm spring day and several course members had dragged chairs outside to watch the flying.

Alcock's first approach was much too high and fast, with the nose of the aircraft pointed downwards at an alarming angle with the throttle closed. As it flew towards us, the noise of the air flowing over the surfaces of the airframe could be heard as a loud hiss. The aircraft neared the start of the runway, descending at a high rate; the student failed to raise the nose early enough to check the excessive descent rate and hit the runway hard. The shock absorbing undercarriage took the force of the impact and bounced the machine back into the air, where it hung suspended for a micro-second before dropping towards the ground. Just as the nose began to drop, we heard the engine noise increase and the aircraft recovered and climbed away. The instructor had taken over.

The remainder of Alcock's landings were as bad or even worse than that one. He seemed to position himself too high or too close in on final approach, so that his problems in getting the aircraft onto the runway at the correct speed and position were compounded almost as soon as he started his approach. At the end of his flight with the Wing Commander, the result was inevitably predictable and we murmured our sympathy as Alcock walked back from his aircraft for the last time.

An entirely different type of incident occurred to another pupil – Geordie Stephenson. With a nickname like that, it wasn't difficult to tell where he came from – Newcastle. He was a big fellow, aged about twenty and possessed an impressive list of academic credentials. Another intellectual! Geordie had been instructed by a sharp-tongued South African with a rather nervous temperament. When one of this instructor's students did anything wrong, he would take over control, correct the mistake then admonish the pupil, contrary to the Air Force's approved instructional technique. The correct procedure was for the instructor to demonstrate a particular manoeuvre, then let the pupil have a try and discuss it afterwards. For example, if a pupil was learning steep turns and began losing height, it would be better to wait for him to correct the mistake and learn from the experience. Afterwards, it probably wouldn't be necessary for the instructor to explain to his student why they'd lost height nor to tell him how to avoid making the mistake again.

Geordie unfortunately hadn't had the benefit of this type of instruction.

After an average amount of instructional time, his instructor decreed it was time for him to fly solo. They had been practising circuits and landings at High Ercall and the instructor taxied to the holding point beside the Chequers caravan, climbed out of the aircraft, and after securing all loose straps and harness, waved his pupil on his way.

Geordie ran through his cockpit checks, called the tower and was cleared for take off. He held the aircraft accurately on the runway centre line and the aircraft left the runway with gentle back pressure on the column and seemed to climb away normally. Things proceeded fairly normally until the final approach when observers on the ground noticed Geordie having difficulty keeping on the approach path. He was overcorrecting, causing the aeroplane to approach the field in a series of 'S' turns. He was also much too high so the continuous turning looked even more alarming because of his high rate of descent.

Geordie crossed the airfield perimeter well to the left of the runway and would have settled into marshy ground on one side if he hadn't applied full power and gone round again.

His second attempt at landing was as bad – but different. He managed to align the aircraft with the runway at the last moment but was too fast. With the long length of runway available to him, he could probably have eventually slowed down to a safe touchdown speed and landed, but now a further complication arose.

His instructor began talking to him from the ground. "You're too fast, man. Christ man, you're miles too bloody fast, go round again!" The engine roared and a distraught Geordie overshot again.

On the next approach, his instructor told Geordie everything he was doing wrong without once offering any constructive advice. "Get lined up on the runway and look at your height, man. How in Heaven's name do you expect to make it from that position? And look, you've shot through the centre line again, come on for Chrissake man, you're still too bloody high. Look at you . . . "

This situation continued for three quarters of an hour! Other aircraft doing circuits and bumps were sent back to Ternhill, leaving the airfield empty for Geordie's sole use. I don't know how many attempts he made at getting the aircraft down but it was obvious his confidence and fuel were running out fast. And without adequate quantities of those two ingredients, flying becomes difficult . . .

Eventually the inevitable happened; Geordie got the aircraft onto the runway, where it bounced and swerved alarmingly before running off the edge of the concrete into the marshy ground. The main wheels immediately became bogged in the grass and mud, tipping the aircraft up on its nose and damaging the propellor and lower cowling. Geordie climbed out, shaken but mercifully unhurt.

The aircraft was returned to flying condition in fairly short time but Geordie never flew solo again. He did resume his instruction, incredibly with the same instructor, but his confidence had been completely destroyed. Finally he was chopped.

By the end of the twelfth week of the course, all who were going solo, had done so.

There had been a sad procession of chopped pilots down to the railway station at regular intervals. Most were offered the opportunity to re-muster as navigators, which most accepted to keep flying.

One wonderful thing about the flying business was waking up in the morning thinking 'Oh good, I've got to go to work today.' I consider myself extremely fortunate that this attitude accompanied me throughout my flying career.

After my first solo and a few subsequent solo details, life began to take on a rosy glow. Here I was, eighteen years of age, being paid to do something I loved. Living conditions were good, the company of fellow pilots exhilarating and only the presence of young female company was needed to complete this paradise.

The elementary flying training stage of our course was now a quarter way through and we became entitled to some leave.

None of us had forgotten the antics of the 'Famous Five' who'd travelled to Ternhill on one ticket, so being determined to save money by emulating them, we announced we'd be traveling to London for virtually nothing. Nobody paid much attention when the 'Famous Five' muttered they'd do better than that.

Singer, Big Dick, and a rather sleepy individual we'd christened 'Mlig' after he'd fared rather badly in a Morse test and only received the letters MLIG in a message containing the words 'PhantoM LIGht', took the Pheasant Plucker while David Brown, Kiwi Green, Switches Phipps and Mike Parry the barrister chose to join me on the train. It was unanimously decided I would buy the one required ticket to London.

The train steamed into the station on time and we boarded with me clutching the ticket. We derived sadistic pleasure in noting The Famous Five were nowhere to be seen; then just as the guard blew the whistle to announce departure, they arrived at high speed and leaped aboard the moving train as it pulled out of the station.

I exchanged smug glances with the others; the Famous Five weren't as smart as us, they hadn't allowed themselves sufficient time to buy the important ticket!

Five minutes after departure, four of the 'Five' joined us in our carriage. "Haven't seen any sign of the ticket inspector, have you?" one enquired innocently.

"Nope but he could come along any time" we chortled smugly, wondering what their fine would be for boarding a train without a valid ticket. At that moment the door at the end of the carriage rattled loudly.

"Holy shit, it's the bloody inspector already!" the first of them exclaimed, standing up alarmedly. We were smarter and faster than they were and reached the toilet compartment well before them.

A small space designed for a single adult was a snug fit for five of us but we didn't have to endure the discomfort very long. A repetitive voice asking for "Tickets please, thank you," advanced nearer and nearer, finally knocking on our door.

"Tickets please," it repeated and I opened the door a fraction and passed it through the gap. We waited for maybe thirty seconds for it to be returned. After a minute, it hadn't been and I became worried, did the inspector somehow know there were five of us bottled up in the cramped compartment? After two minutes I signalled to Mike Parry something had gone badly wrong. He gestured to do nothing and remain silent.

After five minutes we realized our quandary. The inspector hadn't returned our ticket but we couldn't do anything about it. It was becoming hot and uncomfortable in the small space, the windows and mirror were steaming up, and standing on one leg is uncomfortable after even a short time.

"Got any suggestions?" I whispered, closing the door. Four heads shook in unison.

Our situation finally corrected itself when the door handle rattled and the anxious voice of a small boy jumping up and down enquired how much longer we were going to be. We almost fell over each other when I unlocked the door. The youngster threw himself into the compartment and locked the door.

We looked in the next carriage for signs of the inspector but found no trace.

"Might as well rejoin the Famous Five," I suggested. "They can tell us what happened." We trooped back to our seats and were surprised to find no trace of our five companions.

Our train journey continued through the industrial Midlands then further southward through the beautiful Oxfordshire and Hertfordshire countryside towards the capital. An hour later, we had ceased worrying about the inspector and our missing ticket. This was a big mistake, for half an hour before our arrival at St Pancras, a dark uniformed figure loomed in our vision and requested our tickets.

"You've already had it," I exclaimed.

"I'm afraid not, young sir," the uniformed inspector regretted. "I only boarded the train at Watford."

"But somebody asked to see our ticket when we left Wolverhampton!"

"I'm afraid not, Sir. Now may I see your tickets please?"

We had no choice but to admit we didn't have any. The matter could have become quite serious if Mike Parry hadn't employed his advocate's skills to plead our case and persuade the official we had been deceived by persons unknown.

"I'm going to have to ask you to pay for tickets then," the inspector finally pronounced. We grudgingly handed over the required amount of money and fumed over the incident for the rest of the journey.

On arrival at our destination we saw the Famous Five ahead of us and hurried after them.

"Did you get stung by the second ticket inspector?" we enquired, not mentioning what had happened to us.

"Naagh, we got down here for nothing," one of them announced breezily as they leaped aboard waiting taxis.

It took us several days to work out what had happened.

Chapter 12

Romeo Romeo, Wherefore Art Thou Romeo Romeo?

Once home again, I enjoyed recounting details of my flying career so far to the boys and girls I'd grown up with, but after a few days I became bored and anxious to return to flying.

A week later, and back in the camaraderie of the mess, we swapped lies over our exploits and conquests during our leave, then returned to the business of learning to fly.

With first solos completed, we were now in the middle of what the service called a 'consolidation period'. In plain language this meant flying solo as often as possible to increase our confidence, flying skills and experience. A normal morning's flying might start with helping the ground crew push the aircraft from the hangars before attending the day's met' briefing to learn what the weather was expected to do. At the same time we'd be advised of any other factors likely to affect our flying, such as work in progress on the airfield, royal flights, and active danger areas. Then we'd fly to the satellite airfield at High Ercall with our instructor, drop him off at 'Chequers' then do an hour's circuits and landings under his and several other instructors' watchful eyes. During one of these consolidation details, Little Dick had an unusual experience that was exciting for everybody but him.

Provosts on the tarmac, with Sunshine hangar in background.

The time of the incident was mid-morning; half a dozen aircraft were proceeding round the circuit with their pupil pilots, landing, turning off the runway, taxiing slowly back to the holding point, lining up on the runway when cleared, taking off and repeating the exercise six or seven times in an hour.

The Provost's engine was an Alvis Leonides radial of 550 horsepower, quite a powerful and complicated piece of machinery for an ab initio training aircraft. Our instructors had placed great emphasis during our dual sorties on the importance of monitoring the engine's temperatures and pressures in flight, for should some malfunction go undetected, for example the oil pressure beginning to drop below the normal operating range, then the engine would receive insufficient lubrication and begin to overheat. Initially the oil temperature would rise, followed by the cylinder head temperature until eventually the engine would 'cook' and finally seize up. The unfortunate pilot would then be faced with the choice of either a dead stick forced landing (without power) or a parachute jump over the side. Neither of these alternatives was particularly desirable so we quickly developed the habit of continuously monitoring our instruments.

On the ground, when the engine was only ticking over, temperatures and pressures could be expected to drop below the normal operating range.

Little Dick was on his third solo detail. He had soloed for the first time just before our leave and was now about halfway through his solo consolidation period. Dick had obtained a mathematics degree before joining the Air Force and was something of an academic.

I was also flying that day and had just turned down wind on my third circuit when I heard Dick's call. "High Ercall, this is Romeo Romeo, my oil pressure is only 15 psi."

There was a pause on the radio channel. Ahead of me I could see Singer at the end of his downwind leg while another aircraft on finals I knew to be Kiwi Green and his instructor returning from a dual detail, and another two other aircraft were on the ground taxiing. After some delay, the voice of Little Dick's instructor came over the radio.

"Romeo Romeo, what is your oil pressure now?"

"Fifteen pounds still," Dick answered calmly. Fifteen pounds per square inch was a dangerously low figure. The minimum acceptable in-flight figure was 60 psi and the normal operating range varied between 70 and 80 psi. Such a dangerously low figure could be an indication of imminent oil pump failure or a bad oil leak somewhere in the system. Dick's instructor gestured to the duty air traffic controller to get the station engineering officer on the phone.

"OK, now whaddabout your oil temperature, is that excessively high?"

"Negative, it's sixty degrees."

"All right, that's well within limits, now open your oil cooler fully and tell me if you can see any oil streaks on the windshield or fuselage." A brief pause ensued while Dick checked for traces of oil.

"No signs of oil anywhere that I can see," he reported.

"Fine, now what's your cylinder head temperature?" the instructor demanded. This question was the important one for if the cylinder head temperature was soaring above its usual limit of 230 degrees Centigrade, the engine wasn't receiving sufficient lubrication and would seize. The trainee pilot would then be faced with the awesome task of a dead stick landing in whichever field or paddock he could find in the sixty seconds before the aircraft hit the ground.

"A hundred and fifty degrees," Little Dick's voice replied quietly and calmly.

"I've got the engineering section on the line but the senior engineering officer is away at Shawbury today," the air traffic controller reported. Dick's instructor grimaced; it would have been good to have had his opinion on the problem.

The air traffic controller now joined the plot. "All solo aircraft in the High Ercall circuit continue circling at circuit height. Romeo Kilo and Hotel, you are to proceed back to Ternhill without your instructors, remainder keep orbiting." Each aircraft rogered its understanding of these instructions; the circuit was being cleared for an emergency. In the fire section adjacent to the tower, the fire truck's engine started into life as the fire crew prepared for action stations.

Now Little Dick's instructor spoke again, in carefully measured tones. "OK, Romeo Romeo, the final approach and runway have been cleared of all aircraft. What's your oil pressure now?"

"Er fifteen . . . but . . . "

"OK, is it steady or fluctuating?"

"Fluctuating, sometimes it drops to twelve."

"OK, don't worry too much about the amount of pressure; just be glad some lubrication is still getting to the engine." There was another long pause on the radio. I turned crosswind after flying the length of the runway at circuit height and tried to imagine Little Dick alone in the cockpit with oil pressure problems. His chances of successfully carrying out a dead stick landing away from the airfield without damage or injury were slight. The Provost was a heavy aircraft compared to the earlier generation of Tiger Moths; it glided at over a hundred miles per hour and came down fast. Everybody would be hoping like hell that Dick's oil pressure held out long enough for him to make it back.

The air traffic controller and instructor conversed briefly together before the latter picked up the microphone. "Romeo Romeo, the approach path and runway are clear. Now try moving the pitch lever back about three inches. This should stabilize the oil pressure, then check your oil cooler's fully open."

After a short pause, Little Dick's voice answered, confirming he'd done as instructed.

"Oil pressure fluctuating or steady?"

"Still fluctuating. Pulling the pitch lever back didn't make any difference to the revs."

"Shit! That means there's an oil leak in the propellor CSU[1]" Dick's instructor exclaimed to the air traffic controller. "The temperatures and pressures will go off the clock once the oil's drained away." He picked up

---

1. Constant Speed Unit. This device uses engine oil pressure to hydraulically alter the angle of the propellor blades.

the microphone again. "Romeo Romeo, head straight for the airfield and do a straight-in approach for runway two three . . . or one seven if you prefer, the wind's a light southerly. What's your present position?"

"Parked on the taxiway at the intersection of runway two three and three five!"

Dick had been on the ground all the time, taxiing back from his previous landing! While taxiing back to the take off point for another circuit, with the engine ticking over at minimum power, he had checked his engine instruments and noticed their readings were considerably different from what they normally registered in flight. In best academician's manner, he had reacted in the manner he thought best.

The Air Traffic Control service learned something that morning, as well as Little Dick!

Chapter 13

Gentlemen, Start Your Engines

Another pleasant facet of returning to flying after our short period of leave was the opportunity to move from the rather cold ex-wartime huts of the officers' mess annexe into the infinitely more comfortable surroundings of the mess.

Until moving there, we had been looked after by our two civilian batmen. Mine had a very debilitated appearance, with protruding bloodshot eyes, puffy lips and heavy jowls. Singer described his appearance very aptly when he remarked, "He looks like I feel in the morning." Our batman was usually the first thing we saw on regaining consciousness after a heavy session in the bar the night before and the sight of him did little to improve our already fragile condition. The wake up call was also accompanied by a cup of undrinkably strong tea which I had invariably tipped out the window.

So had everybody else, for while we were moving our personal effects from the annexe, I noticed a bare withered patch of lawn outside each bedroom window. Even the weeds had withered and died as if sprinkled with some deadly toxin.

It was very pleasant to leave the cold conditions of the annexe for the comfort of the mess.

It was also a refreshing change to get away from the batmen's two dogs, which as I have already mentioned, when they weren't sleepily depositing hairs and fleas on our beds were busy copulating on the lawn.

The Ternhill Mess was the large pre-war type, shaped like a letter 'H', built of brick with ivy climbing up its outside wall to give it a country club appearance.

I was allocated a ground floor room on the South west corner overlooking the sports field. Singer, Kiwi Green and David Brown had adjacent rooms on the same level while Big Dick was in the same wing but upstairs directly above my room. We now only had to walk thirty paces along the corridor to reach either the anteroom, dining room or bar, depending upon the time of day and our inclinations. Even more important, it wasn't so far to stagger to your room if you had got a little the worse for drink that evening.

Every Tuesday, except public holidays, all APOs not engaged on night flying or away on leave were required to attend a dining-in night. Sometimes the dining-in night was replaced by a guest night, when instead of just members of the mess being present, the Station Commander and his wife would attend, along with various wing commanders, squadron leaders and most interesting of all, outside guests.

Despite strenuous efforts on our part, most of us were still very aware of the scarcity of young females around Ternhill. Shropshire being a farming county, habitation was fairly sparse and the closest large towns were over fifteen miles away. Ever since the incident in the Pheasant Plucker some weeks earlier, neither Big Dick or I had encountered much luck in securing willing female company in our off-duty hours. We were beginning to show the symptoms of a malady which the vet on our course described as 'Noacytol' and which others described as "not getting it regularly".

A pretty girl in a ripe dress claimed everybody's attention when the Station Commander arrived for our first guest night with his wife and their twenty-year-old daughter Sonjah. I would bore the reader with the details of the CO and his wife but Sonjah remains indelibly imprinted in my mind.

She was what English mothers are fond of calling 'big boned', a genteel way of saying she had smooth white broad shoulders, firm well-proportioned breasts, very shapely hips and thighs, and a pretty face with an inviting look in her eyes. Less genteel folk would have said she had 'nut-cracking tits and bollock-cracking thighs'.

During the pre-dinner cocktail half hour, APOs clustered round Sonjah like bees around honey, completely ignoring the other guests who mainly comprised prominent businessmen and their wives, and a few local landowners. We left these people to Henry Bilek and his instructors to charm with their broken English; we had more delightful fowl to pluck.

During the opening gambits in the anteroom before dinner, it became quickly apparent that Big Dick seemed to have found the most favour in Sonjah's eyes, for she held onto his every word. In view of what happened subsequently, we often wondered what the mysterious something or other was that attracted her so strongly; was it his height (six feet eight inches), his youthful good looks, sparkling conversation, pleasant personality or something else? Later we decided the thing that appealed most to her earthy nature was his nickname.

When dinner was served, Sonjah seated herself beside Big Dick and listened to his every word. To his credit, he didn't monopolise the conversation and Sonjah did her share of talking.

We learned she had attended a well known girls' private school on the south coast of England but had had to leave suddenly so had gone to a very exclusive finishing school in Switzerland. She decided she didn't like the Swiss way of life and returned to England to enrol on a kindergarten teacher's training course. This had also met with her disapproval, although she giggled when she admitted this, and she had returned to the parental fold to decide what she'd like to try next.

In the hour and a half that dinner lasted, with a brief speech at the end, it became readily apparent that Sonjah was a young girl bored out of her mind desperately looking for a bit of excitement in life.

It looked like she had found it by the end of the evening. She had been heavily smitten by an attack of amorosa acuta (the vet's words) and was eagerly looking forward to seeing more of Big Dick.

The rest of us had spent the remainder of the evening conversing politely with the other mess guests, realizing we weren't in the running for Sonjah's attentions.

At the end of the festivities, I tottered the thirty or so paces to my room to grab some sleep before tomorrow's flying. I fell asleep instantly and slept so well that I missed a mysterious sound in the ivy above my bedroom window.

Now we were about a third of the way through the Elementary Flying Training syllabus and beginning to feel and look a bit more like professional aviators. The initial self-consciousness of dressing up in flying overalls and other impedimenta was now long gone and after wearing the equipment almost daily for three months, it had become very much our working dress. Familiarity with Air Force routine and discipline had also become ingrained. The Provost aircraft we flew were now as familiar to us as our left and right feet. We still occasionally lost a pilot to the 'chop', usually for failure to make sufficient progress, which meant the particular person had reached his personal intellectual plateau and was incapable of mastering the more advanced stages of flying training. Often an apparently perfectly good pilot would find great difficulty with some phase of his training. I have already described how some students failed to go solo; others failed to make sufficient improvement in the consolidation period after first solo while some never managed to cope with flying and navigating simultaneously. Throughout the course, we lost the occasional member at the instrument flying stage, during periodic progress check flights, night flying and formation. The thing we feared the most was a chop for OQs, two letters standing for officer qualities, a phrase which covered a multitude of sins from how you held a knife and fork to some reactionary political view you might be thought to hold.

By the middle of the course, our numbers had been halved by the 'chop'. The result was that we tended to look over our proverbial shoulders more frequently than usual, lest Damocles' sword be poised above our heads, but eventually most settled down to enjoy the flying, with the attitude that 'if you gotta go, you gotta go'. Once we stopped worrying about it, we flew better and the chop rate seemed to decline. It was certainly infinitesimally lower at the end of the course than it had been at the start, and in the later advanced (jet) stage of training, we only lost two members, one through lack of progress and the other a fatality.

After completing the required amount of solo consolidation circuit flying, we were introduced to navigation and aerobatics. The ground school lecturers covered the theoretical side of what we were going to learn in the air before we tried it with our instructors.

So having learned the theoretical side of navigation, we set about putting theory into practice. This was achieved by sending us on simple dual navigational exercises with our instructors before sending us off a second time to do it again solo. My first dual cross-country was to Worcester and back to Ternhill. As it didn't seem to pose any great problem to me, I was sent off next day to repeat the exercise solo.

After weeks of pounding the circuit, it was exciting to get away from it at last. After take-off, I turned onto course over the airfield, noted the time on my knee pad flight plan and concentrated on flying an accurate compass heading, altitude and airspeed. The en route waypoints came up as planned, I arrived overhead Worcester close to my estimated time of arrival (ETA) and turned back to Ternhill. I landed back in the late afternoon as the aircraft were being pushed into the hangars for the night.

Several members of our course came over to question me as I climbed out of the cockpit. "You were on Nav-Ex Two, weren't you? How did it go?"

"It went fine. It's only half an hour to Worcester so it's pretty hard to get into much trouble in that short a time."

"Try telling that to Big Dick, he seemed to encounter a few problems."

At this moment a somewhat embarrassed Big Dick came over looking rather furtive and recounted the details of his flight. He had been sent off on the same navigational exercise to Worcester an hour ahead of me. On reaching the correct quadrantal altitude overhead the airfield, he had glanced down at the columns of figures on his knee pad looking for the first course to steer, and had begun steering his ground speed! When his track over the ground didn't tie in with that on his map, he became confused. This was hardly surprising for his ground speed to Worcester was probably about 120 knots and the compass heading should have been 165 degrees. He was steering 45 degrees off the correct heading, getting rapidly lost. When he could make no sense of a comparison of his map with features on the ground, he exclaimed to himself "I'm all fucked up."

Unfortunately for him, he'd involuntarily pressed the transmit button as he spoke, which was easy to do since when flying solo, the only time you spoke was to a ground controller and pressed the transmit button to do so. Big Dick realized immediately what he'd done and hoped his transmission hadn't been noticed. Unfortunately it had; the tower operator responded immediately "Aircraft using bad language, what is your call sign?"

Dick sat there, going at two miles a minute in the wrong direction, not wishing to get into further trouble for using incorrect and obscene radiotelephony procedures. While pondering his fate, he realized his navigational error; he was steering 45 degrees off course. Feeling much better at having resolved one problem, he turned onto the correct heading, happy that he at least knew where he was now going.

"Aircraft using bad language, repeat your call sign," the tower operator insisted. Big Dick felt a lot more confident now as he replied, "I'm not that fucked up!"

Tower operators are human and most have keenly developed senses of humour so no further investigation was made to find who the phantom 'fucker up' was.

Gentlemen, Start Your Engines

Once again it was the weekend and now that we were more financially stable, other members of our course began to pool their funds to buy motor cars. In addition to our beloved Pheasant Plucker there was now a very sporty looking Morris open tourer, an ambulance and Lady Chatterley's Lover, the stately Daimler that had belonged to a senior course. Somebody else arrive in a Citroen with a crumpled rear bumper, which we immediately christened 'Citroën Presse '. The entourage was completed by Little Dick arriving in a very old London taxi he'd driven up from London in seven hours, claiming he could have completed the journey in three hours or less had the back doors not flown open every time he passed a cab rank.

With so many vehicles available to us, we decided to enter the Station Motor Club's Weekend Car Rally. After checking the mechanical details of our vehicles, we attended the drivers' briefing at lunchtime on Saturday. I was still rather concerned about the Pheasant Plucker's mechanical condition for although the oil pressure problem was cured, the headlight still had the disconcerting habit of going out on sharp bends or over large bumps in the road. Additionally, the holes in the rear passenger compartment floor had enlarged with use and only our familiarity with the car's structure prevented any of us from stepping through the carpet onto the road below.

The president of the Station Motor Club explained the rules of the rally. Entry was open to all paid up members of the Sports and Social Club, which meant that that as well as APOs, there would be instructors and their wives, accounts officers, engineering staff, ground crew and most important of all, a long retinue of female 'hangers on'.

The rally started on the tarmac then meandered across Shropshire to a hill called The Wrekin, then through Wellington before finally backtracking to one of the better local pubs, the Magpie and Stump in the middle of the low-flying area.

Speed was not the prime object of the rally, instead, drivers had to drive accurately to average 15 mph to the first checkpoint, where they would be handed a clue telling them where the next one was. Marshals would check each car through subsequent checkpoints to confirm they had successfully navigated to them and also to check how accurately the required *average* speed had been maintained. Now although 15 mph is a low speed for any sort of car, it becomes a different matter when it is a required average speed. If a particular car crew managed to navigate accurately by the shortest possible route, maintaining an average 15 mph posed no problem, but getting lost or spending too long deciding which way to turn drops your average speed. To maintain the required average, the driver must now go faster for the remainder of the course. As most of the entrants seemed to get more and more lost towards the end of each sector, their speed tended to increase in direct proportion to the uncertainty of their position.

Those who tried to beat the system by driving faster from the start, merely got lost sooner!

On this, our first motor rally, I set forth at the controls of the Pheasant Plucker with Singer, Mike Parry and F'karwee, the chief navigation instructor, who contributed absolutely nothing towards the successful completion of the course except to repeat at monotonous intervals the phrase 'man is not lost'.

The rally started on the tarmac area in front of what was known as 'Sunshine Hangar', named after a German intruder who had dropped a stick of bombs across the airfield during the war, hitting only the number two hangar and destroying its roof. For reasons known only to itself, the Air Force never repaired the roof and so the open structure became known as 'Sunshine Hangar'.

The clerk of the course recorded each entrant's details, relieved the driver of ten shillings, which he assured us we'd drink in beer later, and told us the starting order. There were twelve entrants. Each would be despatched at five minute intervals, to prevent a following car stalking the one in front – a dubious advantage since it would be doubtful whether the front car knew where it was going! Entrants would start in reverse order of speed, slowest first and fastest last, to ensure the rally didn't drag on too long and interfere with the evening's drinking later!

The Pheasant Plucker started third, with Singer navigating from an Air Force half-million topographical map while Mike Parry kept his eyes and ears open for signs of mechanical problems in the old girl and F'karwee continually reminded us "man is not lost".

The first stage took us down the A41 for a fairly straightforward run to the first check point. Singer had measured the distance as ten miles and we covered it in forty minutes, achieving an average speed of exactly 15 mph. Our time was noted down by the marshals and a white envelope handed to our navigator, with instructions for him not to open it until we were on our way again. I mentally noted the time as I put the Pheasant Plucker into gear and Singer tore open the envelope to find where we were headed next. Pulling out a single sheet of government notepaper, he began to read aloud as we approached the first of several cross roads.

"Which way now?"

"Dunno, hold on a bit."

"Come on fer Chrissake, you're the navigator. Not lost already, are you?"

"Man is not lost," from the back seat.

"Just pull over a minute and tell me what you make of this lot . . . "

I slowed the Pheasant Plucker to a stop and listened as Singer read the next clue.

When Shropshire's sun is sinking low,
And shadows wonder too and fro,
There is a place that lovers true,
Drive up to, perchance to view.
To that place now you must repair,
Check In with marshals atop there, who
Will Record Each Kar's Identity Number,
Then tell you on your way to lumber.

We repeated the verse several times before discussing its possible meaning.

"Where could lovers go at sunset?" Mike Parry mused aloud.

"Some motel maybe?" Singer suggested.

I overruled this suggestion, pointing out that the poem mentioned a view of the sunset.

"Couldn't they get a room with a window facing west?" Singer persisted. Mike pointed out the hopelessness of checking every motel in Shropshire, adding he thought the poem referred to some beauty spot with a view.

Then Singer had a brainwave. "What about the Wrekin then?" he referred to the 700 foot hill with a road running up it that lay to the south of our present position. I thought for a few seconds – there was a road to the top of the Wrekin with a car park at the top, a perfect point for the rally marshals to scrutinize each car then send it on its way again. The car park at the top was also renowned as a romantic place to take a girl friend on a Saturday night.

Mike finally clinched the matter for us. "Listen to this," he ordered. "Will record each kar identity number – why is the word 'car' spelt with a letter 'k'? Because by taking the first letter of each word, we come up with W R E K I N! That's it. The next checkpoint is the top of the Wrekin."

He made sense. I put the Pheasant Plucker into gear, above the sound of our fourth member reminding us 'man is not lost' and turned right for the Wrekin.

The Wrekin is 1,335 feet above sea level, conspicuously higher than the surrounding flat countryside. One of Shropshire's earliest aeronautical events took place there, when a glider designed and built by a local nobleman in 1853, was launched from the summit with his unwitting coachman aboard. The glider made it to the bottom of the hill OK, despite being excessively tail heavy and stalling several times on the way down, but broke apart on landing. The coachman emerged from the wreckage, white faced and badly bruised, and immediately resigned his position.

In 1956 a tar-sealed road led to the summit, where we found the rally marshals awaiting us.

The arduous climb to the summit had taxed the poor Pheasant Plucker's energy to the limit, and she was wheezing and spurting steam from her radiator cap as we pulled into the car park. In our haste to find the Wrekin we had ignored our average speed and it was rather gratifying to learn we had averaged sixteen miles per hour over the sector.

"Keep this up and you'll stand a good chance of winning," the chief marshal encouraged us as he handed Singer an envelope before waving this chequered flag to send us on our way.

I coasted slowly down the hill to cool the engine. Stately old ladies of the Pheasant Plucker's vintage aren't supposed to climb high hills and I was anxious to ensure she complete the course without suffering a mechanical haemorrhage. It would be quite an achievement to win the rally in such an ancient vehicle.

The next clue took us towards Shrewsbury, and Mike successfully navigated us to the next checkpoint at an average speed of 16 mph again. The marshals were highly impressed, we were now past the halfway mark and well ahead on points. Only a mechanical disaster or similar mishap could prevent us securing a high place at the finish.

Singer and Mike had now acquired quite a knack for deciphering the clues. Perhaps because of this we became overconfident and unfortunately turned left when we should have turned right, wasting ten valuable minutes before discovering our error. I turned the Pheasant Plucker onto the correct heading and made for the Welsh border. We now had to backtrack seven miles travelled in the wrong direction plus another fifteen to the next checkpoint in forty minutes. To do this we'd have to maintain an average speed of thirty-three miles per hour. To achieve this kind of speed through the twisting winding roads of Shropshire, with the weekend traffic from the big industrial towns to the east slowing us down, might be possible in a Jaguar or Austin Healey with a top speed over 100 mph, but in an ancient Austin Tourer, whose top speed downhill with the wind behind us was little more than 40mph, was almost impossible. We therefore decided to make up the points lost on this section by making more points on the last two.

With my right foot flat to the floor, we headed towards checkpoint number four. We felt considerable elation when passing several other entrants driving in the wrong direction, and it occurred to us that if enough of them made the same mistake, we might still score the highest points for this part of the course and retain our lead.

The Pheasant Plucker sensed the urgency and went splendidly, the needle of the speedometer seldom falling below 40 mph. It was now after lunchtime and everybody was looking forward to some refreshment at the next stop.

Singer leaned over the back of my seat clutching the RAF topographical map to give me further instructions. "Turn left at the next crossroads and keep on the main road," he instructed. "We've got about five miles to go so once we're on the main road, give the old girl her head and we'll get there without losing too many points."

I nodded my understanding and planted my foot hard down on the accelerator. Singer and Mike wound up the windows to reduce drag. Ahead of us but several miles away I could see what I thought were rally marshals waiting at the next checkpoint. As we drew near, it became obvious from their lack of activity that we were going to be the first past the post. The crews of the cars preceding us must have made the same mistake as us and were now probably heading off into the Midlands. I smiled an inner sense of satisfaction as we hurtled downhill and the speedometer crept towards fifty. In the back seat, Singer and F'karwee were holding onto pieces of the vehicle's structure to prevent being thrown around by the vibrating and shaking. It looked like we might retain our lead.

If it hadn't been for a sneaky little motorcycle cop suddenly pulling out of a side turning, we would have romped home to checkpoint four well ahead of the field on time and points. Unfortunately Fate had decided otherwise. The cop pulled out of his side turning unseen by us, drew alongside the Pheasant Plucker and turned on his siren. The sudden noise gave me such a shock I swerved violently and the old car began to

Dutch-roll alarmingly[1]. Singer and F'karwee clung to various parts of the vehicles structure while I struggled to keep on the correct side of the road and brake to a stop.

For us the rally was over; the cop would undoubtedly book us for exceeding the speed limit in a 30 mph zone, resulting in automatic disqualification. The rules of the rally were quite clear on this point; any infringement of the Highway Code and you were out.

Mike climbed out of the car while I was thinking these sad thoughts.

With a curt "I'll see to this," he approached the upholder of the law. We waited crestfallen for him to return and tell us our rally was over.

To our surprise, after a very short exchange with the officer, he got back in the car and bade us, "Get going for Heaven's sake, in case he changes his mind. Some of the others are coming up behind."

Mystified, I started the engine and managed to make good time to the next checkpoint. As we drew to a stop beside the first marshal, Singer reported the cop was stopping the other entrants.

As captain of the Pheasant Plucker, I decided now would be a good time for a short refreshment break before embarking on the next stage. The others helped me erect a picnic table beside our vehicle where, sitting on the running board, we discussed events so far.

"Bad luck about the last clue," I mumbled while munching on a sandwich. "But it looks like almost everybody made the same mistake. They've also been booked by that nasty little motorcycle cop."

Singer turned to Mike wonderingly. "What the Dickens did you say to him to get away so fast? I was certain he was going to book us for speeding – maybe dangerous driving too."

---

1. Dutch-rolling is an aeronautical term associated with swept wing high speed jet aircraft when they bank one way and turn the other.

Mike smiled mysteriously and only after being pressed for details did he reveal the answer: realizing it was all or nothing, he took a desperate gamble. It was after lunch time, about two thirty and the policeman was a large florid-faced typical beer drinker. Gambling on his legal intuition or leaning heavily on luck, Mike enquired in his severest court room voice: "Officer, do I detect the smell of alcohol on your breath?"

We won the rally, although it was touch and go right up until the end. As we drove the last half mile to the finish, the Pheasant Plucker's engine emitted an apologetic burp and stopped. The road was flat all the way to the finish and I thought at first we might coast over, but it was not to be. One hundred yards from victory, the gallant old girl rolled to a stop. We were beside ourselves with disappointment; we had been well in the lead after overcoming the forces of law and nature successfully, only to have victory dangled in front of us then snatched away. The Pheasant Plucker had let us down.

We hadn't counted on her friends when we resigned ourselves to defeat. Like many old aristocratic ladies, she had friends all over Shropshire and right on cue, one of them came to her assistance – Lady Chatterley's Lover, the stately old Daimler limousine that belonged to other members of our course, hove into view behind us. Mike waved them down, explained our predicament and persuaded them to push us the last hundred yards to victory. I felt a slight bump from behind as Lady Chatterley's front bumper made gentle contact with the Pheasant Plucker's tail feathers and suddenly we were speeding along the highway again.

Even at the last minute, victory tried to elude us. A traffic policeman was on point duty at the entrance to the car park of The Magpie and Stump where the rally ended. He held up a white gloved hand as we neared him, indicating for us to stop. I applied the Pheasant Plucker's drum brakes, cautiously at first then when she showed no inclination to slow down, I increased my pressure on the pedal. Still the old girl failed to respond and I suddenly realized that Lady Chatterley was still pushing from behind, oblivious of the policeman signalling us to stop.

I sounded the horn continuously and the Pheasant Plucker flashed her lights; the policeman realized something was wrong and leaped out of the way at the last moment. We coasted into the car park and rolled to a stop between two other entrants from the rally. Behind us, Lady Chatterley's Lover wheezed into the car park, her mission accomplished.

The last marshal recorded our time and bade us make for the Magpie and Stump's comfortable saloon bar, where the post-rally festivities were about to start.

When the last rally crew had made it over the finish line and the rally officials had totted up the scores, we were comfortably in first place. Our whole course had performed quite creditably on our first rally; an ex-ambulance had gained second place, probably because they had been the only other entrant to talk their way past the nasty motorcycle cop – by turning on the ambulance bell as he pulled out of his side turning.

Lady Chatterley's Lover was in fifth place. Considering they had competed against modern sports cars with an age advantage of twenty-five or more years over our venerable old ladies, we thought they had done reasonably well.

The evening's festivities carried on well into the night; the station skiffle group arrived shortly after 7 p.m. and by the middle of the evening everybody was working hard on tomorrow's hangover. Big Dick borrowed Lady Chatterley's Lover early in the evening and returned thirty minutes later with Sonjah, the CO's nubile daughter. Mike Parry and I established diplomatic relations with two French girls who'd been 'hangers-on' at the rally; F'karwee got pissed out of his mind and told everybody "man is not sloshed" at least a thousand times. At the end of the evening, eight of us were crammed into Lady Chatterley's spacious interior when somebody asked the way home.

"Ask the chief navigation instructor, he should know."

"Man ish not sloshed."

"Well, we're bloody close to it! Anybody remember the way home?"

"Steer two six zero for base," somebody volunteered. It was a call I'd hear frequently when leaving the pub late of an evening. The Magpie and Stump was slap in the middle of our low-flying area, due east of the airfield. There would be many a time that a student, low flying with his instructor, would suddenly be asked the course to take them home. If he was lucky, or a beer drinker, he'd recognise the Magpie and Stump and impress the instructor with the speed of his mental calculation by answering, "Steer two six zero for base."

Big Dick drove us back to the officers' mess before disappearing into the night with Lady Chatterley's Lover and the beautiful Sonjah . . .

Chapter 14

On a Wheel and a Prayer

Sometimes the long arm of coincidence can create situations more incredible than any writer of fiction can imagine.

The morning after my first solo cross-country, David Brown was sent off on the same navigational exercise (nav-ex) to Worcester. He completed the necessary pre-flight preparation and was soon airborne and climbing to cruise altitude.

The Provost's communications radio had two controls, an ON/OFF switch and a channel selector, marked with the letters 'A' through to 'J'. Channel 'A' was used for taxiing and circuit flying, channel 'B' was used as a listening out frequency when away from the airfield; pilots reported in over turning points on cross-country flights. It was a relatively quiet channel compared to channel 'A'. The other channels were used for formation flying, airfield common communication, emergency etc.

Each channel used two crystals, one to transmit and the other to receive. Sometimes after a period of inactivity, one crystal would drift off frequency and when this happened to, say, a receiver crystal, the pilot could still transmit but not receive – the aircraft could talk but not hear.

As David Brown climbed away from the Ternhill circuit, he clicked the channel selector from 'A' to 'B'. Unknown to him, the receiver was inoperative on this channel; he could be heard by others but he couldn't hear them.

While he was setting course overhead, consternation reigned below when the senior air traffic control officer (SATCO) in the tower spied a round object rolling across the airfield. He dispatched the duty fire crew to retrieve the object and report back to him.

Three minutes later, a rather out of breath corporal fire chief reported back to the SATCO carrying a Provost main undercarriage wheel. It took less than a minute to establish the wheel had fallen from David's aircraft setting course overhead. The SATCO called him on channel 'A' and, when he got no reply, deduced he had already changed to channel 'B'. He quickly instructed the controller monitoring that channel to advise the aircraft of its predicament.

No reply. They tried a second time and while they were debating the possible reasons for this, David called up: "Ternhill, this is Romeo Charlie overhead at 4,000, setting course for Worcester on Nav-ex Two."

The SATCO was first to grab the mike. "Romeo Charlie, you have lost a wheel from your undercarriage, return to the circuit and await further instructions. Do not land yet. Acknowledge."

They waited for the reply. None came.

"Romeo Charlie, this is Ternhill director, do you receive me?" the SATCO called. Still no reply.

"That's him up there," the deputy air traffic controller announced, gazing skyward at a small monoplane overhead. "Still continuing on his nav-ex. Why the devil doesn't he acknowledge?"

A corporal radio technician making the morning coffee ventured an opinion. "Prob'ly lorst 'is receiver, Sir. 'appens sometimes when the aircraft 'aven't been used for a while." He went into a technical explanation of how a crystal can change its frequency slightly.

The SATCO phoned the wing commander flying, who listened carefully before issuing instructions. "Get another aircraft and two instructors from

Headquarters Flight," he ordered. "Tell them to intercept him and indicate by signs that something's wrong. Tell the pilot I'll be down in two minutes to brief them on what I want done. Meanwhile, keep calling the aircraft in case his radio begins working again. Let me know immediately if you do re-establish radio contact with him."

The wing commander emerged from his office and clattered down the metal stairway to the tarmac below, where two pilots in full flying kit had pulled up in a Land Rover. "One of the students has lost a main wheel and the tower can't contact him by radio," he explained to them. "He's away on a nav-ex to Worcester so I want you to take off immediately, intercept him then formate on him at a safe distance. Now, listen carefully because I want you to take a wheel with you in the cockpit and when he sees you, formate a bit closer, hold the wheel up and point first to your undercarriage then to his. He should then realize there's something wrong with his aircraft."

The instructors nodded their understanding and lost no time getting airborne and setting off in pursuit.

It was now that the long arm of coincidence flexed its muscles twice. First when by a million to one chance, a main wheel dropped off their aircraft as they became airborne! Then, as they changed to channel 'B', their receiver stopped working. They could speak but not hear, and there was no way the controllers on the ground could advise them of their similar predicament.

Meanwhile, David Brown was enjoying his flight. The weather was fine and clear, the cockpit heater maintained a pleasant temperature and the nav-ex was going well. Beyond his starboard wing tip he could see the snow-capped Welsh mountains on the horizon, and to his left the squat shape of the Wrekin Hill could be clearly discerned. He glanced down at his chart for a track and ground speed check and decided he was on track and a minute ahead of his estimated time of arrival at his turning point over

Worcester. The aircraft was performing well, engine instruments checked out OK, heading was good, airspeed a trifle higher than usual but only by three or four knots. David settled back to enjoy the flight.

Ten miles behind him, two tense-faced instructors, unaware of their personal predicament, coaxed every last knot from their machine while squinting forward through the perspex windshield for a sighting of their quarry. Mental calculation had told them the other pilot was probably cruising at a ground speed of 120 knots. They were making 145 knots at a higher power setting and hence, assuming they were ten miles apart, they should be overtaking the other aircraft in about 24 minutes.

David checked his position again. Ahead and slightly to the left, he could discern the dis-used runways of Halfpenny Green disappearing beneath the left wing. He had made up two minutes on his flight plan ETA.

Overhead Worcester, he consulted his knee pad for the new heading back to Ternhill and smiled contentedly as he anticipated that in another hour he'd be back in the camaraderie of the mess, laughing, drinking and talking flying with his fellow students. This was better than being in the family business, which his father was always urging him to do.

As he levelled out on the homeward heading, he spied another aircraft travelling in the opposite direction, converging towards him from the right. He watched it anxiously for several seconds, it seemed to be at the same height and he was well aware of the usually inevitable outcome of mid-air collisions. The other aircraft had seen him, for it banked towards him and formatted alongside. As he watched, the canopy opened and a gloved hand waved to him. He grinned beneath his oxygen mask as he returned the wave. "That must be Switches," he thought, he was off on the same nav-ex today and maybe he wanted to indulge in a bit of dogfighting, a forbidden activity spiced with excitement, danger and fun which he would particularly enjoy.

The other aircraft drew closer . . .

The other aircraft banked closer. David was about to push the throttle and rpm levers to full power when he saw a second occupant in the other aircraft. This puzzled him, for students never carried passengers, other than their instructors on dual details, and he knew that dogfighting was frowned on. No instructor would engage a student in an unauthorized dogfight.

While he was puzzling this out, the other aircraft drew closer to his port wing tip. One occupant was struggling with something heavy, eventually managing to hold it aloft.

Even more curious, their right main undercarriage wheel was missing! David concentrated on keeping his aircraft straight and level while watching the wheel-less aircraft.

The passenger in it was holding something aloft, it looked like, yes it was, a wheel!

David was dumbfounded; somehow they had removed a wheel in flight and had it in the cockpit. He was convinced this was some sort of practical joke but couldn't begin to imagine how they'd done it.

Knowing the other two would be on the same channel 'B' as he was, he pressed the transmit button. "Terrific, now let's see you put it back on again!"

David returned to Ternhill and when he switched to channel 'A', air traffic control were able to advise him of his problem. Henry Bilek came to the tower and briefed him on the best technique for a single wheel landing.

Bringing the aircraft in on a long low approach, he set the serviceable wheel onto the runway while holding the other side off with aileron. Gradually reducing power, he cut the switches just before the broken undercarriage leg settled to the runway in a shower of sparks. The aircraft continued in a straight line for a few seconds then ground looped, ending up facing the opposite direction undamaged.

Taking into account his minimal experience, David Brown had done a remarkable job in getting the aircraft down without damage. The Air Force thought so too, because they subsequently awarded him a 'green endorsement', a sort of written pat on the back that was pasted into his logbook as a permanent record of his meritorious achievement.

The day's problems didn't end with David's safe arrival, however, for when the second aircraft arrived back with the instructors and the wheel, they resolutely refused to believe they had suffered a similar predicament. Not even the SATCO could convince them their colleagues in the tower weren't playing a practical joke on them.

Above the earnest assurances of just about everybody, they went ahead and landed conventionally on two wheels, finally becoming convinced when they ground looped shortly after touch down and ended up with the aircraft mounted astride the wing commander's Land Rover, damaging both vehicles and their professional pride extensively!

Chapter 15

Accidents Will Happen

Now we were halfway through the course. The flying was becoming increasingly more interesting. After the thrill of first solo, consolidation and cross-country navigation, we learned aerobatics, low flying, forced landings and later in the course came instrument flying, night flying and finally formation flying. I began to realized how fortunate I was to have Ian Wilson as my instructor, for as well as being an excellent pilot, he had the remarkable knack of being able to communicate his skill to his pupils. Furthermore, his main delight in flying was aerobatics, which we practised for a few minutes every day we flew. The result of this dedication to aerobatic flight was that his pupils quickly became very adept at handling the aircraft in any attitude, right side up or down. As an additional bonus, he was a very approachable person and sincere friend.

Monday morning following the motor rally, a rather pale-faced collection of APOs filed into the briefing room to listen to Deep Depression Dan, the station meteorologist[1], guestimate what the weather was going to do. After he had said his piece, the duty squadron commander stood up and advised us of any NOTAMS or Notices to Air Men. These would usually be in the form of airfield unserviceabilities, for example the grass at a satellite airfield might be unusable due to overnight rain or a royal flight

---

1. Most Air Force technicians like meteorologists and dentists usually had nick names. The other met' man was Cu Nim Jim (named after the infamous Cumulo Nimbus clouds or Cu Nims as they were referred to) and the station dentist was Fangs' O' Flanaghan).

might be transiting our air space and we were to avoid it at a safe distance. Other items might be prohibited areas, military firing areas, rocket ranges, and anything else affecting the safety of flight.

Pupil pilots and instructors noted down significant items on their knee pads or scraps of paper. The backs of our white leather flying gloves were used to write down essential information like emergency procedures, radio channels and similar gen. Looking round the briefing room that Monday morning after the motor rally, I couldn't help but be struck by the changes the Air Force had wrought in us in only nine months. Everybody's appearance in particular had changed from schoolboys in uniform to something a lot more mature; oil stains on flying suits were proof of continued use. Gloves, boots and bone domes all bore scratches or scars from continuous use. Technical phrases now came readily to mind and we no longer had to think what a QGH or SBA was.

Our numbers had changed too; fifty per cent of the original course hadn't survived the chop. Some had been chopped for officer qualities, most for lack of flying ability, some had resigned for personal reasons while others had been off sick so long that it was thought better to assign them to a lower course rather than to try to cram them to catch us up.

Of all the delights in flying, aerobatics and low flying held the most fascination for me. The Provost's ample wing area and powerful engine made it a delightful aircraft to aerobat and during my time at Ternhill the engine was upgraded in power by the manufacturers. We were now allowed to go up to eight pounds of boost, an enormous increase in power over the previous limit of plus four. The additional power was mainly appreciated during aerobatics – upward rolls were a lot easier and an extra 'half roll' could be coaxed out of the aircraft. At long last I was able to perform a decent half loop with a roll off the top, having always failed on previous occasions.

Aerobatics became even more enjoyable now that it was summer; often we would climb to eight or ten thousand feet above Shropshire and look westward into Wales, eastward into the industrial murk of the Midlands, north towards Snowdonia and south towards Salop. Finding an empty piece of blue sky clear of cloud, you could stand the aircraft up on one wing tip to carry out a 360 degree clearing turn to ensure nobody else was in your piece of sky, then commence a sequence of aerobatics while endeavouring to remain in that same patch of sky so that any imaginary spectators wouldn't lose sight of the aeroplane. The best way of achieving this was to string various aerobatic manoeuvres together to ensure you continually passed through the same point. This wasn't as simple as it sounds because the wind aloft tended to lure young aviators downwind unless some allowance and correction was made for it.

A typical aerobatic routine might be to lower the nose to increase the airspeed to 160 knots for a loop, then easing back on the control column to raise the nose up into a loop, relaxing the back pressure slightly at the top then allowing the nose to rise again at the conclusion of the manoeuvre until the aircraft pointed vertically upwards. Chopping back the power and applying rudder and opposite aileron produced a stall turn. The speed would build up rapidly in the ensuing dive and use of power and a bit of careful handling would be just right for a slow roll. At the conclusion of the slow roll another reversal manoeuvre would bring you back to centre stage for the next manoeuvre, which might be another loop, a Cuban Eight, barrel roll, Immelman, four point hesitation roll or anything you fancied.

The combinations were infinite and depended upon the skill and imagination of the pilot, for although a good instructor could train you to do aerobatics satisfactorily, a necessary sparkle of imagination had to be there already to make a really good aerobatic pilot.

Low flying was as much fun as aerobatics but infinitely more dangerous, since apart from the obvious hazard of flying into a tree, high tension cable, hill or tall building, the temptation to go below the minimum altitude of 250 feet was invariably too much for anybody. Many an aircraft had returned to Ternhill with twigs and branches dangling from the undercarriage. One memorable Saturday morning, *two* students hit objects while low flying. The first indication we had that something was amiss was the sight of a Provost in the circuit trailing vegetation from both main undercarriage struts. A buzz quickly spread round 'Flights' that it was Lord Jim, the Irish peer. He had become quite well known as a bit of a hellraiser on the ground and had now apparently extended his activities into the air.

After circling for half an hour, he approached the duty runway with fire engines and ambulances standing by, and performed a superb job of landing his aircraft safely without the wheels jamming and the plane ending up on its nose. He was taken off flying for a short spell while his incident was investigated then allowed to resume flying training.

The second incident the same morning was a lot more serious, although fortunately the student pilot survived. He had been on a solo cross-country nav-ex and either misjudged his pull-up to go over a large elm tree or was caught by a freak wind shear and literally flew through it. Only the immense bulk and inertia of the Alvis Leonides engine enabled the aircraft to ram its way through such an impenetrable object as a Shropshire elm. When it emerged on the other side, there was little left of the airframe to keep it flying for the propellor blades were bent and hopelessly out of balance, the engine's air intake was choked with leaves and branches and the aerodynamic shape of the wing was so badly distorted that it took all the pilot's skill to dump the aircraft into a convenient paddock on the other side.

The crashed Percival Provost.

On the Monday evening following the motor rally we were discussing the previous weekend's events over a few quiet beers in the mess. The prestige of having won the rally lingered on for many weeks after the event, probably because most aeroplane enthusiasts are usually also pretty interested in cars and couldn't fail to be impressed by a stately old 1935 Austin Tourer beating late model Triumph TR2s, MGAs, Austin-Healeys and other exotic automobiles. While we insisted to everybody that it was "nothing really", we didn't tell any admirers about the incredible sequence of luck that had accompanied us that afternoon.

Big Dick had suffered a close encounter of a strange kind after leaving us on Saturday nigh to drive Sonjah home. On arrival at her parents' house, he had parked at the end of the long driveway, intending to walk her up to the house. Sonjah couldn't wait that long for what was to follow and shortly after getting out of the car began necking furiously with him against the gatepost of the group captain's official residence. Dick realized tonight was definitely his lucky night and debated whether it might be better to return to the car and head off to a less conspicuous venue. By the time he'd finished thinking about it, such a course of action would have been impossible since Sonjah was smothering him with kisses while her eager young hands busied themselves about Dick's clothing.

He decided that amour was better than discretion and kissed her up against the gate post. Suddenly the night was rent by light, causing Dick to pause in his enjoyment of Sonjah as a large staff car pulled up beside them. The window wound down and the Station Commander's voice told Dick and Sonjah to "Get the hell out of here."

Dick mumbled something appropriate as he removed his hands from Sonjah's firm young breasts but the CO's voice roared "And take that slut with you!"

That night our conversation in the bar revolved around the forthcoming guest night, when the station chaplain was to be dined out. Air Force chaplains generally are a unique breed – infinitely patient and understanding and he had displayed all these characteristics at our weekly padré's hour, which was a welcome change from the high pressure academic pace of ground school. The idea was that this one hour in the week could be used to improve our souls and the padré tried to do this by answering any questions we might wish to ask. It says a tremendous lot for him that the only questions we ever asked were completely irrelevant, such as "Are we going to get Jet Provost trainers, Padré?" or "Who do you think will win the Epsom Derby next Saturday, Padré?". He would answer our questions with a very patient "I really wouldn't have the faintest idea," while ignoring any heavy snoring from the back of the class room.

The chaplain had been immensely popular among the student pilots, possibly because he had been a Rugby player of international standard and still played pretty well. There were a lot of New Zealanders at Ternhill, and as summer turned to autumn, rugby became a popular subject of conversation, after flying and girls.

The dining out night was a smash it. By 10 p.m. the speeches were over and the serious business of enjoyment had begun. The station skiffle group were playing in the bar, belting out innumerable songs on their improvised double bass, washboard and a couple of guitars. Few of the songs had any Air Force content, least of all *The Demon Barber of Clapham Junction*.

> *I am the demon barber of Clapham junction, last night*
> *I pulled my pud,*
> *It did me good,*
> *I knew it would!*

> *Chorus:*
> *Ease it, squeeze it, bang it on the floor,*
> *Ease it, release it, slam it in the door . . .*

During the evening, every officer and wife present came over to bid the departing padré a very fond farewell.

As I had a progress check with Henry Bilek, the flight commander, next morning, I left the proceedings earlier than the others, to try and get some sleep before the morning wake-up call. Singer and several others kept the festivities going into the early hours.

As I reached my room, I heard a strange slithering sound in the ivy outside. Sliding open my bedroom window, I glanced left and right but saw nothing. I was about to give up searching when I heard the window of the room above mine slam shut. I shrugged disinterestedly; maybe Big Dick had thrown something out the window before retiring.

Chapter 16

Biggles Flies Undone

Although most of our circle of friends in the Mess tended to be National Servicemen like ourselves, there was also a large percentage of career officers on the same course, who had signed on for eight or twelve year short service commissions. Since they were prepared to give the service considerable benefit from their training by eventually becoming members of operational squadrons, the Air Force was naturally reluctant to chop them unless they proved themselves completely unsatisfactory for the job.

Most of these career officers were perfectly normal intelligent fellows who intended to make a career out of flying; however, there is always an exception to any rule and this was true on our course.

His name was Robin Leach but his friends quickly christened him Biggles. Early on in the course we had noticed he wasn't quite up with the play. A subtle point, innuendo or joke in any conversation would have to be patiently explained to him before he could understand it.

For example, there was the instance of the flying instructor discovered having a love affair with a squadron commander's wife. Everybody expected the wronged husband to divorce his erring wife, citing the other officer as co-respondent. Since the worst two crimes for an Air Force officer to commit were bouncing a cheque or being cited as co-respondent in a divorce action, the flying instructor's days in the service seemed to be numbered. It therefore came as quite a surprise when the squadron commander and his wife were reconciled and posted to Hong Kong for two and a half years. Even more surprising was the presence of the wife's former lover at the farewell, laughing and drinking with his former mistress and her husband. Even more perplexing was the arrival of a beautiful light blue Austin-Healey sports car in the flying instructor's carport a few days later.

A few of us were discussing this one evening in the privacy of the Magpie and Stump, for it would have been indiscreet to discuss the subject in the mess. The evening had been a very quiet one and conversation had ranged over most topics of the day before settling on this latest piece of station scuttlebutt. We knocked the matter around for a few minutes then fell into silent speculation of what had really happened in that 'eternal triangle'. Had the husband paid the boyfriend off or had he agreed to leave the other's wife alone for a fee? Somebody finally put an end to the topic when he said, "Well, the one good thing about it is that the instructor's wife has stood by him throughout the whole affair."

We were about to murmur agreement and move onto another subject when 'Biggles' Leach astonished us with one of his rare utterances. "I don't see how a wife could stand by her husband when he's making love to another woman and not notice."

Everybody considered Biggles' remark with absolute amazement. Somebody finally suggested to him that 'she probably had A VERY GOOD BOOK'. This seemed to satisfy him and he remained quiet again.

Things continued slowly but fairly routinely for Biggles until one morning about a third of the way through the course, when he had spent an hour with his instructor practising spins and stalls. After returning to Ternhill to refuel, he was sent off again to practise stalling and spinning on his own.

We were forbidden to fly higher than 10,000 feet because of the danger of oxygen starvation to the brain (anoxia) in the higher and more rarified atmosphere above. Biggles decided, for reasons which even he couldn't explain later, to climb to 13,000 feet. This unusual decision was about to save his life.

After performing the necessary checks at the top of climb, he put the aircraft into a spin. With the throttle closed and control column hard back in his midriff to reduce airspeed, he kicked the rudder to the right as the aircraft entered a stall. He began counting each revolution as the aircraft span earthward . . . one, two, three . . . time to recover!

Now, incredibly, he realized he'd forgotten the correct spin recovery technique! Meanwhile, the aircraft continued spinning downward while he tried to sort out his spin recovery procedure. After four, five, six turns they had descended below seven thousand feet. He had the control column hard back and over in the opposite direction but still the aircraft refused to respond. Seven, eight, nine turns, he gave the engine a burst of full throttle but still continued earthward. He waggled the control column from side to side, opened and closed the throttle several times and generally tried everything he could think of. He even tried trimming hard back on the elevators but it didn't seem to make any difference.

Still the earthward dive continued: ten, eleven, twelve turns of the spin and the altimeter was unwinding like a demented Catherine wheel, the hands almost unreadable they were spinning down so fast. He continued trying to recover as he plunged through 4,000 feet, plunging into a thin layer of cloud at 3,000 and shooting out the base at 2,700 still pointed vertically at the earth below; an anxious glance at the altimeter made him realize he probably wouldn't recover before hitting the ground.

We had been told the minimum safe height to bail out was 1,000 feet above the ground and Biggles decided that this was no place for a growing lad. Removing his hands and feet from the controls, he reached out towards the canopy emergency release handle; he was going to bail out.

The moment his hands were off the controls, the spin slowed then stopped! The wings levelled, and the nose began to rapidly rise to a position above the horizon. Biggles gave away the idea of bailing out and concentrated on levelling the nose back on the horizon. After a lot of re-trimming, the aircraft was back in straight and level flight. Keeping his hands and feet firmly on the controls, he decided that was enough spin practice for today.

After landing back at Ternhill, he decided not to mention his close shave with death to anybody, preferring to fill in the routine paperwork before proceeding to the crew room to sit down and wait for the shaking to stop.

Nobody was any the wiser until next day, when a different instructor told his pupil to go out to the same aircraft ' . . . and do the pre-flight check while I sign the paperwork'. By the time he'd reached the aeroplane, his student was strapped in and the engine was running.

The instructor climbed up onto the wing and stroked his chin puzzledly, something was wrong with this aircraft, the upper surfaces of the wings should have been curved and smooth, but on this one they were wrinkled and buckled, like a sheet of corrugated iron. He glanced at the 'G' meter in the cockpit to determine whether the aircraft had perhaps been over-stressed. It read an incredible thirteen 'G'! Biggles had overstressed the aircraft the day before, subjecting it to thirteen times the force of gravity, over double its safety design factor. It was designed to safely withstand 6 'Gs', which was ample, for an average pilot would begin to 'black out' somewhere between four and five 'Gs'.

Biggles was questioned but incredibly he was allowed to continue his training. We all waited for the next incident.

A few weeks later, he set off on a two and a half hour solo cross-country that would take him a considerable distance away from his home base. During this time away, he got himself badly lost, so lost in fact that he had absolutely no idea where he was.

After considering several alternatives, Biggles had a sudden rush of shit to the brain and decided to land and ask somebody the way, reasoning that he was rapidly using up his remaining fuel in getting further and further lost.

Just as he made that decision, he spotted a conveniently large green area below, with plenty of room on which to land his Provost trainer. This grass area was to the west of a very large town which he'd been unable to identify on his map. (Subsequent investigation revealed the town was London, a curious landmark to sight when his original flight plan had been to Waddington in Lincolnshire then up to Sheffield before returning back to base. He had literally almost flown 'off the map'.)

Descending to a thousand feet, he carried out an investigatory circuit prior to landing. The area looked absolutely perfect, with a large mown grass as smooth as a cricket pitch, and a large country house on one boundary, where Biggles was confident somebody would be able to tell him where he was.

Luck was with him that day, for after touching down on the smooth grass area and rolling to a stop, a handsome young couple walking their dogs approached the aircraft to see whether he needed assistance. The husband leaped up on the wing root, slid open the cockpit canopy and quickly pointed out their position on the map when Biggles explained his predicament.

Biggles thanked him for his kind assistance and was soon airborne and setting course back to Ternhill. His last glimpse of his helpers was the tall slim figure of the husband walking with his hands clasped behind his back across the lawn to where his wife waited with their corgi dogs.

Once again, Biggles didn't mention this escapade to anybody, not because of any subtlety on his part, but simply because he saw nothing wrong in stopping and asking the way!

Next morning, the media were full of an account of a light aircraft landing on Smith's Lawn[1] at Windsor and asking Queen Elizabeth and the Duke of Edinburgh the way! There had been no other observers to the

---

1. Smith's Lawn is a polo ground in Windsor Great Park.

incident and nobody had noted the registration number of the aircraft, which was thought to be an Air Force machine, although there was considerable doubt what type it was.

Four of us were discussing the matter after lunch over coffee in the ante-room when Biggles amazed us all by declaring "Oh, that must have been me. I wondered who the couple with the corgis were. I meant to get their name and address to write and thank them."

It was several seconds before any of us spoke, for the enormity of his revelation had overwhelmed us. We finally recovered the use of our tongues, and emphasized to Biggles he must never breathe a word of this to anybody if he wanted to remain in the Air Force.

The only other incident I witnessed with Biggles was when a crowd of us went pigeon shooting one Saturday afternoon. The disused hangars on the far side of the airfield housed large flocks of pigeons, so while strolling over to the hangars, we drew straws to decide who would go into the hangars to scare the birds out for us to shoot.

It goes without saying that Biggles drew the short straw.

While we pushed the hangar doors open a few inches, Biggles sneaked through a small door at the other end. Once inside, he began shouting and banging on the corrugated iron walls to scare the pigeons out. He succeeded quite well, the birds panicked and most of them flew out through the narrow gap between the hangar doors. As each pigeon emerged, it was speedily killed by a lethal dose of twelve gauge lead shot from our waiting guns.

After the initial flurry of birds through the door, the remainder displayed a marked reluctance to leave the safety of the hangar to get shot. Biggles continued shouting and banging away inside the hangar, causing the last few birds to emerge in ones or twos at irregular intervals. Meanwhile, we waited outside, with our guns aimed at the narrow gap between the doors and fingers on the trigger ready to fire.

Having flushed out the last pigeon, Biggles walked through the gap between the doors, announcing, "That's the lot, let's move on to the next hangar."

Nobody knows why he didn't get shot eleven times as he emerged!

Eventually, when we progressed to more advanced exercises in our flying training, Biggles began to lag behind and failed to reach the required standard in the allotted time. He was subjected to the usual procedure of check flights, first with a different instructor, then with Henry Bilek our flight commander, who passed him further up the chain. Everybody who flew with him was unanimous he'd never reach the required standard of flying required of an Air Force pilot. His main problem was navigation, although general aircraft handling was also below standard.

We were in the bar before dinner when Big Dick came in with the news of his chop. "Hey, heard about Biggles?"

"Naagh, what's he done this time? Defected?"

"No, nothing like that, he's been chopped for navigation, or so I understand."

"Sorry to hear that but it doesn't surprise me. He wasn't the brightest of individuals, was he? I mean, that incident on Smith's Lawn, he should have been chopped for that alone."

Dick agreed then continued. "Yeah, maybe, but anyway, he's been chopped for navigation but as he's on a short service commission, guess what they've offered him?"

We couldn't guess.

"Navigation training! They've chopped him for navigation and now they've offered him a job as navigator. Isn't the Air Force amazing?"

We agreed; it was Mike Parry who had the last word on the matter. "I'm surprised they didn't transfer him to RAF Intelligence," he commented.

We never saw Biggles again but we heard about his exploits

occasionally. He passed his navigator's course successfully, despite passing fifty miles to the wrong side of Mount Snowdon on his final check out, and became a navigator on Beverlies – a large very slow aircraft, which in the words of an ex-Beverly pilot, could transport either a fully equipped battalion of troops eighty miles, or one Weetabix round the world.

Chapter 17

Messerschmitts at Eleven O'Clock

It wasn't unusual for the station adjutant to receive regular requests from Rotary Clubs, Air Scouts, local flying clubs or other organisations for some of the more highly decorated flying instructors to give talks of their wartime flying experiences.

Although such talks were excellent public relations for the Air Force, as well as being much appreciated by the audiences, they were detested by the speakers, who feared accusations of 'line shooting' from their colleagues back at base. So when a last minute request arrived one morning from the Salop Country Women's Guild for one of these talks, every available instructor hastily grabbed a student and pleaded that pressure of work prevented his participation.

In desperation, the adjutant phoned around Flights and felt an enormous sense of relief when he found Henry Bilek engaged on administrative duties in 'A' flight. Without any preamble, he informed Henry he was to talk to the Country Women's Guild in two hours' time.

Henry's participation as a Hurricane pilot in the Battle of Britain equipped him admirably for the task but his heavily accented English would be difficult for any audience to understand. He informed his caller that he had no desire to waste "twenty or sirty focking minits spicking to a group of ploddy vimmen" when he had far more important things to do. The adjutant sternly informed him this was a direct order from the station commander which he would obey or else . . .

Singer and Big Dick had just returned hot and sweaty from flying when Henry exited his office in a foul mood. Recognising there was strength in numbers, he ordered them to come along for moral support. After a quick wash and a polish, they accompanied him to Market Drayton, where the Anglican vicar, a nervous young man in his mid-twenties, met them at the village hall. He was delighted that somebody had appeared at such short notice and informed them he was an avid enthusiast of Second World War aeronautical history and had read almost every book on the subject.

"Dowding, Bader, Adolph Galland, Stanford Tuck, I feel that I almost know them personally," he effused enthusiastically as he led them into his study, where the bookshelves were lined with beautiful plastic model aircraft of that era. He picked up a Spitfire and caressed it lovingly.

"Beautiful, weren't they?" he turned to Henry for affirmation. "Although I believe the early models were no match for the Focke-Wulfes and G model Messerschmitts?" Henry refused to be drawn into discussion, which left the clergyman no option but to lead them into the village hall, where their excited and expectant audience awaited.

A short flight of steps led them up onto the stage, in front of which an audience of thirty or more elderly ladies in flowered hats twittered excitedly with anticipation. From their vantage point on stage, the flowers hid the audience's faces, giving Henry and his companions the weird experience of confronting a human herbaceous border.

"Today we will have the pleasure of listening to Flight Lieutenant er sorry, I've forgotten your names . . . " the vicar turned to Henry.

"Bilek."

"Er yes, how silly of me, Bill Leck and two students from his station whose names are . . . ?" He turned back to Henry.

"Singer," Bilek pointed to his left. "And Big Dick." Several ladies blushed, others giggled.

"Er yesss, well Flight Lieutenant Leck and er, his two companions, will now entertain us with a blow-by-blow account of the air war over southern England in the summer of 1940." The clergyman stepped back, leaving Henry at the centre of attention.

He used a convenient blackboard on which to draw a map of Central and Southern England and the north coast of France, drawing dividing lines across England denoting the various Fighter Command Groups responsible for the defence of Southern England – 11 Group under Keith Park and 10 Group under Leigh Mallory. The French coastal areas became peppered with various Luftwaffe units.

"After overrunning France, Belgium and Holland in 1940, zer ploddy Chermans zenn decided to advance on England," Henry began an explanation of where the various squadrons were stationed, placing some emphasis on the Polish squadrons. Singer and Big Dick were as enthralled as the rest of the audience as Henry's first-hand account of fighting in the Battle of Britain unrolled. He seemed to remember everything from that summer of 1940 – squadron numbers, strengths and types of aircraft, aircraft and pilots downed by the Luftwaffe, enemy losses, until he reached the critical first week in September when it became a simple arithmetical question of whether the small number of RAF fighters remaining would be sufficient to repel the enemy bombers intent on reaching London and other major cities.

The excitement of reliving those times resulted in Henry becoming highly agitated and sometimes running out of words, causing him to resort to the use of profanities in every sentence, much to the embarrassment of the vicar, who coughed loudly whenever a profanity was uttered. Eventually Henry became irritated at these interruptions and would stop in mid-sentence to glare angrily at the clergyman for several seconds, hoping to stop his censoring.

The audience were enthralled and held onto his every sentence as he started to recount his own squadron's involvement on September 15, the day the Battle of Britain could have turned either way.

"Zen Uxbridge scrambled us for a sird sortie chust before ploddy lunch and vectored us towards unidentified bastards at twenty sousand feet over zer ploddy Channel," he recounted. "Vee were flying into zer sun, climbing to get above zem before going in for zer attack." Big Dick later told us they could have heard a pin drop as this first-hand account of history unrolled. In the excitement of the moment, Henry at last seemed to have become oblivious of the occasional interruptions of loud coughing from the vicar.

"Zen chust as vee got above zeese buggers (coughing), my number two reported twenty plus Fokkers (more coughing) five sousand feet above us, attacking out of zer sun . . . "

"Er perhaps I should explain to you ladies that a Fokker was a type of German aeroplane," nobody paid any attention to the vicar when he interrupted the Battle of Britain, in an attempt to minimize the audience's embarrassment. Henry ignored him, busily explaining how the enemy aircraft below them were a diversion to draw his squadron's attention away from the larger swarm of fighter aircraft above.

"Zees Fokkers dived out of zer sun . . . " Henry gesticulated excitedly with his hands as he spoke.

"Er, I think you really should explain to these ladies that these Fokkers were the new Focke-Wulfe 190 German fighters," the vicar pleaded rather than suggested. Henry stopped in mid-sentence and eyed the cleric with exasperation. "Fokker refers to the type of German fighter, doesn't it . . . ?" the vicar pleaded lamely, conscious of having made his speaker very angry. Henry Bilek gave this source of so many interruptions a ten second withering glance before responding. His patience had been stretched paper thin.

"Zees fokkers were in ploddy Messerschmitts," he informed the vicar angrily.

Chapter 18

Torture

The course numbers now appeared to have stabilized on fourteen of the original thirty and we began to hope the 'chop' was now something of the past.

Unfortunately, when we began to learn instrument flying, it reared its ugly head again. This time in my direction.

I had always been mystified when I heard a member of a senior course had been chopped for instrument flying, and even confided to friends that I couldn't understand the problem, since we used the six instruments on the blind flying panel every time we flew. What difference did it make if you couldn't see outside and had to fly by sole reference to them? I couldn't understand why the Air Force had to cover up the cockpit windows and teach us to fly by instruments alone, it seemed a complete waste of time because we could already fly on instruments!

I hadn't heard of the effects of the ampullary canals, those little ducts in the ears which enable us to keep our balance. As long as man is on the ground, with his eyesight available to back up what the ducts in his ears are telling him, all is well and he is able to maintain a vertical equilibrium. But if false sensations confuse the canals, for example as on some fairground rides, the eyes will normally detect that the information from the canals is false, and will override the false sensations. Take away the sense of sight by covering the cockpit windows, and you have only the wrong signals from the ear canals to guide you. They will invariably lead you astray.

So in an aircraft, when the outside visual reference is lost, as happens in cloud, the brain's only source of attitude information comes from these canals, which can be hopelessly misled by the aircraft's accelerations. It is for this reason that nobody is able to fly in cloud without mechanical devices to tell him which way he is pointed and even which way up he is! This inability to distinguish the right way up is termed disorientation; it normally takes a pilot less than a minute to end up in a spiral dive when his visual and mechanical references are removed. This spiral dive is known as the 'graveyard spiral' because of its often lethal consequences.

My first introduction to the monster 'disorientation' came one afternoon, when we had arrived at flights after the lunchtime met briefing, with everybody keen to get into the air. The day had looked so promising that even Deep Depression Dan, the miserable meteorologist, had been quite cheerful during briefing.

I shrugged philosophically on seeing from the programme board in flights that I was down for a dual detail with my instructor; a solo aerobatic detail on an afternoon like this would have been delightful but Ian would probably conclude our flight with ten or fifteen minutes of aerobatics anyway.

My thoughts were interrupted were interrupted by the arrival of our instructors in a gaggle, already clad in flying clothing. Ian was carrying something that looked rather like a pair of ski goggles.

"Afternoon Guy. Feeling fit and well, I hope?"

"Afternoon, Sir. Yes, I'm feeling fine; it looks like a wonderful day for flying."

My instructor wrinkled his nose distastefully. "Yes, well, er, come into the briefing room, will you. I want to talk about what we're going to do today."

I followed him down the passageway into the small room beside the crew room. Instructors used it to brief their students on what they were about to teach them in the air. It contained a table and two chairs, a blackboard and chalk. Ian closed the door and spoke in a serious tone.

"Instrument flying for you today," he held up the goggles by way of explanation. I already knew from other pupils that these dark goggles were used to simulate being in cloud. The goggles allowed the student to see inside the cockpit perfectly but amber screens covering the windows prevented him seeing outside, because the combination of blue and amber is black. The Air Force had contrived a marvellously cunning way of allowing the instructor to see outside while his goggled student could only see the controls and instruments in the cockpit. This was the standard method of teaching instrument flying in the 1950s and was referred to as 'two stage amber'.

Ian briefed me carefully on the forthcoming exercise, frequently referring to disorientation. "Don't trust what the seat of your pants is telling you," he stressed. "It's more likely to be wrong. Just watch the six basic blind flying instruments and keep the aircraft in trim at all times."

I took all this in rather disbelievingly; instrument flying was going to be a piece of cake, a mere formality before going onto more exciting things like night flying and formation.

We took off on the sou'westerly runway for my first attempt at instrument flying, with Ian doing the take-off. Turning left, we cleared the aircraft traffic pattern and once the aircraft was stabilized and trimmed in the climb, he handed me the goggles while he slid the amber screens across the cockpit windows.

"Into the torture chamber you go," he joked. "Just watch those six blind flying instruments and try to ignore any sensations your body might give you."

I placed my right hand on the control column and watched the instruments. The nose of the little aircraft on the artificial horizon was slightly above the horizon line, with the wings level. The climb and descent meter indicated a rate of climb of five hundred feet per minute, the compass remained steady on south and the airspeed indicator seemed locked on 115 knots. I concentrated on using small control movements to keep the various instruments' needles in the required positions. It all seemed so easy, what was all this fuss about instrument flying about?

"Don't forget to spare an occasional glance at the engine instruments. Boost pressure's dropping off with increase in altitude so you'd better do something about it."

I glanced at the centre engine instrument panel and saw the engine's boost pressure had indeed dropped from the normal climb reading. I moved the throttle lever forward with my left hand while concentrating my attention on the boost pressure gauge until it read the correct figure.

"Watch your altitude all the time," Ian's voice admonished gently in my earphones. I spared time to glance at the blind flying panel – dammit, the nose had dropped in those few seconds and we had entered a descending turn. "Level the wings first, then get the nose on the horizon. Come on, level those wings. Hey that's the wrong way!" I tried desperately hard to correct the turn we had entered. The nose was well down below the horizon and the engine was still set on climb power The airspeed began to increase – 140 knots, 150, 160, good Heavens, we're fast enough for a loop; 170 knots, the compass had swung to 100 degrees and despite my every effort, we were still turning. I pulled back on the control column to stop the airspeed increasing; the needle was now dangerously close to the maximum limiting speed.

"Level the wings first, Guy," the soothing voice instructed. I moved the control column further to the left; I could tell we were now in quite a steep right turn. I moved the stick further to the left and pulled back harder. Still the compass card kept turning and the airspeed was now over 200 knots. The altimeter was unwinding fast, we had lost 1,500 feet already.

Suddenly an unaccustomed glare of light hit my eyes as Ian removed the goggles from my sweat-plastered face.

"Look outside, will you? We're in a steep spiral dive with the wings now past the vertical, which is why you couldn't decrease your airspeed by pulling back. Now follow through on the controls with me and we'll try again." Ian recovered the aircraft to a more normal position and we commenced climbing again.

"Level out at 6,000 and keep scanning those instruments," my instructor's voice tortured me.

I stole a glance through the clear Plexiglass panel above my head, which didn't have an amber screen across it. It was a beautiful English August afternoon; a mile below us, people were playing cricket, drinking cold beer in pubs or working in cool air-conditioned offices while I was embroiled in this Plexiglass sweat box, trying to control a dervish that took every opportunity to twist itself into impossible attitudes.

"Keep scanning those instruments," Ian repeated unnecessarily. I was about to remind him that my airspeed was spot on the correct figure, when I remembered my heading – the artificial horizon told me the wings were banked fifteen degrees to the left and the gyro compass confirmed we had deviated from our heading by twenty degrees or more. I banked back onto the correct heading, watching the airspeed, then remembering the vital engine instruments, took a quick glance at the boost and rpm gauges. Boost pressure was a bit low so I nudged the throttle forward and the needle returned to the correct indication.

"Don't forget the oil temperature too," my torturer continued.

"Fer Chrissake, I can't watch everything at once," I thought to myself while the sun beat down on the Plexiglass canopy and sweat rolled down my forehead, under the goggles and into my eyes then inside the oxygen mask. The oil temperature was high so I opened the oil cooler control a notch.

"Keep that scan going!"

I shot a glance back at the blind flying panel, confident that nothing much could have happened in the ten or fifteen seconds I'd devoted my attention to the engine instruments – surely I would have felt if the aircraft had begun another spiral dive? We were descending slightly and the airspeed had increased. I checked the wings were level before easing the nose above the horizon and we resumed our climb. The airspeed indicator returned to the correct climb figure and I checked the other blind flying instruments. Airspeed I knew was OK, the artificial horizon told me the wings were level and the nose fractionally above the horizon, climb and descent indicator read 600 feet per minute climb, turn and slip were centred, the compass indicated we had deviated off heading again. I banked back onto one eight zero.

"I said level out at six thousand, remember?"

A quick glance at the altimeter and I realized I had forgotten Ian's instruction to climb to and level out at 6,000 feet. We were now passing through 6,500 and still climbing. I eased the control column forward and the climb and descent indicator told me we had begun to descend. As confirmation, the altimeter began to unwind – 6,400, 350, 300, must be careful not to go through 6,000. I watched the hundreds hand of the altimeter as it neared the top of the dial.

"Keep that scan going; don't concentrate on one or two instruments at the cost of the others."

To hell with it! I needed a second pair of eyes, the airspeed had increased again – of course, I'd left climb power on! I pulled the throttle back a few inches and fiddled with the rpm lever. "Twenty-two hundred rpm and minus two pounds of boost pressure should bring the speed back to the required figure. Come on now, 2,200 rpm not 2,250, the airspeed's returning back to the correct figure, increase the boost to maintain that speed. Bloody hell, look at the altitude, we've gone through 6,000 again! Put the power back up to the climb setting, watch the speed, raise the nose. Approaching 6,000, level out now. Look at the heading! We've deviated off twenty-five degrees!"

"Keep that scan going! Don't forget your engine instruments, level the wings, you're descending. Raise the nose, lower the oil temperature. Turn on to North, climb to 7,000, increase the power first. Come on, more power, scan, oil temperature, heading, airspeed, altitude, boost, rpm, bank. Keep that scan going . . . " The hot August sun blazed down on my torture chamber and sweat rolled off me in rivers.

"OK fine, I've got control. Take the goggles off. Whaddabout some aerobatics?" Ian had taken me to the limit of my intellectual endurance and realized it would be unproductive to go further. I pushed the horrible blue goggles up and looked around at an almost completely clear sky, with clouds only evident over the distant Welsh mountains.

"Mind if I practise a few aeros for a change?" Ian enquired in a casual tone, banking vertically to the left onto a clearing turn to check for other aircraft. When he was satisfied there were none around to interfere with our antics, he allowed the nose to drop as he rolled out of the turn. The airspeed increased, 140 knots, 150, 160. Back on the control column, the nose came up through the horizon, past the vertical, over the top in a perfect loop and down the other side. Speed increasing again, reduce the power, level out then raise the nose slightly above the horizon again, and put the power back up again for a hesitation roll – aileron left, check, hold it with rudder, aileron left again, stick forward to stop us diving, aileron again, check, lots of left rudder then aileron it back to level flight again. Now keep the power on and let the nose drop to increase our airspeed before pulling up into a stall turn, check the wing tips are vertical with the horizon before feeding in right rudder, chop the power and apply a bit of opposite aileron, now the nose is pointing vertically down again, ease back on the control column and feed in the power as the nose comes back to the horizon.

"Had enough for one day?"

I nodded miserably, well aware of the poor performance I had put on. There was so much to do, so many things to watch, if the airspeed wasn't galloping away the altitude was; if both were OK and you looked away from the blind flying instruments to check something else, by the time your attention returned to the panel, everything had gone haywire. It didn't help my confidence to known that today was only an introduction to IF (instrument flying) and infinitely harder lessons lay ahead – QGHs or controlled descents through cloud, using commands from a ground controller, SBA (standard beam approaches) using a radio beam that transmitted As and Ns in Morse code either side of a continuous beam, recovery from unusual attitudes (on instruments!), steep turns and a whole host of other tortures.

Neither of us spoke more than was absolutely necessary as Ian flew us back to Ternhill. Back in the briefing room, he went over the worst of my mistakes.

"The first time is always a bit of an eye-opener," he encouraged. "Anticipation is the name of the game, anticipation and scanning. Keep the aircraft in trim at all times so that when you do have to divert your attention away from the instruments, it won't start to deviate by itself."

I couldn't think of anything to say. How could I have thought instrument flying was going to be easy?

That evening I was the only thoughtful member of an otherwise light-hearted group. At afternoon tea we met the new padré for the first time; it was difficult not to compare him with his predecessor, who had been an exceptional man and good company at all times. The new padré, in contrast, seemed more of an academic, who would probably have felt more at home roaming the quadrangles and cloisters of some seat of higher learning rather than a flying training station.

He politely declined our offer of a drink before dinner when the bar opened at six, choosing to retire to his room instead. This was convenient for us for we had something vital to discuss.

Big Dick had been temporarily suspended from flying training on the express orders of the Commanding Officer!

Apparently the relationship with the CO's daughter Sonjah had blossomed to the point where, as Singer had so succinctly put it, "He was getting it away." Since this was a position which none of us were in, we felt more than slightly envious of Big Dick.

After swearing us all to secrecy, he took us to the bar and related how the trouble had begun.

"It was after a dining-in night," he began. After walking Sonjah home, he had received the message loud and clear that any amorous advances from him would be gratefully received. Having nowhere to take her, he had kissed her goodnight and returned to the Mess.

During the night he had the most incredibly erotic dream of being pinned down by a beautiful full breasted nubile siren, who first pinned his arms to the bed before lowering her naked body upon his and conjugating with him. Big Dick had become erect with excitement as he felt her ample breasts rise and fall on his chest. From the way in which he described it, the dream must have been incredibly vivid. When he got to the part where his manhood was thrusting deep into her, he woke up!

"So you missed out on the best part?" Singer snorted, angry at being left up in the air by such a story. Disappointment clouded our faces and the barman resumed polishing glasses.

"No! That was the most incredible part of the whole thing," Big Dick explained. "When I woke up, it was for real. My bedroom window was open, half a gale was blowing through the room, there was a full moon outside and some bird had climbed into my bed and was er . . . "

"Helping herself?" Singer suggested rather neatly.

"Yeah exactly, very nicely put, thank you."

We digested this information thoughtfully, each turning a light shade of envious green.

"You mean, she was actually, er, well was she?"

"Who was it for Heaven's sake?"

"Who do you think? Sonjah!"

I remembered the strange rustling sounds outside my room late at night.

This idyllic situation had continued for several weeks until Sonjah announced she was pregnant. She lost no time in telling her mother, who relayed the news to her husband the Station Commander. He did the first thing he could think of and suspended Big Dick from flying training pending an enquiry into the matter.

"And the worst part of all is that I've been moved out of my comfortable room back to the annexe," Dick lamented.

We sympathised, remembering how cold and uncomfortable the annexe had been, not to mention the horrible early morning cup of tea and the batmen's copulating dogs leaving hairs everywhere. We commiserated with Big Dick but realized there was very little we could do to help him. His future in the Royal Air Force was out of our hands.

After so much excitement in one day, I slept soundly and forgot to worry about my difficulties with instrument flying. It wasn't until next morning, when I walked down to Flights after attending met' briefing, that I remembered the horrors of the day before. Once again I was scheduled for another dual IF (instrument flying) detail. Ian briefed me meticulously "Keep the scan going at all times. Don't concentrate on any particular flight instrument, monitor all of them," he urged. I paid considerably more attention to his briefing this time, for now I could understand how students got chopped for IF.

The second day's training went as badly as the first, possibly worse because now I knew what to expect. The weather had remained sunny and clear, and the sun shone through the Plexiglass again, broiling me medium rare. Perspiration ran from every pore.

The problems seemed to be the same as the previous day; if I took my eyes away from the flight instruments to make an engine power correction, the aircraft would lose or gain height, the heading would change and we were either in, or well on the way into, the infamous graveyard spiral.

"Keep the scan going, level out at 5,000, adjust the power, watch your bank angle, don't let the nose drop, keep the scan going . . . "

By the end of the second day's torture, I despaired of ever being able to fly on instruments. Ian's voice had lost its usual patient tone and was sometimes quite irritable. We returned to Ternhill in moody silence, neither of us speaking unnecessarily until after we had landed and parked the aircraft. Walking back to the flight hut, Ian broke the silence. "Not taking this personally, are you, Guy?"

I assured him I wasn't, although there had been times during the flight when I could have shouted at him in frustration. He debriefed me thoroughly, once again listing my faults and errors. "You must keep that scan going, anticipate what you're going to do next and keep the aircraft accurately trimmed all the time."

I knew what he meant. In every type of flying it is essential to be at least one move ahead of the aircraft; when climbing to an altitude, anticipate the level out by a hundred feet, when turning onto a new heading, start the roll out before you get to it so that you don't go past it and have to turn back. I didn't appreciate that the aircraft was flying me; I would suddenly find myself at the assigned altitude and have to abruptly shove the nose down to arrest further climb. Oops, the airspeed's increasing, better take some power off, don't let the nose drop, watch your height, here we go again . . .

I returned to the officers' mess in very low spirits that evening, terribly aware that unless I could conquer this monster called instrument flying, I would be chopped. Word of my problem seemed to have got around among other members of the course and people tended to avoid me unless I approached them first.

Suddenly it was the weekend again, time to forget the worries of the week. The duty batman approached me during breakfast. "Telephone for you, Sir. Flight lieutenant Wilson on the line." I wondered what Ian could want me for on a Saturday morning, especially when relations between us had become rather tense since the start of instrument flying training.

"Morning Guy. Barbara and I wondered if any of your lot were doing anything this afternoon?"

"Don't think so, Sir. Did you have anything in mind?" At least he wasn't phoning up about my lousy instrument flying!

"We've got to drive south this weekend, but thought about driving via Bagington Airport to watch the King's Cup Air Race and the Lockheed Aerobatic Trophy on the way. It's about an hour by car, probably only three quarters of an hour in that velocipede of yours; Barbara says she'll prepare the food if you'll provide the drink."

It was another beautiful August day, perfect for flying, or if you couldn't fly yourself, for watching somebody else. I told Ian I'd ask around and find out how many were interested then phone him back.

Saturday afternoon found eight of us at Bagington Airport, comfortably seated round a picnic basket, waiting for the afternoon's flying to start. To lovers of aeroplanes, there is something magical about air displays and rallies; I believe the light aeroplanes flying in the 1950s were infinitely more interesting and exciting than the aluminium 'Spam Cans' that pass for private aircraft today. There were Percival Gulls, Proctors, de Havilland

Moths, French Stampe biplanes, Czech Zlins, Italian Ambrosini racers, a privately owned Spitfire, Miles Hawks and Comper Swifts. We watched every aircraft as it took off, completed its demonstration and landed. The weather remained good, the company was excellent and the hours flashed past like minutes.

Towards the end of the afternoon, a brightly coloured radial engined biplane took off for an exhibition of aerobatic flying. I have already mentioned that aerobatics had become an interest of mine; Ian and I nearly always carried out a few minutes of aerobatics during our dual flights together and because of this we had become critics of aerobatic displays. We also reckoned we weren't at all bad at aerobatics ourselves.

What we saw in the next fifteen minutes has remained indelibly engraved in my memory. I had expected to see a wealthy young man take off in his aged biplane, treating it gently as would be appropriate for its vintage, climb to safe height and perform a few gentle aerobatics with moderate skill. Indeed I remember thinking now might be a good time to wander along the flight line to admire a few of the visiting aircraft.

Thank heavens I didn't, for that day I witnessed the incredible Count Cantacuzene in his Bücker Jungmeister World War Two German biplane. Somebody with better writing skills than mine was there that afternoon and twenty-two years later, while browsing in a bookshop, I came upon James Gilbert's fine piece of descriptive writing of what we both saw:

There can be few more wondrous and astonishing events than the first time you see a Jungmeister properly flown. The moment is impossible to forget. For me it came in England twenty years ago at the little country airfield, bumbling with bees, where we were cadets learning to fly. An airshow had been arranged to break up the mid-summer calm and the great Cantacuzene was coming all the way from Spain to perform. He flew a Jungmeister and he was, our elders and betters had told us, something to see, so we lay on our backs in the clover and chewed on grass stems and waited. We flew Tiger Moths, so bi-planes, and we liked to think, aerobatics were our business too.

When Cantacuzene flew in on the misty warm morning of the show, we were astonished at how tiny his Jungmeister was. Its narrow swept back wings seemed no larger than those of the model aeroplanes we so laboriously made and so quickly broke. As he touched down on the turf, those tiny balloon wheels on that ridiculous, forward jutting undercarriage seemed to reach down for the earth like the paws of a jumping cat. Yet it was clearly a thoroughbred aeroplane. Its lines had a classic racehorse grace that set it apart from our clumsy maternal Moths.

Cantacuzene was a royal prince of Rumania and woe betide anyone who forgot his rank and title. He would occasionally venture forth (for a princely fee) to demonstrate his fantastic flying prowess, the amazing precision and almost impossible audacity of his flying that made it so enthralling to watch. For no more than an infinitesimal instant was he ever in level flight. Mad, insane manoeuvres followed each other with effortless ease. At no time was he ever more than five hundred feet above us, and every manoeuvre seemed to finish with the little bi-plane inverted, its cat's feet stretching up to the clouds, its hanging rudder almost parting the daisies.

We were quite unprepared for his finale. We thought he had finished and was coming in to land. Motor throttled back, he glided down in front of the crowd till his wheels lightly but firmly touched the grass. Then, without warning, we heard the throttle advanced and saw the nose rear up into the summer sky; everything let loose as he entered the wildest snap roll, and we gasped in shock, for he was only twenty feet above the grass.

As suddenly as it had started, as soon as the Jungmeister was right way up, the roll stopped. The throttle closed and he landed, for all the world as though that crazy gyration had never happened.

It was, we learned later, a speciality of Cantacuzene, this landing flick, and probably could only be done in a Jungmeister . . .

Cantcuzene, against everybody's prognostications, died conventionally in his own bed.

There was an awed silence among the eight of us from Ternhill at the end of this incredible display of aerial mastery. We, who until this afternoon had fancied ourselves as pretty nimble aerobatic pilots, suddenly realized how green we were, performing our manoeuvres at a good safe height, with plenty of space to manoeuvre in. Furthermore, our aerobatic manoeuvres were simple compared to this Spanish nobleman's. Loops, rolls, stall turns seemed old hat now compared to his tailslides, Lomcevaks and snap rolls at literally ground level. I think that afternoon's humbling experience did us all a lot of good, for it reminded us there was an awful lot about flying we hadn't learned about yet.

We returned to Ternhill late that night, weary after a wonderful day of 'messing about around aeroplanes'.

Thanks to Ian's suggestion to watch the King's Cup, I had got away from worrying about my problems with instrument flying, and equally important, Big Dick, now exiled to the mess annexe after his episode with Sonjah, had also been jolted out of his gloom.

Next morning, Sunday, we rose late and after a leisurely breakfast were reading the Sunday newspapers when Kiwi Green spoke up. "Anybody interested in going to church this morning?" he enquired. We lowered our *News of the World*s and regarded him curiously.

"Hadn't thought about it, quite honestly. Any particular reason for going?"

Trev fidgeted embarrassedly in his seat. "The squadron commander mentioned the new padré was preaching his first Sunday service today, and suggested it would be a nice gesture to attend."

"To lend a bit of moral support maybe?" Switches suggested.

" Yeah, Ian said a similar thing to us yesterday," a dim recollection came back to me. "Well, I suppose it wouldn't be a bad idea to give the new chaplain a good welcome. I can't say he impresses me terribly, looks very studious and boring." We reluctantly agreed among ourselves it would be a nice gesture to lend our support to the new cleric.

Most of us had sat through our share of innumerable boring sermons before so nobody expected anything sensational as the new chaplain walked to the pulpit and waited for the hymn to finish. It was therefore a pleasant surprise to find that he delivered a forceful sermon with enthusiasm and conviction. When we rose for the last hymn, everybody had changed their opinion of the mild-mannered cleric.

I still recall the text of his sermon. It was from Psalm 13, vs. 6. 'I will sing to the Lord because he has dealt bountifully with me.'

Only later did the source of his inspiration become apparent.

Chapter 19

Fur and Feathers Fly

Another Monday morning; late summer was turning into autumn and low cloud brought rain to accompany my mood of deep depression as I sat between Dave Brown and Big Dick at Met briefing, listening to Deep Depression Dan give his opinion of what the weather was going to do.

I anticipated that today would be another session of dreaded IF training, which was confirmed when the duty squadron commander stood up at the conclusion of briefing and told us that because of the worsening weather, only dual flying would take place that morning. Dave Brown grumbled at this news for he had successfully passed his IR (instrument rating) test on the previous Friday and was now qualified to fly in cloud. I felt a pang of envy towards him for I wondered whether I would ever pass mine.

We discussed Big Dick's predicament as we headed back to Flights.

"Have you heard anything further from the CO?" Dave enquired sympathetically. Big Dick shook his head in negative reply; he was being kept in limbo, a subtle form of torture, not knowing whether he was to be disciplined, ignored, chopped, challenged or horsewhipped by Sonjah's father. Even worse, his suspension was causing him to fall behind in flying hours, and unless it was lifted soon, he might have to be moved down to a more junior course. After spending a year with us, he was reluctant to break the bonds of camaraderie binding him to us.

I made appropriately sympathetic sounds while reflecting that I was lucky to still be flying.

By the end of the morning I was convinced my flying days were numbered. As anticipated, I was down for IF training with Ian – not once but twice. We took off on the first detail and climbed to seven thousand feet to practice a few manoeuvres before carrying out a controlled descent through cloud procedure. Although the day was cool and the cockpit heating turned down low, I perspired heavily. Furthermore, Ian's voice was beginning to annoy me with its constant litany of my mistakes.

"Watch your height now. OK turn onto zero niner zero, I said watch that height. Start levelling out now, you've overshot your heading, remember to anticipate the level out. Come on, Guy, look at your height . . . "

Couldn't he see I was working like a one-armed paper hanger, trying desperately hard to control the aircraft?

At the end of the first detail we walked back to the Flight hut together, with me feeling terribly depressed after this last display of ineptitude. Ian therefore surprised me when he remarked. "You've improved a bit this time, probably the weekend break from flying. Keep it up."

I muttered something or other, I have no idea what, convinced he was saying this for lack of anything else to encourage me with.

Back in Flights, Singer and Little Dick were jubilant at just having passed their instrument rating tests. Now three of our number were qualified to fly in bad weather by sole reference to the aircraft blind flying instruments and ground based radio aids.

We offered them our congratulations as we gulped our morning coffee. Mike Parry was due to take his test at the end of the morning and I reflected that I was no nearer an instrument rating now than I had been at the start of the course. Singer must have read my thoughts.

"It'll suddenly click," he promised. I looked up startled.

"What the devil are you talking about?"

"Instrument flying. Everybody finds it difficult, almost bloody impossible at first, then one day you go up and it's as if the aircraft is on rails, everything goes right."

I replied grumpily that I didn't think this was ever likely to happen to me, just as Ian entered the room . "Ready for another torture session?" he enquired briskly and we made our way out to the aircraft.

The next session went much as the previous. Ian kept telling me to anticipate and scan all the instruments while I struggled desperately to exercise some form of control over an aircraft that was way ahead of me. If the height and airspeed were correct, the compass heading had changed, then when I rectified that, the airspeed was too low and the altitude too high. Nothing seemed to go right but Ian continued to sit beside me and offer occasional bits of advice – "Keep the scan going, look at your height, that's better, now your airspeed, put some power on, watch your heading, don't forget to check the engine instruments."

It seemed hopeless. When we landed after the second detail, I was convinced my instrument flying was now worse than it had been on the first day. After a quiet lunch, Singer, Mike Parry, Big Dick and I walked down to ground school together.

Halfway through a mid-afternoon navigation lecture, Big Dick was summoned by the CGI (Chief Ground Instructor). He stowed his notebooks into his briefcase and left the room. Several of us wished him 'good luck', aware that his future was about to be decided in the CO's office.

The rest of the afternoon was spent trying to concentrate on navigation and aerodynamics. Dick returned to ground school in time for the afternoon tea break at three o'clock. We crowded round, anxious to know how he had fared.

"Dunno yet. I went and saw the CO and he asked me a few questions about his daughter, then he said he wanted to see me in the mess at five o'clock and suggested I bring two officers along to represent my legal interests."

We ruminated on this information thoughtfully. There was little reason to believe things had taken a turn for the better.

"Who will you choose to represent you?" I wondered, thinking he would approach somebody in the legal branch.

He looked at me before replying. "Mike Parry and anybody else who's available. Whaddabout you?" I must have looked surprised but before I could say anything, Dave Brown continued. "Mike has the gift of the gab. After all, he's a trained barrister; look at some of the things he's talked us out of."

"But what can I do?" I demanded.

"Dunno actually er well maybe you can act as a moderating influence. Too much of Mike could go too far, but if somebody could moderate his tempo, I think Dick might at least get a full hearing."

It was agreed that Mike and I would accompany Big Dick at five o'clock.

The mess anteroom had been rearranged by the staff to look something like a court room. Four writing tables had been pushed together at one end, with five chairs for the presiding officers of the Court of Enquiry to sit behind. Two upright chairs had been placed in front of this improvised bench, one for the accused and the other for a witness. Further back in the body of the court, several rows of comfortable mess arm chairs had been arranged for the use of anybody else attending the proceedings.

Big Dick and his defence arrived just before five o'clock.

The CO and his wife were already there, accompanied by their daughter looking very innocent and fragile. Henry Bilek, our flight commander, was also in attendance. Without any form of preamble, the CO bade us all sit down. He then closed the door and set the proceedings in motion.

"I want to establish precisely what occurred between this officer," he gestured towards Big Dick, "and my daughter before I decide whether any further action should be taken." Beside him, his wife nodded approvingly.

He turned towards Sonjah. "You have already told me this officer lured you back to his room after administering a large quantity of alcohol to you in the Magpie and Stump public house, is that correct?"

"Of course it's correct," Sonjah's mother replied from her seat beside him. Her daughter nodded her head, trying to look woeful.

"Queen's Regulations are most explicit on the subject of officers entertaining ladies in their rooms," the CO cautioned. "Now let's hear your side of the story." He motioned for Big Dick to stand up.

Mike Parry sprang to his feet, clasping the lapels of his battledress jacket in best barrister fashion and advanced on the line of tables.

"Group Captain, Sir, Mrs Group Captain and members of this enquiry," he began. "I am here, at the request of Pilot Officer Howard, to give his account of the events that took place." The group captain and his wife looked at Mike startled. The squadron commander's face was a study in curiosity and I detected the ghost of a smile on Henry Bilek's face.

"Why can't the officer himself tell us?" the group captain enquired after a hurried consultation with his wife. "After all, he was there, wasn't he ... ?" Henry Bilek gave a throaty chuckle before a ten second glare from the group captain's wife silenced his mirth. Mike Parry waited for complete silence.

"The officer concerned could tell you," he agreed. "But feels that his version might be somewhat biased or distorted in view of the catastrophic effect this matter could have on his future flying career. I understand, group captain Sir, that you informed him he could bring along two fellow officers to represent him. Is that no longer correct?"

The group captain appeared flustered and consulted with his better half again. "Yes, that's true but I thought he'd have selected officers better qualified to represent him than two students on his course. What about getting somebody from the legal branch?" Beside him, the group captain's wife nodded her head approvingly. On his other side, Sonjah smiled coquettishly at the prisoner.

"Be that as it may, the officer has chosen us," Mike replied, gesturing to his right. The group captain's wife whispered in her husband's ear again. He listened obediently then looked at Mike.

"Do you have any legal training?" he demanded. Mike nodded his head and reeled off his academic qualifications to practise law.

"Have you any experience?"

Again Mike nodded his head. "I appeared in court several times before joining Her Majesty's Royal Air Force," he stated definitely. This time several of us had to struggle to suppress chuckles for we remembered hearing of the time Mike had been prosecuted for being in charge of a brewer's dray as a law student. The case had dragged on for weeks as Mike's law tutors and fellow undergraduate law students used every piece of legal ammunition to fight the case, eventually getting off on a technicality.

The CO ignored his wife's whispering while he considered Mike's reply. "Very well," he finally conceded. "You may proceed."

"Thank you, Sir. Now before we hear the defendant's side of the story, I'd like to ask the plaintiff a few questions," Mike began.

"Who's the plaintiff?" the mother asked suspiciously. Mike pointed towards Sonjah. "What about, young man?" Mother demanded. Her husband shushed her quiet and she sat back in her chair and watched the proceedings commence, her mouth a thin tense line.

"Miss Sonjah, you have known the defendant, Pilot Officer Howard for how long?"

Sonjah counted on her fingers. "Four months."

"Four months? I see. Now on the night in question, where did he take you?"

Sonjah brightened as she recalled the evening. "We started off in the mess for a drink then we went to the Magpie and Stump, where a few other members of his course were drinking."

"And you left there at what time?"

"Oh, about ten thirty."

"About ten thirty eh? And what happened next?"

"He drove me home."

"Please tell the court who 'he' is."

"Big Dick."

"You mean of course, Pilot Officer Howard?"

"That's what she said," the mother's voice replied.

"Pilot Officer Howard drove you home," Mike reiterated. "What happened when the defendant arrived at your house?"

Sonjah blushed. "We kissed for a few minutes." She giggled involuntarily at the recollection.

"Where did you kiss?"

"Well, I started everything by kissing him on the ear first and he kissed my neck then my throat, then . . . "

Sonjah's mother began turning a deep shade of furious magenta.

"No, I mean where you were when you first kissed?" Mike hastily interrupted.

"In the car then up against the gatepost. I'd kissed him in the car and as we were passing the gatepost, he pushed me against the gatepost and kissed me back. He's ever so strong . . . "

"Sonjah," her mother hissed. "Just answer the questions."

"Please continue," Mike encouraged the witness.

"We kissed up against the gatepost and er, kissed some more until . . . "
A tense silence enveloped the courtroom.

"Until what . . . ?"

Sonjah giggled again. "Until Mummy and Daddy arrived home and saw us and told, well, you know . . . "

Mike drew himself up to full height and, clasping his hands to his lapels, finished the sentence for her. "Told you to 'get out and take that slut with you' is that what your father said?"

Sonjah coloured a delightful shade of pink. At the bench, the group captain fidgeted with papers while his wife directed her venomous gaze at Mike.

Mike continued. "And then Pilot Officer Howard, feeling rather awed at being discovered in a compromising situation by a senior officer, bade you good night and returned to the officers' mess, did he not?"

Sonjah nodded affirmatively then looked flustered. She knew what was about to come next; she turned to her mother for help.

"You mean he lured my daughter back to his room. Don't you?" Mother demanded. Mike waited an unusually long time before answering. Just as he was about to reply, the door of the anteroom opened and the new padré appeared, carrying a folded copy of the *Church Times*. He looked around at the unusual configuration of the tables and chairs.

"Oh sorry, am I interrupting something private?" he ventured timidly, preparing to leave. The group captain motioned for him to come in and sit down.

"That's quite all right, Padré, come in. There's plenty of armchairs at the other end of the room. We were just holding an investigation into a matter that occurred here recently . . . "

"Of a quite immoral nature, completely contrary to the teachings of the Church," the wife added. The squadron commander added something facetious about breaking one of the Ten Commandments. The padré brightened.

"Well, perhaps my place is here, in that case," he suggested hopefully, settling himself comfortably into a mess armchair and opening his magazine.

Mike Parry waited for complete silence before resuming the case for the defence. This time he directed his words towards the group captain's wife.

"It remains to be proved whether or not Pilot Officer Howard lured your daughter to his room . . . " Further speech was made impossible by Mrs Group Captain standing up and interrupting Mike.

"Absolute stuff and nonsense!" she stormed at Mike. "As far as I'm concerned, there's nothing to prove. Somebody's got Sonjah in the family way and I'm going to find out who it is." Several members of the hearing tried to silence the irate mother but her voice drowned out their efforts.

"You over there, what's your name again, Howard, isn't it? Stand up boy, stand up I say."

Not even Mike Parry's eloquence could halt the fury of a mother in full rant. Big Dick Howard stood slowly to his six foot eight inches and eyed Mrs Group Captain across the room.

"Yes, you're the one, I recognise you, you've been taking Sonjah out for several months now. Well tell me young man, did you sleep with my daughter on the night in question?"

Mike Parry again tried to intervene. "Madam, this is all quite irregular, he began. 'We are trying to establish whether or not the accused is guilty of the alleged offence . . . "

The CO's wife scoffed at his words. "You're just trying to get round the truth," she accused.

"But by doing so we hope to encompass it," Mike countered but she paid no heed, her attention was directed towards Big Dick, now trying desperately to think of the best reply to her question.

"Did you sleep with my daughter?" the mother repeated, emphasising the question by hitting the table top with a rolled up copy of *Fur and Feathers* magazine. Big Dick shuffled awkwardly from one foot to another; nobody spoke. "Did you or did you not sleep with my daughter?" the questioner screamed. Everybody in the room held their breath. Finally, as she was about to repeat the question for a third time, he drew himself up to his full height and looked the mother full in the face.

"Not a bloody wink, madam!" he blazed.

The male members of the committee convulsed in laughter at the unexpected reply. I stole a sideways glance at Mike and saw even he was chuckling at this unexpected turn of events.

The CO's wife banged her magazine angrily on the table to restore silence. She glared across at Big Dick while formulating her next question. She realized her adversary wasn't going to be the easy victory she'd anticipated. Unless she cached her questions with considerable care, she and her daughter were going to end up the subject of considerable ridicule. She swept the room with an angry glare to silence the last sniggers before continuing.

"Pilot officer Howard," she began in an almost conciliatory voice. "Do you love my daughter?"

The question caught Big Dick completely by surprise. He'd braced himself to withstand the big guns of her questioning, now she was talking of love. What would this dragon know about love? He suddenly realized the question contained a hidden barb – the obligation to marry the daughter if he answered 'yes' to the question. On the other hand, to answer in the negative could result in an accusation of ungentlemanly conduct, which could quickly be construed as 'lack of officer qualities' in Air Force parlance. The inevitable result would be a chop for OQs. Big Dick turned to Mike and I for assistance but even the unflappable Mike Parry was lost for a suitable answer.

The atmosphere was suddenly rent by Sonjah's mother banging the table again. "Do you love my daughter?" she repeated angrily, adding emphasis by banging the table after each word. An extra loud bang at the end of the sentence nearly destroyed the magazine.

Every pair of eyes was on Big Dick as he cleared his throat nervously before replying "Er, well hmm, yes, parts of her I love, parts of her are excellent . . . "

The answer created complete pandemonium in the makeshift court room. *Fur and Feathers* finally flew apart as Sonjah's mother angrily beat the table top in a vain attempt to restore order. Beside her, the group captain had turned a deep shade of convulsive purple as he struggled to regain his breath between loud guffaws. Beside him, the squadron commander held a handkerchief to his eyes, shoulders shaking uncontrollably. To his left, Henry Bilek had fallen from his chair and was rolling helplessly on the floor.

Sonjah's mother glared angrily at her daughter, who was beaming delightedly at hearing parts of herself described as excellent. Mother now turned her anger towards her husband and began beating him about his head and shoulders with the remnants of her magazine. He didn't feel a thing, the magazine was empty.

Five minutes later, some semblance of order had begun to return to the proceedings when Mike stood to address the judges. "Group captain and other members of this enquiry, I think we have just witnessed a graphic illustration of how the course of justice cannot be short-circuited," he commenced. "Because of the informal nature of this enquiry, I now intend to question Pilot Officer myself, unless of course, anybody else has any other question she'd like to ask?" He left the question hanging in the air while staring at Sonjah's mother, who had difficulty in returning his gaze.

"You men wouldn't understand a matter of this nature," she muttered sullenly.

"We are merely trying to administer justice," Mike held his arms out to simulate the statue of justice. "Both men and women are equably capable of that. Are they not?"

"But the statue of justice is a woman," she smirked triumphantly.

"And therefore capable of an occasional miscarriage?" Mike suggested gently. She glared into space, pretending not to have heard the brilliant rejoinder. Henry Bilek and the squadron commander looked hopefully at her, hoping for more light entertainments but none came.

Mike led Big Dick through a series of questions which gave the members of the enquiry a clear picture of what had happened. Dick described how he had said good night to Sonjah at her parents' house and after driving back to the mess had gone straight to bed. Further questioning revealed how he had woken during the night to find the bedroom window open and Sonjah's nubile body astride him. If thoughts were audible, every male voice in that room would have echoed the words 'Lucky bugger'.

"Stolen service," Lord Jim, who had been listening to the proceedings from the back of the court, suddenly interrupted. All eyes turned on him and Mike Parry asked him to explain.

"Stolen service, a horse racing term, used to refer to the practice of smuggling a mare into a prize stallion's stable usually at dead of night to avoid paying stud fees to the stallion's owner," he explained. "Sort of an equine term for rape."

Mike nodded dismissively at this information but before he could resume his questioning, Mrs Group Captain was back on her feet again, banging the tattered remnants of her magazine on the table. "Lies, absolute lies, he lured my daughter into his room then had his way with her, isn't that right, Sonjah?" She turned to Sonjah, who nodded obediently like a trained seal.

A few details of the case were now beginning to intrigue me. I realized the strange noises I had heard outside my room late at night had been Sonjah climbing the ivy to the room above mine. If this constituted rape, who was the assailant?

Even more interesting, who had taken over occupancy of Dick's room since his banishment to the mess annexe?

Mike looked at me helplessly. "Got any questions you can think of asking?" he implored, sitting down abruptly for we both realized that although events so far had provoked considerable mirth, we had done nothing to help Dick out of his predicament. I stood to my feet without the faintest idea of what I was going to say. Sonjah sat closer to me than Big Dick so I directed my questioning at her.

"Sonjah, you climbed the ivy running up the outside of the Officers' Mess to get to Pilot Officer Howard's room on the first floor," I began, but Sonjah's mother interrupted that line of questioning by reminding us she had already established that her daughter had been lured to Big Dick's room under the influence of alcohol.

Mike attempted to interrupt her by suggesting it would have been impossible to have scaled the ivy while under the influence of alcohol but Sonjah's mother drowned his words by insisting rape had already been established. Mike looked at me as he sat down dejectedly.

"What happened after he raped you?" I enquired. A whimsical smile crept over Sonjah's face while she thought for a few moments.

"Then we smoked a cigarette together and he raped me again."

The magazine finally disintegrated completely and Mother beat the table with her clenched fist to quieten the pandemonium that arose. By now the armchairs and other seating places had been taken by casual passers by attracted by the sound of merriment in the anteroom. The group captain was the first to control his mirth; sitting up very straight, he announced the court of enquiry was adjourned. Some were still chuckling as he left the room. His wife threw a wad of shredded magazine pages at Henry before hurrying after her husband. She began saying something to him as they disappeared out the door but was silenced by her husband's instruction: "Lydia, next time you have a good idea, keep it to yourself and shut up!"

Big Dick, Mike Parry and I made for a corner of the bar, where we discussed the case in detail.

"The trouble is," Mike explained, "it isn't good enough to establish Dick's innocence. The court is ruled in the first case by Mrs Group Captain, who decided he was guilty long before the trial started. In the second instance, even if we prove Dick's innocence, or they fail to prove his guilt, the CO only has to say 'lack of officer qualities' and Dick's chopped, and he's kept his wife happy."

We sadly considered this information as the bar filled with pre-dinner drinkers. Several came over and offered us drinks but we weren't in the mood.

Like it or not, we now had to await the group captain's verdict.

Chapter 20

Saved!

A surprise awaited me down at Flights next afternoon. Ian had been called away for some reason and I was down to fly with a different instructor, Flight Sergeant Bright, an NCO pilot of considerable experience. Our first dual detail together was to be instrument flying, which in the excitement of yesterday's court room drama, I had forgotten was proving a problem to me.

My new instructor spent little time briefing me for the forthcoming exercise – I already knew the format by heart. We chatted idly as he signed the flight authorisation Form 700 and we strode out to the aircraft. Strangely, I didn't feel particularly concerned or nervous about the coming detail.

Within ten minutes we were airborne and climbing to 6,000 feet. The flight sergeant pulled the blue goggles down over my eyes as we passed through 500 feet, forcing me to concentrate on the blind flying instruments. It was a moderately turbulent day and the aircraft demanded my full attention to keep on the correct heading and airspeed. I remembered to open the throttle further to maintain climb power as we climbed. The airspeed fluctuated occasionally passing through areas of turbulence but recovered under my direction. I anticipated the level out at 6,000 feet and reduced power slightly once we were cruising straight and level. Flight Sergeant Bright had sat silently in the instructor's seat saying nothing. Now he spoke.

"OK, let me see a right turn onto a heading of zero four five, maintaining this altitude and airspeed," he suggested rather than commanded. I banked right until the needle of the turn and bank indicator pointed to the first graduation, taking care to maintain height and airspeed. The airspeed decreased fractionally, only a couple of knots, as we continued the turn and I inched the throttle forward to correct the excursion.

We continued turning, the airspeed and altitude now steady as we passed through north. It would soon be time to start levelling the wings just prior to reaching the required heading. The gyro compass card continued turning, zero one zero, two zero, three zero, take the last of the bank off now and we're heading zero four five. I remembered to reduce power as the compass card stopped its turn.

"Now a left turn onto two four zero, descending at 500 feet a minute to 5,000, maintaining this airspeed," was his only acknowledgement that we had achieved our new heading. I banked left and pulled the throttle back to prevent the airspeed building up in the descent. The vertical speed indicator immediately shot down to a thousand feet a minute and the airspeed increased ten knots until I raised the nose of the little aeroplane on the artificial horizon. The rate of turn had obligingly found its way to the correct position and the compass card was turning again. Descending through five and a half thousand feet I noticed our heading passing through three three zero. The rate of descent was fractionally greater than 500 feet per minute; I eased the nose up half a degree and nudged the throttle forward to correct it. We were now passing through two five zero degrees and the height was coming down to 5,000. I realized I would have to level out at the new altitude while simultaneously rolling out onto the new heading. Five thousand one hundred feet, heading coming round onto two four zero. I levelled the wings and simultaneously raised the nose to halt the descent. As if by magic, the hands of the altimeter stopped precisely in 5,000 and the gyro compass indicated the required course. As I increased power again to maintain airspeed in level flight, I noticed the engine oil temperature had dropped to the bottom of the operating range in the turn. I closed the oil cooler a notch.

My new instructor gave me several similar exercises to perform before announcing he had control. Leaning across to my blind flying panel, he locked the gyro compass before increasing the engine rpm to the higher setting for aerobatics.

"Just a couple of unusual attitudes to recover from, nothing very different from what you've probably done with Ian," he explained, banking to the right and closing the throttle. For a moment we both hung weightless as the aircraft hung poised in the sky then the altimeter began unwinding towards the earth, the vertical speed indicated four thousand feet per minute down and the artificial horizon toppled as I looked at it. I had no way of knowing which way up we were.

"OK, recover now," the calm voice on my right requested.

The turn and bank indicator needle was hard over to the right stop; I nudged the control column to my left to return the needle to the mid-position. The altimeter continued to unwind until, with wings level, I applied gentle back pressure on the control column and the descent halted. The altitude steadied on 4,000 and I applied power to stabilise the air speed on the cruise figure.

The flight sergeant took control of the aircraft again and opening to full throttle, raised the nose as he commenced a climbing turn. The airspeed began to decrease despite the 550 horses generated by the aircraft's Alvis Leonides engine.

"OK you have it, now recover," he removed his hands from the controls. The airspeed was now critically low; I pushed forward on the control column to prevent further loss of airspeed but it continued to fall. The aircraft was now marginally above the stall and the controls were reacting sluggishly. The engine began surging as I pushed harder on the control column but still the airspeed fell; suddenly, above me through the unobstructed part of the perspex cockpit canopy, I saw the ground below. We were inverted! No wonder the airspeed wouldn't recover when I pushed forward. I glanced down at the turn and slip, it was hard over. I applied aileron to get the needle back to the mid-position before easing the column forward. The wings were now level and the airspeed increasing, the engine had resumed its continuous roar. As the airspeed increased through ninety knots, I raised the nose to check the descent. The aeroplane accelerated in level flight and I reduced to cruise power.

"Good effort, most people don't twig to that one," Flight Sergeant Bright had taken over again. "I rolled us upside down with the nose pointed way up in the air, expecting you to push forward to regain your airspeed. Don't forget to always level your wings first. OK that's enough of unusual attitudes, re-synchronise your compass and we'll ask control for a practice controlled descent through cloud"

We occupied the remaining flight time with practice QGH approaches – better known as controlled descents through cloud, a procedure where the air traffic controller on the ground talks the aircraft to a position overhead the airfield then instructs it to commence descending at a predetermined rate and airspeed on a heading away from the field. At an appropriate moment he then instructs the aircraft to turn back to the field and gives a series of instructions to bring the pilot to a position where he is aligned with the runway at the correct height, distance and airspeed for a landing. The first QGH is rather impressive, the demands of instrument flying don't leave the pilot much time to figure out where he is exactly, so it comes as a tremendous surprise (the first time) to look up out of the cockpit and see the home runway in front of the nose.

As well as QGHs, Flight Sergeant Bright also taught me Standard Beam Approaches (SBA), a procedure where the pilot endeavours to fly along the centre of an electronic beam radiating from the airfield. If he deviates to one side, he will hear the letter 'N' in Morse code in his earphones; if he deviates the other way, he'll hear the letter 'A'. A continuous note tells him he is correctly located 'on the beam' in the centre. Fortunately for me, both types of approaches went well.

"When are you taking your instrument rating test?" the flight sergeant enquired conversationally as we rejoined the circuit to land. I had just removed the dreaded blue goggles, allowing me to see through the cockpit windows unimpeded. I confessed to him no mention had been made of a date on which to take the dreaded instrument flight test, while prudently refraining from telling him the reason!

"Want to take it this afternoon?" he enquired. "I could get somebody over from HQ Flight." Headquarters Flight were the standard setters, who conducted instrument rating tests.

I gulped at the prospect of taking the test but agreed. Only now at the end of our flight did I realize instrument flying had suddenly clicked with me, just as Singer had assured me it would. My only regret was that it hadn't happened while flying with Ian, my regular instructor.

Once back at Flights, I filled the take-off and landing times in the flight authorisation sheet while the flight sergeant phoned through to HQ Flight for an examiner.

Before I had time to develop pre-instrument test nerves, a cheery young flying officer bobbed into the Flight hut, looked at me and enquired: "Are you the lucky lad; Clapshaw, isn't it?" I admitted I was and after a quick briefing, we went out to our aircraft for the test.

Nothing eventful happened during the IR Test. Flight Sergeant Bright must have decided I was up to standard, otherwise he wouldn't have made the arrangements. For me, things had developed so fast that I didn't have the time to consider the possibility of failure. I passed OK and

Flying Officer Foreman, my examiner, ran over a few minor points in his post-flight brief.

Suddenly we both noticed it was unusually quiet outside; there was no sound of aircraft engines or voices from the crew room. He looked at his watch, startled. "Five o'clock by crikey! I'd better get home to the wife and family. OK, good work, congratulations, you'd better hurry over to the mess now, your mates are probably waiting for you to buy them all a drink in the bar. Cheerio!"

I walked down the passageway of the flight hut, immeasurably relieved that the dreadful problem of learning to fly on instruments was now resolved. Passing Henry's office, I spotted his corpulent form behind the desk, filling in the masses of paperwork that seemed to go with flying. I tapped on the door and saluted him as he looked up.

"Good night, Sir."

"Good night," Henry replied, setting down his pen and looking up. "Sank Christ you passed zer fokking instrument rating test, eh?"

"Yes, thank you Sir."

Dear old Henry, not only was he a superb pilot, he was also a wonderful guy.

Back in the mess, things were winding up for a big thrash.

While passing entrance to the bar en route to my room for a quick change and freshen up before starting the evening's fun, I was startled by the din emanating from within. My attempt to pass by unnoticed was doomed to failure; a dozen or more loud voices called my name as I slunk past. Sheepishly I entered the bar, explaining away my behaviour with the excuse that I had intended to return after a quick wash.

"Waddya wanna wash for? Only dirty people wash!" an already inebriated Mike Parry enquired, spilling most of his beer down himself.

Somebody else enquired how the IR Test had gone, and everybody cheered and thumped their empty glasses on the counter top when I held my thumb up in victory fashion.

"Heard the news about Big Dick?" Dave Brown enquired immediately. I recoiled away shamefacedly for in the euphoria of passing my IR Test, I hadn't spared a thought for my colleague figuratively chained to the ground awaiting the verdict of his bizarre trial.

"The CO sent for us an hour ago," Mike slurred drunkenly. "We looked for you but you were still flying, so anyway, he called us in, told me to shut the door and said he'd thought the matter over very carefully and had decided not to take any further steps. He also mentioned casually that Sonjah wasn't in the family way after all. Said something about a false alarm."

I breathed a deep sigh of relief for Big Dick, thankful he could now rejoin our course. Mike was talking again, holding up a small purple packet. "Then he told Dick to be good in future and giggled and said if he couldn't be good, be careful, and he gave him this packet of condoms! Jolly decent of him, eh?"

I agreed. Life was wonderful at the moment, without a care in the world; I was paid to do a job I loved, in the company of friends who shared my passion for flying. I signalled to the barman for a round of drinks. I had a lot of catching up to do.

My only recollection of the rest of the evening was confiding to Mike Parry that I'd heard rustling in the ivy outside my room on many occasions but hadn't realized what or who it was. Then I suddenly remembered I'd heard the sounds the previous night!

"Good heavens, doesn't Sonjah realize Dick isn't in that room any more?" somebody asked. We began speculating on who the new occupant of the room was. Singer had a sudden inspiration and hurried over to the mess manager's office to check the room register. He returned laughing.

"I will sing to the Lord because He has dealt bountifully with me," he intoned reverently. "Psalm 13, verse 6. Sound familiar to anybody?"

We clamoured to hear who the lucky new occupant was; the whole bar roared its approval when we heard.

It was the new padré!

Chapter 21

Nautical Interlude

News of Mike Parry's successful defence of Big Dick's case had soon spread to nearby stations, bringing him further cases to sharpen his legal skills on.

The first person to require his services was an air traffic control officer from nearby RAF Shawbury, who after a Guest night had been observed running stark naked through the corridors of the mess in pursuit of a similarly attired young female WRAF officer. Normally anything like this would have been forgotten in the cold light of the following morning, but this particular incident had been witnessed not only by the headmistress of a prominent girls' school and the Bishop of Shrewsbury, but also the Chief Constable of the Shropshire Constabulary and the local Member of Parliament, who had all been guests at the dining-in night. In the circumstances, the station commander was left with no option but to order a court martial to be convened. The officer had been charged with three breaches of Queen's Regulations – being incorrectly dressed, conduct unbecoming to an officer and a gentleman and conduct likely to bring discredit on the service.

As was customary, he had been relieved of all duties while awaiting trial. Having heard the hilarious and unusual details of Big Dick's trial, he requested Mike Parry as his legal representative.

The relentless academic pressure of flying training made such an appointment inconvenient for Mike, who having received no training in military law, realized many hours would have to be spent first discussing the details of the case then poring thorough hundreds of pages of Queen's Regulations (QRs) and the Manual of Air Force Law (MAFL) to learn its vagaries in order to devise some form of defence. Recognising that it would be almost impossible to represent the accused while learning to fly, Mike asked to decline the case.

He was promptly informed by a member of the Legal Branch that he would obey orders and represent the accused at the forthcoming court martial trial.

We soon began to notice his absence from ground school lectures while he was away discussing details of the case with his client. Flights also didn't see much of Mike, and by the end of the month, Henry Bilek had become concerned that his flying hours were falling below the required monthly average. Nobody would have worried if this had happened during spells of bad winter weather because the hours could be made up when finer weather returned, but in Mike's case the flying conditions were perfect and it was his legal duties causing the problem.

When Mike called in to the legal branch to seek advice on preparation of the case, he was fortunate to make contact with an officer with previous experience in this particular legal area.

"There are only two points to consider," the legal eagle assured him. "Firstly, remember the presiding officers are human beings and fellow officers, who will view the matter with sympathy and good-natured amusement while secretly thanking their lucky stars they're not in the dock."

"And the second?" Mike enquired eagerly.

"They will readily grasp any good excuse to throw the case out of court, provided they can be seen to have conducted a fair and correct trial."

"How can I help them do that?"

"If you can find a reference in Queen's Regulations or the Manual of Air Force Law covering the circumstances of the case, that will overcome any evidence or logical argument," his mentor assured him. "So I suggest you take a long detailed look in QRs."

The advice was good, for next afternoon Mike attended ground school and seemed quite relaxed about the forthcoming trial now less than a week away. Next morning he reported to 'Flights' and completed a dual navigation exercise followed by a solo general handling detail. Henry Bilek beamed with relief; at this rate his pupil would soon catch up on his flying hours.

"Got everything ready for next week's trial?" Big Dick enquired at the bar that evening, and Mike assured him he felt quietly confident of the successful outcome of the case.

After breakfast the following Wednesday, an RAF staff car took half an hour to transport Mike to RAF Shawbury for the trial while we reported to Flights for a morning's flying.

It came as quite a surprise to find him celebrating with several other officers in the mess bar at lunch time. To judge from the number of champagne corks on the floor, he had won the case.

"The case was dismissed," Mike replied to our questioning. "So the time spent studying QRs was worthwhile, for Queen's Regulations covered the situation very nicely."

"You were brilliant!" A statuesque blonde WRAF flight lieutenant, with prominent breasts and a mischievous look in her eyes, interrupted to refill Mike's champagne glass.

Next morning down at Flights, Mike recounted the details of the case.

"I'd already worked out this was an emotive issue which wouldn't have normally come to court if there hadn't been so many prominent members of the public present," he explained. "The advocate general's advice to look for a relevant passage in QRs was good."

"What did it say?" Big Dick demanded. Mike consulted a notebook before replying.

"The relevant section on Dress Regulations, is quite specific on the first charge of being incorrectly dressed," We waited expectantly for him to continue. "An officer shall be appropriately attired for the sport he is pursuing," he quoted. "And I don't think anybody could have argued the defendant wasn't appropriately dressed for the sporty young thing he was pursuing on the night in question!"

Everybody who remembered the nubile WRAF officer in the bar at lunchtime yesterday had to agree.

"What about the other charges?" Kiwi Green demanded.

"No case to answer. The remaining charges were contingent upon the first charge being proved, so the president threw the whole thing out when it was established the defendant was appropriately attired."

"Parry!" his instructor's voice bellowed from the corridor.

"Coming, Sir," Mike turned to us apologetically. "Sorry fellahs, gotta go and learn to fly!"

By the end of the month he'd caught up on his flying hours and copied our notes of the lectures he'd missed.

Now it was early autumn and football replaced cricket as the premier station sport. There was intense rivalry between the Army, Navy and Air Force to demonstrate their superiority at all forms of sport. The Ternhill soccer team had started the season well by defeating an Army team from the local AOP (Air Observation Post) squadron resident on the opposite side of the airfield. This gave the station's Physical Fitness Officer the excuse to challenge the Royal Navy.

An unexpected raid on the bar by the Physical Fitness Officer (PFO) one evening resulted in several of us being roped in to play soccer for our station. The forthcoming match was an away fixture against the Navy at Dartmouth. Because of the distance involved in transporting the team plus supporters and various hangers-on, arrangements had been made to borrow a twin-engined Valetta transport aircraft from RAF Shawbury. The aircraft duly arrived at the promised time and we climbed aboard for the hour's flight to Dartmouth.

We were met on arrival by a group of eleven officers who introduced themselves as the Navy's team. After escorting us to their comfortable mess, their captain informed us they were holding a guest night that evening in our honour. We received this information with mixed feelings for although the festivities would be tremendous fun, we had just received a stern lecture from the PFO on the importance of winning tomorrow – or as he put it, 'thrashing the living daylights out of the fish heads'. Drinking and partying into the early hours wasn't going to increase our chances of victory against the Navy league. Reluctantly we tried to beg off.

The fish heads would have no part of it. The captain explained the guest night was held for us – what would a guest night be without guests? "Besides," he added conspiratorially, "the Navy team will be there, the Air Force isn't going to chicken out, is it?"

What could we lose? When he put it that way, we had to agree it would be churlish not to attend.

So after showering and hurriedly changing into dinner jackets, we reported to the Naval wardroom at six-thirty for seven. The idea seemed to be that we should get to know our Naval hosts over a few per-dinner cocktails. It quickly became apparent that the pre-dinner cocktails had been skilfully blended from ingredients resembling rocket fuel, nitro-glycerine, dynamite and a few other secret ingredients. The effect on our team became apparent almost immediately. I found great difficulty in pronouncing words, while Mike Parry was affected by a tremendous spirit of *bonhomie* and insisted on putting his arm round the shoulder of the Naval Commanding Officer.

The pre-dinner drinks affected other members of our team in various ways but the overall result was we were all gloriously drunk by the time we entered the dining room. However, any anxiety we might have felt about our team's worsening condition affecting the outcome of tomorrow's match was allayed by the members of the Naval team exhorting us to "have another one, we're on our fourth!"

Dinner was a rather confused two hours of boring conversation, mercifully saved by excellent food and copious quantities of good wine. I sat between two rather dull paymaster accounts officers, good career men whose conversational skills did not extend past the Royal Navy and the important part they played in its efficient running. Fortunately the Naval stewards were very attentive in ensuring our glasses were never empty. I blanked out the boredom of the paymasters with plenty of wine.

After-dinner speeches from the representatives of both services dragged the evening on till 11 p.m., at which time the senior officers departed and we headed for the bar.

I re-established contact with my team members. Big Dick was in great form, bursting into occasional song, ranging from excerpts of Gilbert and Sullivan on the higher intellectual plane down to all verses of 'Eskimo Nell'. From his height, there was no problem in making himself noticed.

Singer had arranged a schooner (beer drinking race) against the opposing team, who we were relieved to note, were still present and probably drinking faster than we were. All the members of our sporting detachment were enjoying the guest night to the full.

By 3 a.m. even the strongest had begun to wilt. Bodies lay around the bar and mess rooms in various stages of unconsciousness. The Naval team continued propping up the bar, exhorting us to "have one more for the road, don't worry about tomorrow's game, we're not so why should you?"

A particularly boring career Naval officer trapped me in a corner and expressed his concern and surprise on learning our team was mainly comprised of conscripts. My reply that both World Wars had been fought by conscripts didn't seem to register with him; he began telling Mike Parry, who had just arrived in our corner, that he was a fourth generation Naval officer, able to trace his ancestors back to Nelson's time. Mike was totally unimpressed and upset the fish head by telling him that was a rather one-eyed achievement which proved absolutely nothing. He emphasised the Air Force dealt in practicalities and was more interested in an officer's professional competence rather than who his ancestors were. Fish-Head was stung by these remarks and countered that the senior service was founded on customs and time honoured traditions, adding rather snidely that we, as conscripts, were not true serving officers and therefore unlikely to appreciate the significance of such things. I noticed a steely timbre creeping into Mike's voice as the conversation continued.

The arrival of yet another round of pint tankards of West Country beer prompted a visit to the men's room (labelled 'heads' in nautical parlance). Fish-Head showed us the way.

It was only when I tried to walk in a straight line that I realized how drunk I was. With every step forward, the walls moved out and struck me. Mike was having similar problems.

Fish-Head however, was in much healthier shape; he reached the entrance to the 'heads' and held the door open while watching our efforts at walking straight with smug amusement. I banged into him going through the doorway and started to apologise but he interrupted me and assured me it was "Quite all right, I understand. In the Navy they teach us to hold our liquor." I noticed Mike bristling at the implied innuendo.

Once away from the noisy smoky atmosphere of the bar, I suddenly felt sick. I managed some sort of revival by splashing cold water on my face until the feeling went away. Mike was similarly affected, he stood very still for several moments before suddenly regaining his composure. All this time, the smug little Fish-Head supplied a running commentary on what the Royal Navy taught its officers.

"Dress is another important consideration in the senior service," he droned on, emphasising 'senior'. "No self-respecting career officer would dream of attending a guest night unless he wore correct uniform." He stared pointedly at our civilian dinner jackets. "Of course for the Air Force's part-timers, it probably doesn't matter. Do they teach you to dress correctly for dinner?"

Mike grunted something unintelligible in reply as we finished relieving our distended bladders. I couldn't possibly face any more drink that night and decided to go to bed to snatch what little sleep I could before tomorrow's match.

Fish-Head droned on monotonously as we buttoned our pants and headed towards the door. "Yes, if we're going to do a job, the Navy teaches us to do it properly," he continued as we exited the 'heads'. "Oh and another thing, of course, the Navy teaches us to wash our hands after going to the toilet." He delivered this last remark with a snide snigger. Mike paused momentarily, eyeing him up and down. For a moment I thought he was going to thump him.

"That's bloody good of the Navy," he admitted. Fish-Head preened himself. "But in the Air Force," Mike continued. "They teach us not to piss all over our fingers. Good night!" He slammed the door with a definite bang and staggered away while Fish-Head slunk away to the safety of the bar.

Next morning I felt as if I'd woken up dead! My mouth tasted worse than the bottom of an elderly parrot's cage and a thousand hammers beat an irregular staccato rhythm inside my skull. My whole body ached from the self-inflicted wounds of the previous night – the rocket fuel cocktails, the excess of wine during dinner, the mess games, all topped off with unlimited gallons of strong West Country ale. I opened one eye cautiously lest I bled to death on the pillow. A cold cup of tea on the bedside table confirmed the late hour. A glance at my watch confirmed it was twelve thirty; the match kicked off at two o'clock.

The phone rang as I swung my legs over the side of the bed and the PFO's voice told me I was awake, lunch was now being served in the ward room. He added that our bus would leave for the football field at one thirty.

My head reeled as I stood up. I can recall little of the lunch; a steward placed a selection of cold meats in front of me; I picked at the vegetables for a few seconds before giving up and pushing the plate away. A cup of strong coffee was the only thing I could face.

Approximately half the team assembled in the mess reading room, gathered in a small circle round the PFO listening to him conducting a council of war. It was of no consolation to find the rest of the team were in similarly bad shape to me – some were even worse. Everybody silently hoped our drinking companions of the night before hadn't staged a lightning recovery. It had surprised me that no form of restraint had been placed on their drinking by their team manager. Instead, their overindulgence if anything had been encouraged. I had thought at the time what a seedy looking lot of characters they looked to be representing their service at soccer. All were grossly overweight, smoked and drank heavily and were still holding up the bar when Mike and I bade everybody a curt 'good night'. We all derived much consolation that the Navy would be feeling as hungover as us – possibly worse!

A coach took us on a short five minute drive to the football field where our supporters were already gathered on the side line. Their leader led them in a cheer as we stumbled onto the pitch.

The Naval team could be discerned at the far end of the field, practicing energetically in front of the goal. The referee blew his whistle to summon both teams to the centre of the pitch. The Naval team ceased their practice and jogged to the centre of the field, looking remarkably fit for a team who'd still been drinking heavily at 3 a.m.

Suddenly the truth came to us as a horrible shock. The team jogging towards us comprised eleven healthy, fit-looking young players in top physical condition. I looked round at my team mates.

"They're not the team we're playing!" Singer exclaimed as a strong very fit looking youth approached us.

"Hugo Ponsonby-Waterford, captain of the Naval soccer team," he introduced himself then the rest of his team.

"B . . . but we weren't drinking with you lot last night!" Singer exclaimed. In the background I could hear Big Dick spewing behind the goal post. The Naval captain feigned ignorance.

"We're the only soccer team here," he assured us.

"Whaddabout the team we were introduced to yesterday," we chorused together. The Dartmouth captain feigned complete ignorance of the whole matter and insisted theirs was the only team.

At this juncture the PFO strode onto the pitch and delivered a strong lecture. "You stupid bastards have been outmanoeuvred by a bunch of bloody fish-heads," he announced. "That was their drinking team that entertained you last night, keeping you up most of the night while their soccer team got their regular ten hours' rest!"

We looked shamefaced at the PFO's revelation; he was right, we had been out-manoeuvred by the senior service.

The ensuing match was a slaughter. The senior service's fit, well-rested young men ran rings round us, literally, scoring goal after goal. When the final whistle blew, they had scored thirty goals to our one! Even our solitary goal had been an act of magnanimity on their part in the final minute of the game.

As we slunk off the field after our humiliating defeat, I passed close to my boring dinner companion of the previous night, who remarked in a voice deliberately loud enough for us to hear: "What do you expect from a team of part-time officers?"

After showering and changing, it was time to bid our naval hosts farewell. I queued between Singer and Big Dick to board our aircraft back to Ternhill.

"Well, at least we didn't have to pay for all the booze we drank last night," I ventured for our hosts had been more than generous in offering us drinks.

"Wrong again, I'm afraid, Guy," Mike looked grim as he handed me a folded piece of paper. "In the Navy, when somebody invites you to have a drink, tradition dictates that his drink goes on his bill and yours goes on yours." I groaned aloud when I saw the amount at the bottom of the mess bill. Five pounds! Two weeks' pay for a part-time officer!

Chapter 22

The Flying Pheasant

Next Monday morning started with ground school but was followed by a free afternoon to rest before starting night flying that evening. I had been looking forward to this part of the course immensely after having read almost every book ever written about night fighters.

We were now approximately eighty-five per cent of the way through the elementary part of our flying training, and after night flying only one or two navigational exercises, then formation flying, remained before we took the final exams and the Final Handling Check. After all that, we would be off to an Advanced Flying Training School to learn to fly jets.

The initial reaction to night flying is to marvel at how beautiful the lights of the world below look. Ian Wilson my regular instructor had returned from his time away and took me on my first night flying sortie. Taking off from runway two three, we immediately transitioned to instrument flight for there was no clear horizon with which to judge our attitude. Below us, the dim blue taxiway lights meandered round the airfield perimeter while a line of brighter yellow lights marked the runway. The most illuminated part of the airfield was the dispersal area, where bright sodium lights bathed everything in a strange yellow/orange glow. Outside the airfield perimeter, pinpricks of street lights traced the path of roads leading to adjacent towns.

For our first detail we climbed to 7,000 feet to give me some idea of how the world looked from the air. The sky was partly cloudy, with broken flat stratus cloud below and the occasional wisp of nimbo-stratus above. The canopy of stars overhead seemed much larger, probably because there were no earth-bound objects like trees or buildings to restrict our field of view.

I could see the street lights of towns below. Ian's voice came over the intercom: "See those lights in front of the nose? How far away would you estimate they are?"

I looked forward at the lights he'd mentioned. They seemed to be about a mile away, possibly two. "Probably Market Drayton?" I ventured confidently, knowing that was the closest town to the airfield in that direction. "About a couple of miles?"

"Negative, that's Shrewsbury, fifteen miles away," Ian shook his head. "Deceptive, ennit? That's one of the things to bear in mind when night flying, it's very difficult to judge distances accurately. Remember that!"

We concluded the detail with a few circuits and landings. Although the basic flying was not terribly different from daytime, it was important to listen to everything on the radio, for another aircraft calling downwind as you were about to turn downwind yourself should tell the trained mind there was another aircraft a short distance ahead. It would therefore be a very good idea to keep a weather eye open for it while maintaining the correct speed downwind, lest you catch the other aircraft up and create a very real likelihood of a mid-air collision. Similarly, on hearing another aircraft call downwind shortly after you, should tell you another aircraft is coming up your tail. Once again, it would pay to keep an eye and ear open for him and maintain either the correct airspeed or a few knots faster.

The greatest difference with night flying was the different landing technique, for whereas in daytime the runway was visible during the later stages of the approach, at night the whole airfield had the appearance of a gigantic black hole surrounded by a border of very dim lights and bisected by a line of goose-neck flares which gave hardly any illumination but told the pilot where the sides of the runway were. Initially it is very difficult to land at night but soon the technique of lowering the aircraft into a long wide dark trench is mastered and you wonder what the problem was with landing at night. As soon as I began to imagine this trench into which I had to lower the aircraft, my landings improved and I went solo on my second circuit detail.

After an hour of night solo consolidation, we began night navigation exercises (night navexes), which it seemed to me were mainly a question of by guess and by God! These nav-exes were relatively short in duration and consisted of triangular tracks around the surrounding countryside, each leg normally taking about twenty minutes. Radio bearings were obtained from local airfields and used to guestimate our track made good and estimated time of arrival (ETA) at the next turning point. An occasional patch of light could be identified as a particular town but apart from that, night map reading was rarely used. No doubt mountain ranges and coastlines could have been used for map reading, but the instructional staff were careful to ensure their trainee pilots crossed neither, especially at night.

On the second evening of night flying, I witnessed something rather puzzling. Most of our off-duty social partying went on in any of the hospitable pubs in the surrounding countryside, with the exception of the Bustard, a pub across the road from the guard room, which the NCOs and airmen frequented. We were requested not to use it.

As there were plenty of other choices, this didn't worry us.

Late that particular night, Singer and I had popped across the road to the Bustard for sandwiches to take back to Flights. As we walked through the car park, we paused to examine a beautiful carmine red Aston-Martin DB-4 coupé.

"Nice set of wheels if you can afford five thousand pounds," Singer murmured admiringly, for Aston-Martins were then at the forefront of high performance sports car design and manufacturing.

While we waited inside the pub to be served, I spotted one of our sergeant instructors in the adjacent bar. He was oblivious to our presence for he was listening attentively to an elegantly dressed gentleman in a dark business suit, who was doing most, if not all, of the talking.

"That must be his Aston," Singer commented.

"Who and why?" I enquired uncomprehendingly; Singer explained the elegant gentleman was Sir David Brown, chairman of the David Brown tractor manufacturing organization as well as Aston-Martin.

"Probably been up to see young David," Singer suggested.

"You don't mean Dave Brown on our course, do you?" I asked surprised. Singer then explained Dave was the sole heir to his family's business empire and had endured monumental opposition when he announced his intention of joining the Air Force to fly.

"Dave once told us his father had done everything he could to prevent him flying," Singer explained. "After failing to dissuade Dave, he pressured their local MP, got the family doctor to say Dave was unfit and even went to the station commander to try and get his son taken off the course."

Further discussion was abruptly terminated by the departure of Sir David, with the rather embarrassed looking sergeant instructor at his heels.

After paying for the sandwiches, we went back to our night flying and forgot the incident until a bit later in the course.

Night flying lasted a week and was enjoyed by everybody. Because we were flying at a different time and in a different (darker) environment to everybody else, we were treated differently, for example we would have breakfast around 4 a.m., having picked mushrooms on the airfield for our meal, then go to bed until lunchtime. Ground school and other activities like parades were waived for us and we'd spend a leisurely afternoon reading, writing letters – or discussing flying and girls, usually in that order! After dinner, where we were permitted to remain in battledress instead of changing into a suit or number one uniform, we'd go down to Flights as darkness began to fall and listen to a met' briefing from the irritable Deep Depression Dan, who didn't appreciate being kept away from an evening's drinking by a bunch of Acting Pilot Officers.

I thoroughly enjoyed the fifteen hours night flying on Provosts and found it one of the most enjoyable and satisfying parts of the course. It was a snug feeling to be encased in a warm cockpit on a dark night, looking down at the sleeping earth below as the lights went out one by one. Only later, after having flown multi-engined aircraft, did I worry about flying single-engined aircraft at night, with the possibility of an engine failure and the unenviable choices of a parachute jump into the dark or a blind forced landing.

The day after we finished night flying, I was down for a dual circuit detail with Ian my instructor. I looked at him in aggrieved fashion, wondering why he had put me back seven months in my training. Hadn't he covered circuits adequately before I went solo?

"Hard landings, old son," he replied. When I questioned him further, reminding him that I hadn't done any hard landings at night, he held up his hands to halt my protests. "Nothing to do with your flying, Guy. It's standard procedure for all pupils to do a quick dual check before going off solo again in daytime. The reason for this is that too many pilots were doing heavy landings after coming off night flying."

Having had the reason explained to me, I stopped protesting. After two circuits and landings, which I was very careful to ensure were good ones, Ian signed me out for daytime solo flying again and as if to soothe my hurt feelings, he then authorised me for an hour's aerobatics – solo!

Just as we finished night flying, Mike's previous life caught up with him again when a rather shifty-eyed sergeant in the accounts section was arraigned on a charge of being a peeping Tom. The matter attracted quite a lot of interest and amusement for a few days, during which time Mike kept a very low profile, hoping the legal branch would appoint one of their number to handle the matter.

Unfortunately for him, the accused asked to be defended by Pilot Officer Parry, and Mike's protest that pressure of other work prevented him taking the case failed once again.

"This is just what I don't need," he complained to us shortly afterwards. "Final exams are only a few weeks away and I can't afford to miss any more lectures."

When he called into the station legal eagles' department, a squadron leader legal officer tried to compound an already grim situation by suggesting he'd be better employed in their department than flying aeroplanes.

"Which is the last thing I wanted to hear," Mike protested to us. "I want to carry on flying with you fellows. These two years of flying training are my academic pressure relief valve between three years' study at university and forty or fifty dull but lucrative years practising law."

Predictably, Mike's application to withdraw from the case was turned down. "But the squadron leader did agree not to recommend my transfer to the legal branch," he added gratefully.

"Couldn't you throw the case?" the course bookmaker suggested. "Once you break your winning streak, people will stop asking for you to represent them."

" 'fraid not. I'm a lawyer by heart, so was my Dad and his father before him, and to intentionally lose a case would be unethical – a bit like a jockey pulling back a horse or an accountant fiddling the books."

"Yeah but the accused isn't a particularly likeable bloke, couldn't you just try a little less than normal?"

Mike waved the suggestion aside. "I couldn't live with my conscience if I did that," he stated emphatically. It was fortunate the case was relatively simple and didn't demand too much of Mike's time in preparation. He confided to a few of us that he anticipated no problems in establishing that his respected client had unintentionally stumbled into the plaintiff's house, resulting in some embarrassment for the occupants. His client had no previous record of similar offences and regretted any embarrassment he may have unwittingly caused the plaintiff.

"End of case," he assured us confidently. "The president of the court will comment appropriately and it'll all be over in less than a quarter of an hour and we can all go back to our jobs."

The relatively simple and straightforward nature of the case occupied so little of Mike's time that he was able to attend ground school and continue full time with his flying training. Trial date coincided with a cold foggy morning with no prospect of flying before lunch, so five of us wandered over to Station Headquarters to listen to the proceedings from the back of the court room. Mike's case was listed as the last of five that morning.

By eleven o'clock, the other cases had been heard and there was a brief intermission for Mike to prepare his documents. We moved to seats nearer to where he stood listening to a bit of last minute advice from a flight lieutenant from the Legal Branch.

"Don't ask any witness a question unless you know how he's going to answer," the legal eagle advised our colleague. "And if the unexpected happens, don't try to think on your feet; ask for a five minute intermission to assemble your facts, oh and most important of all, in these sorts of cases, when giving evidence, sergeants invariably revert to their idea of Dickensian English, believing it adds authority and correctness. Be ready for that one."

"What do you mean exactly?" Mike enquired curiously. The other explained that witnesses sometimes tended to use quaint old-fashioned phrases long out of date. Their further discussion was abruptly terminated by the presiding officer calling everybody to order.

It took less than four minutes for the necessary formalities to be completed and the charge to be read out. Mike stood to make his opening address, describing how his client, a non-commissioned officer with many years of loyal service in Her Majesty's Royal Air Force, had unwittingly wandered into a colleague's house at an inopportune moment and thus been branded a peeping Tom. When Mike sat down at the conclusion of his address, none of us doubted the case would be thrown out of court for lack of evidence.

The other side's feeble attempt to discredit Mike's argument left us in even less doubt that the accused would soon walk away unpenalised. It was when Mike stood to cross-examine his first witness that everything fell apart.

"Could you tell the court in your own words the sequence of events that led to you lodging a formal complaint of 'Peeping Tom' against my respected client," he addressed the plaintiff, a rather florid-faced individual who was obviously enjoying being the centre of attention, for he cleared his throat theatrically before grasping the lapels of his jacket and beginning to speak.

"I was apleasuring my wife one Saturday afternoon, as is my wont," he began. "When the defendant 'ere sticks his head through the bedroom window and says "What-ho Charlie, at it again I see.""

The effect of this evidence was immediate, dramatic and hilarious. The president and his fellow board members tried desperately to hide their amusement while the rest of the room collapsed in paroxysms of laughter.

The case for the defence had been destroyed by this one sentence. Mike stood flummoxed, trying desperately to think of a way of saving the situation but even he failed miserably.

Nobody felt particularly sad when the Peeping Tom sergeant was punished by a severe reprimand and six months' loss of seniority, least of all Mike Parry, who had finally broken his winning streak.

This was confirmed when the squadron leader legal eagle who'd suggested Mike join the legal branch rather than fly aeroplanes, pointedly ignored us when we sat at the same table at lunch. Nobody worried one bit, least of all Mike Parry, who could now get on with enjoying learning to fly aeroplanes the Royal Air Force way.

At this stage of the course we lost another member in circumstances which can only be described as incredibly hilarious for everybody except for the unfortunate individual concerned.

The shareholders of the Pheasant Plucker had begun to notice the dear old lady was beginning to show her age. She was rapidly deteriorating in some areas, especially around the body. The metal floor of the rear passenger compartment had almost rusted completely away and the gaping holes had been covered by lengths of wood from wooden apple boxes. Her headlights still went out on sharp bends or over bumps and occasionally they just went out for no reason at all, usually when going through a long tunnel or over a narrow bridge.

The weekend after the end of night flying, Little Dick arranged to take the old lady to a Saturday night dance in Shawbury.

The following morning when I awoke for a late Sunday breakfast, I noted the Pheasant Plucker wasn't in her usual parking place. I thought no more about it, thinking Little Dick had scored last night and would be home later, until a phone call summoned me from the Sunday papers an hour later. One of the mess batmen was holding the receiver as I got to the phone. "It's Pilot Officer Jones . . . Little Dick, Sir . . . " he began. I took the phone from him, imagining Little Dick had suffered a mechanical breakdown in the Pheasant Plucker and needed assistance to get her back to the mess.

"Hello, are you a friend of the patient?" a rather soothing female voice enquired over the phone.

"I dunno, what patient are you talking about?"

"Do you know a Pilot Officer Richard Leon Jones?" the voice enquired patiently. "Also known as er . . . Little Dick?" When I admitted I did, she explained he had been admitted to the Accident and Emergency section of the Wellington Hospital. When I pressed her for more details, she would only reveal the patient was asking for either me, Singer or Mlig to visit him.

I roused the other two and told them we had to go to Wellington immediately on urgent personal business; there seemed little point in telling them more until they had recovered from their Saturday night, which had probably been a heavy one.

Switches Phipps suggested I borrow Lady Chatterley's Lover, and Little Dick's batman let me into his room to select a few essential items to take to him in hospital. I also caught the barman fiddling his accounts and persuaded him to let me have half a dozen bottles of Worthington 'E' beer. He'd refused at first until told him it was for a hospitalised APO then he'd relented.

Wellington lay twenty miles to the south of the airfield down the A442 and Lady Chatterley covered the distance in slightly less than forty minutes. I drove while Singer and Mlig dozed in the back.

By the time we arrived at the hospital, my travelling companions were even more comatose than before. I woke them and persuaded both of them to come in with me. As I picked up Dick's bag of personal effects, I noticed half the bottles of beer were empty.

We entered the main section of the hospital and waited at a window marked 'Admissions and Enquiries'. After only a moment or two, a delightful young honey-blonde nurse slid the glass partition aside and asked if she could help.

I held up Little Dick's bag and explained we were friends of Mr Jones and had brought him a few toiletries and other essential items. As I spoke, a bottle of Worthington 'E' rolled out onto the counter top. Singer quickly grabbed it and muttered something about mouthwash, while behind us, Mlig held up another bottle in emphasis. The nurse emitted a chuckle of feminine amusement.

"Hmm, yes, he's been transferred to my ward," she informed us with a glint of amusement in her eyes. Singer, who had recently become a major shareholder in the Pheasant Plucker, seemed more concerned than any of us about Dick's condition.

"Was it a bad accident?" he enquired anxiously. "Was anything broken?" The nurse assured him everything was all right. The patient had suffered two broken ankles and a bruised dignity but otherwise there was little the matter with either the car or the patient that a little tender loving care couldn't fix.

We followed the trim figure of the nurse along a series of corridors leading to a well lit public ward, with various patients propped up in bed or sitting in bedside chairs. We spotted Dick immediately in one of the first beds.

"Here they are, I told you they'd come immediately," his nurse reassured him, placing a soothing hand on his forehead. He looked up at her appreciatively and stroked her bare arm. She registered a token regulation frown but left her arm where it was.

"What the hell happened to you?" we demanded simultaneously. Dick looked distinctly embarrassed by our question. His nurse, whose name we learned was Dawn, suddenly found a pretext to hurry away in embarrassment, after which he seemed more inclined to talk.

"First of all, you have no need to worry about the Pheasant Plucker," he assured us. We remained puzzled, wondering how anybody can break both ankles and sustain severe bruising in a motor accident without damaging the vehicle. Dick noted our scepticism.

"Well maybe there is a small dent in the rear bumper," he admitted. "But nothing that a good panel beater can't straighten out in half an hour." Singer exhaled a sigh of relief. "Thank Heaven for that," he murmured. "I was worried sick about the car."

Mlig and I remained puzzled.

"What the hell happened?"

"Well, as you know, I took a girlfriend to a party in the Shawbury Officers' Mess," Dick began. "We were getting along absolutely famously, so after the party, on the way back to her place, I suggested a drive to the top of the Wrekin to admire the view."

We listened patiently to Dick's explanation of events. It was interrupted by his embarrassed pauses and our guffaws of laughter. It transpired they had parked in the car park at the top of The Wrekin and begun to admire the view. Human nature began to take its natural course and when Little Dick, now somewhat enlarged, suggested they get into the more comfortable back seat of the Pheasant Plucker, his girl friend had readily agreed.

Now the old car's dilapidated condition began to pose a few problems, for the back seat was too narrow to accommodate two horizontal bodies. The only way they could consummate their evening together was for Dick to remove some of the floor boards and poke his feet through the holes in the floor and stand on the road beneath, while his companion perched on the edge of the back seat and steadied herself with her arms around his neck. Dick continued the story.

"Things were going splendidly and just as we were getting to the best part, with my girl friend in absolute ecstasy crying out "Don't stop, don't stop", I felt this sudden blinding pain in my ankles and a strange sensation of floating off into space. The next thing I knew I'd been loaded into an ambulance and brought here . . . "

The whole thing was very puzzling. We handed Dick his essentials, bade goodbye to Dawn his nurse and headed off to recover the Pheasant Plucker.

Piece by piece, we managed to reconstruct what had happened late that Saturday night. While little Dick was performing in the back of the Pheasant Plucker, the rocking motion caused the lights to flicker intermittently then go out. His girl friend became highly aroused and began calling out in ecstasy. Simultaneously another load of drunken party goers from the Shawbury dance drove up at high speed to the top of the Wrekin, crashing into the darkened Pheasant Plucker, breaking both Little Dick's ankles, ruining his beautiful relationship with his girl friend and pushing the Pheasant Plucker over the edge of the 1,335 feet high car park.

The gallant old vehicle plunged down the side of the hill, her headlights flashing on and off and one of her occupants screaming 'Don't stop, don't stop'. She fortunately buried her aristocratic nose in a wire rubbish basket placed there by the National Trust. Little Dick and his companion were fortunate the wire basket was robust enough to halt the Pheasant Plucker before she had gathered momentum and careened the remaining thirteen hundred feet downhill. As it was, the sudden stop threw him against the driver's dividing partition , knocking him unconscious. The occupants of the other vehicle rescued Dick from his precarious perch atop the Wrekin and called for an ambulance to take him to hospital.

We rescued the Pheasant Plucker from the waste paper basket with the assistance of several sightseers, who helped us push her up the grassy slope back to the car park. To our surprise and relief, her only injuries were a bruised rear end and a cracked tail light. The wire rubbish bin had acted like an enormous spring and compressed on impact, absorbing the force of the impact and preventing any damage to the old lady's visage.

Nobody ever heard or saw anything of the female occupant of the car; probably the embarrassment had been too much for her and she had slunk off home.

During our regular visits to Little Dick in hospital, it became obvious that Dawn, his nurse, was catering to his every need. Our last visit to him was the day before we left Ternhill for Oakington, when he told us he'd been informed by the Air Ministry that due to his unfortunate accident, there was insufficient time remaining for him to complete his national service pilot training. We offered our condolences but Dick and Dawn were sitting hand in hand, completely absorbed in each other. His last words to us were "Don't give it a thought, chaps. The flying was a lot of fun and so was your company but now I'll be back in Civvy Street a year early."

Singer, in a rare attack of generosity, offered Dick his share of the Pheasant Plucker for what he'd paid for it. Little Dick looked at Dawn then pointed to the outline of The Wrekin on the horizon. "Feel like a trip to the top of that hill to admire the view one night?" he enquired suggestively. Dawn swiped him playfully with a newspaper.

"Don't start anything you can't finish . . . " she chided him. "Nobody likes being left up in the air."

Three weeks later we read of their engagement in *The Times*.

Chapter 23

Be Prepared

Now the course was getting into top gear. Final exams were less than four weeks away and the only remaining flying training was formation flying plus a few dual 'brushing up' revision sorties with our instructors before the final handling checks. After that, we'd enjoy a short spell of Christmas leave before moving on to Oakington for jet training.

Surprisingly, Dave Brown started to have problems with his flying at this late stage, which surprised everybody.

Shortly after we'd finished night flying, he'd had a change of instructor, which was not unusual if a personality clash occurred between pupil and teacher, but in this case no such problem existed. Dave's new instructor was the rather unpleasant sergeant pilot we'd seen talking with his father in the Bustard, who seemed to have a permanent chip on his shoulder about commissioned pilots.

Dave had been the first to go solo; all his reports had been good and his previous instructor had been quietly confident his student would collect one or more of the prizes at the end of the elementary flying training stage.

Now he was the subject of a discussion in the Wing Commander Flying's office. Problems had manifested themselves when Dave's new instructor cut short a dual aerobatic detail. Dave was indignant when he climbed white faced from the cockpit.

"It wasn't the aerobatics that affected me," he told a group of us later that evening. "We were in the lee of the Welsh mountains and the turbulence was terrible. I suggested going further inland to avoid the area but my instructor refused. It was a boiling hot day, we were above cloud in bright sunshine, getting thrown around like a bird in a badminton game and the cockpit temperature was almost unbearable. After thirty minutes of this, my instructor looked pretty green about the gills and asked if I'd had enough. We cut the sortie short; I reckon he'd have been sick if we'd carried on. And do you know, the cockpit heat had been on 'High' throughout the whole flight!"

Dave and his instructor were summoned in front of Henry Bilek, who wanted to know why they had remained so long in the turbulent area. When the instructor couldn't come up with a good reason, Henry detected a personality clash. After flying with Dave next day and finding nothing wrong with either his flying ability or his stomach, he decided to reunite him with his previous instructor, with whom he'd made excellent progress throughout the course.

Very strangely, this order was countermanded by higher authority, forcing Dave to continue with the disagreeable sergeant instructor.

Formation flying was an exhilarating experience. For my first detail, Henry Bilek and I were Number Two aircraft in 'Lightman Formation' of three aircraft. I had always been thrilled by the names chosen for aircraft formations: Gingerbread, Mainstreet and Timberwolf are three names that spring to mind and although the names themselves are fairly prosaic, when applied to a formation of military aircraft, they suddenly become very glamorous and exciting.

The take-off looked simple enough. Squadron Leader Arm, the formation leader as well as our squadron commander, called for take-off clearance, was cleared and began his take-off roll down the runway. Henry accelerated behind and to one side of him, our wing tip clear of his, so that in the event of him aborting his take-off, we wouldn't hit him. To our right, Singer and his instructor were in the third aircraft.

Once airborne, it seemed to be just a question of listening carefully to what was said on the radio, and changing to Channel 'D', the formation flying frequency. Henry flew the aircraft in the climb and it all looked very easy to me, then once in straight and level flight in 'V' formation, he informed me I had control.

The first attempt at formation flying is difficult.

As soon as my hands touched the controls, the lead aircraft ahead zoomed up fifty feet. I tried to pull up into position but ended up too high. The first attempt at formation flying is difficult until you, the pilot, realize the lead aircraft is flying straight and level and it is you who are moving out of position. Like instrument flying, it suddenly clicks and you wonder why it was so difficult initially. After a few dual details, we were sent off on solo formation practice with an instructor flying the lead aircraft. On my second dual formation detail, once again with Henry Bilek, we were the lead aircraft. At the end of the sortie he ordered the other two aircraft into line astern formation for five or ten minutes' tail-chasing.

Henry knew darn well that like every other member of the course, I was interested in the lifestyle of a fighter pilot, and he used this knowledge to goad me. "Zere are two fighters on your tail, Clapshaw, you must lose zem, zey are going to shoot you down . . . " I tried every antic in my repertoire of aerobatics – steep turns, full throttle climb, Derry turns – but the other pilots knew as much as I.

"Zose fokkers are still zere. Come on, d'you vant to die?" I began perspiring with the mental and physical effort of this type of flying. I tried rolling rapidly to the left then as the aircraft completed three quarters of the roll, Derry turning to the right, but still the others were there.

"Zey are two fighters, Clapshaw, you vill be shot down of you don't lose zose buggers. Come on now, they're about to open fire!" I fire-walled the throttle and rolled into a vertical turn to the right but the other aircraft saw my ailerons move and anticipated my action.

"You vould be dead now, you know zat?" Henry pronounced sadly. "You must use zer fokking aircraft; here, I show you, I haf control." He rolled the aircraft into a vertical bank to the right, slowly enough for our pursuers to notice his right aileron deflect up. They instantly banked to the right and pulled hard to turn inside us.

I couldn't see how this gambit of Henry's could possibly work. Our pursuers were already turning inside us.

When our aircraft was in a vertical bank, he held it there with a small amount of top rudder and pushed forward on the control column so that the aircraft described an outside turn to the left! After turning through 270 degrees, he levelled out. The sun was directly behind us while ahead and slightly below, the other two aircraft were sitting ducks convinced we were still somewhere ahead.

"See vat I mean? Here, you haf control." Henry had made his point. Within seconds of placing his hands on the controls, he had foxed our attackers into proceeding in the opposite direction to where we were going, enabling us to get behind them in a perfect position to shoot them out of the sky. Now he was handing control back to this slow-witted pupil of his. It had taken him no great effort to lose our pursuers; there was no sign of ruffling of his calm demeanour, no perspiration or stress lines on his face, he had merely performed a feat which he had probably done hundreds of times before, one which he had learned in the hard school of wartime combat flying, where the slow learners died first.

By the end of the formation flying part of the syllabus, we could hold station through most simple manoeuvres such as turns, climbing and descending. We never learned formation aerobatics, which I imagine to be one of the most exhilarating forms of flying.

Every formation detail ended with a 'run and break' over the airfield. For this manoeuvre, which looked and sounded very spectacular to those on the ground, the three aircraft would dive down the duty runway with propellers in high rpm then abruptly turn downwind at one second intervals. The moment to turn was indicated by the leader transmitting: "Lightman formation, turning left, turning left. GO!" He would then bank sharply to his left and pull up to wash off any excess airspeed resulting from the dive down the runway. His number two would follow one second later followed by number three a second after him.

It was essential to listen carefully to which way the leader was turning, as was evidenced on my very last formation trip, when the leader broke right, as he had announced he would, and Singer, who was flying number two, simultaneously broke left towards me. We had become very overconfident by this stage and I had already begun to bank right, so for a split second I had a very close view of a Provost in plain view turning towards me before we both banked away from each other. The experience was rather sobering and left us rather thoughtful afterwards. The formation leader, a very quiet-mannered sergeant pilot who rarely raised his voice or uttered expletives, realized he'd have to do something about this near fatal error. After we had taxied in and shut down, he walked over to Singer's aircraft, climbed up on the wing and glared at him accusingly. "Do you know what you are, Sir?" he enquired. "You're a stupid cunt!" The matter was then over.

A few months earlier, two APOs had done something similar with more permanent results. Their aircraft collided at eleven hundred feet, the minimum height for bailing out by parachute, and both pilots decided to jump. It was the only sensible decision, for both aircraft were locked together and falling out of control. One parachute opened immediately and the pilot landed beside the runway. The other pilot's parachute hadn't opened fully as he disappeared behind Sunshine Hangar. Five of us raced towards the area behind the hangar, not relishing seeing the grisly sight we imagined lay behind it. To our astonishment and delight, we were met by the pilot carrying his chute like a large pile of laundry. His parachute had opened micro-seconds before he hit the ground, below the height of the hangar roof. His actual time under the silk must have been well under a second! After a quick visit to the sickbay and a change of underpants, he was declared fit to fly again.

After formation flying, I had only one more nav-ex to do – a solo low-level cross country, which I had been looking forward to immensely. After that, everybody would have to get down to some serious revision for the end of course exams and final handling check.

Big Dick arrived back from his low-level nav-ex with a hilarious tale to tell: while flying across Trentham Park Lake well below the prescribed height, he had sighted a fly fisherman standing up in a punt casting. Temptation proved too much for Big Dick, who altered course towards the angler, and his last glimpse of the man had been as he disappeared over the side of the boat, a look of horrified incredulity on his face. Dick had flown straight at him to ensure he couldn't note down the aircraft's identity number.

The solo nav-ex was supposed to be flown at 250 feet but I doubt whether anybody ever went that high, for the temptation to fly lower was irresistible. The sensation of flying across the countryside at 120 knots, about 140 mph or over two miles per minute, is indescribable.

On the afternoon I flew my low level nav-ex, five other members of the course were on the same exercise. This resulted in an impromptu air race between six relatively inexperienced pilots, all playing silly games at less than 250 feet! Something dangerous was likely to happen and it did: at one stage of the flight, while hurtling across flat countryside in formation with Switches Phipps, he turned left towards me and passed over my head. I was concentrating more on his relative position than a line of poplar trees ahead, racing towards me at two miles a minute, less than two seconds flying time away. I couldn't pull up without colliding with the underside of Switches' aircraft and I was incredibly fortunate there was a gap in the line of trees wide enough for my aircraft to squeeze through!

Experience is made up of such episodes and I ruminated afterwards that I would rather have done without that one! (Shortly afterwards, the

Air Force deleted solo low-level cross-countries from the syllabus because they were costing the British taxpayer too much in damaged aircraft! Even during our training, a retired wing commander had phoned the station commander and told him he was getting rather sick and tired of looking out of his bedroom window in the morning and seeing Provosts passing below!).

The remarks of the driver of an express locomotive speeding along a long straight piece of track in the Canadian wheat belt one moonlit night were unrecorded. He saw what appeared to be the light of another train hurtling towards him at a hundred miles per hour. He applied the emergency brakes in an effort to avert what seemed like an inevitable head-on collision. As the wheels ground to a halt in a shower of sparks, the approaching light suddenly rose into the night sky and the roar of an aircraft's radial engine was heard above the confusion. Some trainee pilot had flown down the long straight piece of track with his landing light on . . .

Towards the end of our elementary flying training, more and more people began to remark on Deep Depression Dan's increasing irritability. At first there was only light hearted banter at the meteorologist's bad-tempered demeanour.

"What's the matter with Deep Depression Dan? Hasn't fallen into another of his deep depressions, has he?"

"I don't think the weather agrees with him."

Eventually he became recognised as a depressing influence on the light-hearted atmosphere of the mess, or as somebody described him 'the life and soul of a bereavement'.

He was a civilian working for the Air Force, so had been allowed to join the officers' mess. He had a low tolerance level towards APOs and rarely lost an opportunity to complain of their boisterous behaviour, which seemed rather short-sighted to us, because our presence was responsible for his job.

He was at his worst on dining-in nights. His drinking, which I suspect was the prime reason for his unpleasantness, would start before dinner and continue until after mid-night. He suffered from short arms and deep pockets, for he would stand moodily at the bar and accept drinks from others but never reciprocate their generosity. He seemed to enjoy glaring irritably at the antics of the APOs for the Air Force had always enjoyed a reputation for high-spirited mess life and Ternhill was no exception to the rule. On Tuesday dining-in nights, the mess skiffle group would provide after-dinner entertainment with its tea chest double bass, guitars, washboard and anything else that could be persuaded to make sounds. By 11 p.m. the festivities were in full swing, with flying instructors, pupils and miscellaneous hangers-on joining in the fun. Ternhill Tuesday dining-in nights had taken this format since long before we had arrived on the scene and continued after our departure.

Throughout these festivities, Deep Depression Dan would sit at the bar, glowering disapprovingly. Everybody ignored this behaviour until the odd complaint from him began to filter through to the President of the Mess Committee. I have already mentioned OQs, Officer qualities, which were one way an APO could be chopped without question, for the Air Force's future pilots had to be gentlemen and officers – as well as being able to fly aircraft to the standards demanded by the service. The RAF had ceased training NCO (non-commissioned or sergeant pilots), and a whisper of lack of OQs was enough to make any APO tremble at the prospect of the chop. Certain acts were guaranteed to result in axing: bouncing a cheque was probably the best known, being cited as the co-respondent in a divorce case was another but a more insidious and snide way was to hint at a lack of OQs in a particular individual.

Eventually Deep Depression Dan went a bit too far and made a formal written complaint against two members of our course: during the previous

Tuesday night's after-dinner festivities, Mike Parry and Switches Phipps had tried to snap the met' man out of his permanent gloom. Their efforts had the opposite effect – his mood became surlier and his face grumpier. For somebody never blessed with an excess of charm, this made him almost animal-like. He had an extremely objectionable habit of noisily clearing his throat, as if to spit, and then not doing so. The effect was unpleasant for everybody else. His table manners weren't very good either, a request to pass say the salt or pepper would never contain the words 'please' or 'thank you', so his arrogance in suggesting anybody lacked officer qualities was a case of the pot calling the kettle black.

On the evening in question, Mike and Switches had decided to do something about his moodiness.

Dan usually stood at the bar either staring moodily into his glass or glaring at any revellers. While he was staring into his glass, Mike and Switches led a cart horse through the swing doors of the Mess and positioned it directly behind him. Some animal lover bought the horse a packet of cheese straws, which it ate with great enjoyment, surrounded by a semicircle of APOs.

After a long contemplation of the bottom of his glass, Deep Depression Dan turned and gazed irritably at the semicircle of youthful faces behind him. He clicked his tongue irritably and returned to gazing into his glass, appearing not to have noticed the horse.

Every pair of eyes was upon the met man. If he had forecast fire and brimstone at the morning's meteorological briefing, he couldn't have gained more attention. After several seconds, his head suddenly jerked in recognition of what he had just seen. He turned slowly round again. The horse was still there, finishing the last of its cheese straws. It whinnied hopefully and nudged Dan's arm, hoping to inveigle him into providing more goodies. The meteorologist looked around at the others in the bar, all carrying on normally, apparently oblivious of their equine companion.

Dan turned back to the bar, rapidly drained the contents of his glass and held it out for refilling. Quickly swallowing most of his fresh drink, he looked slowly round again.

The horse was no longer there. Mike and Switches had removed it while Dan's back was turned. He gazed suspiciously at the semicircle of poker faces before returning to the solace of his glass. He suddenly turned again, hoping to catch sight of the horse again; it was not there. He seemed convinced it must have been a trick of the light, for he removed his spectacles and cleaned them vigorously with a rather grubby handkerchief.

While he was doing this, Mike and Switches brought the horse back through the other entrance and positioned it at the opposite end of the bar from Dan, where the obliging bar man placed a bowl of cheese straws in front of the animal.

Having cleaned his spectacles to his satisfaction, Dan replaced them on his nose and squinted the length of the bar. His head gave a convulsive jerk when he spied the horse. His glasses fell from his nose and he downed his drink in one gulp. Mike and Switches decided now the time had come to depart with the horse. They exited through the far door, leading their four-legged friend down the corridor.

Deep Depression Dan left the bar shortly afterwards. He was still doubtful whether to believe what he thought he had seen but smart enough not to ask if anybody else had seen a horse. Leaving the bar, he took the corridor to his room; unfortunately it was the same one down which Mike, Switches and the horse had disappeared. On hearing his approach, they quickly hid in a convenient dark alcove under the stairs, confident the met man wouldn't notice them.

Deep Depression Dan hurried past without a glance, anxious to gain the shelter of his room. Unfortunately the horse recognised him, and associating him with cheese straws, whinnied hopefully. The meteorologist stopped, glanced at the indistinct shape, bade it "good night" and hurried to his room, slamming the door closed behind him.

Mike and Switches returned the horse to its field and considered the matter finished. Unfortunately, somebody discussed the hilarious event next morning in Dan's earshot and mentioned names. The meteorologist realized he'd been had by a couple of APOs, and lost no time in lodging a formal complaint with the Mess Manager, himself an ex-wartime air gunner. He took the unprecedented step of warning Mike and Switches about the complaint before passing it to the President of the Mess Committee for action. Normal procedure was for the complaint then to be passed to the Commanding Officer, who would decide whether it constituted a case of 'lack of OQs' and whether to issue the order for them to be chopped.

Mike and Switches therefore had twenty-four hours in which to extricate themselves from the mire. They were both incensed at Dan's actions.

"How on earth did an animal like him become a member of the mess? He's a civilian . . . " Switches exclaimed.

"He's a country member," the Mess Manager explained.

"Yes, of course I remember, but couldn't he be a bit more tolerant?"

Later that afternoon, I headed towards the barber's shop thoughtfully. Despite Mike's previous form, I doubted whether even his agile legal mind could extricate them from this spot of bother. Worse still, knowing Deep Depression Dan's hatred of APOs, I felt certain he'd insist on the gravest punishment. Because he was a civilian mess member making a complaint against two serving officers, he need not be influenced by the CO in any way. The matter didn't seem to concern Mike, who breezed into the barber's shop while I was in the chair.

"Haircut, Sir? Won't be long; take a chair."

"No thanks, just some protectives please."

"Large family pack, Sir? These are electronically tested – very popular . . . " he paused in his snipping.

"The reusable type please," Mike replied. The barber reached up to retrieve a faded package from a high shelf.

"Here you are Sir, try these, she won't feel a thing," he assured Mike. I was puzzled. Was the condemned man having a good night out in lieu of a healthy breakfast?

For the next twenty-four hours, Mike did nothing. He treated the meteorologist normally, sat in the front row at Met briefing and stared intently at him while he tried to predict the day's weather. This rather flummoxed the meteorologist, and next morning he pinned the met' chart upside down on the blackboard, and tried to point out the main points of the synoptic situation. This was comparable to a concert pianist trying to play with his music upside down. Similarly, in the dining room, as well as the bar, Mike treated the meteorologist as if he was oblivious of the complaint he'd made against him.

At breakfast the following morning, Mike sat opposite Dan but appeared to ignore him. The meteorologist, anticipating some remark from Mike, eyes him suspiciously through his glasses. Switches came in a minute after Mike, sat beside him and began questioning him about his previous evening's activities.

"I didn't leave her bed 'til 5 a.m." Mike confided to him in a conspiratorial whisper. Dan's ears pricked up with interest.

"They say she's insatiable. Her first husband had a breakdown and died . . . "

"On the second week of the honeymoon," Mike confirmed.

"You must be starving then?" Switches observed. Mike agreed, adding mischievously that he "could eat a horse". Dan twitched convulsively at the mention of a horse while all the time pretending not to listen in to their conversation. Mike reached across to the assorted packets of cereals and helped himself to a generous portion of Coco Pops.

"These things are supposed to contain energy," he explained to Switches, still affecting a stage whisper. Switches nodded agreement, adding something about being "shot out of guns" as he passed the milk and sugar.

After sprinkling the cereal with a liberal coating of sugar while explaining he had to put energy back into his system, Mike reached into his uniform shirt pocket and pulled out a long reusable condom, which he had previously filled with condensed milk and tied at one end. To anybody not in the know, it looked very 'used'. Untying the knot with his teeth, he squeezed the contents over the cereal. Dan's eyes began to bulge and his Adam's apple bobbed up and down at a high rate.

Mike finished squeezing the last drop from the condom, dropped it into the ash tray in front of Dan and scooped up a large spoonful of cereal. He chewed appreciatively on the vitamin rich nutriment.

"It's supposed to contain all the essential vitamins and minerals," Switches volunteered. Deep Depression Dan had turned a bilious shade of green and his cheeks began to bulge.

"Very important in building up resistance to infection and disease," Mike mumbled between snaps, crackles and pops. "Also carbohydrates for replacing lost energy." Large beads of perspiration had appeared on Dan's brow as he placed a hand over his mouth to fight back a desire to throw up. Mike looked at the met man in alarm.

"You feeling OK, Dan?" he enquired concernedly. "Here, have a mouthful of this, it'll work wonders . . . " he held out a heaped spoonful. The met man pushed the proffered spoon away and began to stand unsteadily. Rivulets of sweat were running down his green face as he ran for the door with one hand over his mouth.

He would probably have made it through the door if the Commanding Officer hadn't happened to enter the dining room on his monthly inspection, accompanied by the Mess Manager and the Station Medical Officer. Courtesy would normally have dictated that Deep Depression Dan stand aside to allow the senior officer to enter the room but Dan was desperate, an area of intense high pressure was developing. He attempted to barge his way through but the Mess Manager grasped him firmly by the arm and suggested he "Have the courtesy to stand aside for the Commanding Officer".

The result was sickeningly messy for all concerned.

Mike and Switches were quickly on the scene; Switches led Dan off to station sick quarters while Mike stayed behind.

"Poor fellow, it's the drink, I'm afraid," Mike muttered audibly enough for everybody to hear.

"Does he drink very much?" the Medical Officer demanded, gesturing in the direction of the departing meteorologist.

"Not really, Sir," Mike replied. "He spills more than he drinks, it's the hallucinations that are the problem. Pink elephants, horses . . . know what I mean?" Behind the MO's back the Mess Manager was having great difficulty stifling his laughter.

Deep Depression Dan's civilian status saved his job but he was very careful in his attitude towards APOs thereafter.

Chapter 24

Cross Roads

Now the course entered a very serious stage. With final tests less than two weeks away, we suddenly realized we would have to study hard to achieve the required pass marks. Every evening, including week-ends, we studied coefficients of lift, drift angles, detonation, inventory forms, clouds, precipitation, fuel systems, Morse code, instruments, adiabatic lapse rates, tephigrams and a thousand other things. Daytime was spent on any remaining flying exercises and 'polishing up' for the final handling check. At this stage of our training a rumour began to circulate that national servicemen would not be going on to advanced jet training. Everybody hoped this *was* just a rumour, but since the Tory government had recently disbanded the Auxiliary Air Force squadrons, it made sense and could be true. If the Air Force was thinking this way, a failed grade in the end of course exams would be a convenient and legitimate way of withdrawing an individual from further training.

One by one, we took our final handling checks. I did mine with the squadron commander, who briefed me very thoroughly on what we were going to do, then seeing I looked rather apprehensive, put me at ease by telling me "You've done it all before and you wouldn't be here today if we didn't think you could handle it."

The test lasted an hour and a half and consisted of a bit of almost everything except formation and night flying. It started with a Fanstop after take-off, with which I coped OK, followed by instrument flying, which was not a problem, forced landings, aerobatics, steep turns, a flapless approach followed by a glide approach and a bit of low flying.

After ten exhilarating minutes in the low flying area, my examiner suddenly asked me our position and the course to steer back to Ternhill. I was completely flummoxed for a while, having been so engrossed in the low flying that I hadn't kept a mental plot of our position. I knew we were still in the low flying area but it was so close to Ternhill that the bearing could be anything from 240 degrees to 360. I cursed myself inwardly for having fallen into such an elementary trap while the aircraft roared across Shropshire at 150 mph.

Suddenly below us I recognized a familiar sight, our favourite pub, the Magpie and Stump. I remembered the many times we had staggered out of that excellent hostelry, reeling towards the Pheasant Plucker or Lady Chatterley's Lover, while some wit would tell the driver to 'steer two six zero for base'. I turned leisurely to my examiner and while trying to appear casual, replied "Loggerheads crossroads, Sir. Steer two six zero for base." He grunted his approval of the answer and announced he had control. I held my hands up and away from the controls to confirm he had command.

"OK, you've passed the final handling check so now I'm going to have a fly. I spend far too much time behind a desk. You don't mind, do you?" I assured him he could fly the aeroplane for as long as he wanted and we climbed up through a grey overcast sky to carry out a quarter of an hour's aerobatics – loops, rolls, stall turns, Immelmans, hesitation rolls, he went through the whole repertoire, talking while he flew.

"Have you enjoyed the course?"

"Loved every minute of it!" I replied.

"Looking forward to jet training, I imagine?" I assured him I was. "Where's the end of course party going to be?" he suddenly demanded.

I had no hesitation in replying. "The Magpie and Stump, Sir."

We flew back to Ternhill and my last flight in a Provost was over[1]. By the

---

1. Untrue! Thirty-six years later, I flew a privately owned Provost that had been on the Ternhill flight line with me, but that's a long time away.

end of the day's flying, half the course had successfully passed their final handling checks. Gradings were fairly uniform, only one person was marked 'Low Average', most of us got 'Average' and the only member of the course to be graded 'above Average' was Lord Jim, who must have got it on ability alone, for he never seemed to do any homework in the evenings.

David Brown's final handling check had been with a Fleet Air Arm former Buccaneer pilot now serving as a 'trapper' with the Central Flying School's examining board.

When we questioned him after the flight, Dave held up one thumb in triumphant affirmation that all had gone well.

"It was blooming lucky really," he began. "The bloke is obviously a bit anti-RAF so I didn't say anything controversial, and he just sat there. He gave me a Fanstop on take off, which went OK then a forced landing which he seemed to think was good. It was one of those days when the aeroplane just seemed to fly on rails 'cause when we climbed up for some general handling and aerobatics, I hit my own slipstream at the bottom of a loop!"

We murmured our grudging admiration, for hitting your own slipstream was the aeronautical equivalent of a hole in one in golf, requiring not only skill but also a lot of luck.

"Yeah, it was pure luck but then when I did a 360 degree steep turn, it happened again!"

"You mean you hit your own slip stream a second time?"

"Yeah, like I told you, it was one of those days when everything went right."

"What did the Fish-Head say?" Mike Parry's contempt for career naval officers hadn't diminished in the slightest.

"Well, it was rather funny 'cause he said 'I bet you can't do that again', and do you know what, the aircraft was in perfect trim and I rolled into another steep turn in the opposite direction and it did it again! Talk about lucky, eh?"

We ruminated on this bit of information. Everybody has good and bad days and Dave had obviously had a good one. It appeared likely he would be graded above average, possibly collecting the flying or aerobatic prize and maybe even topping the course in flying.

A loud bellow from the debriefing room reminded him he hadn't been officially debriefed and graded yet. The naval pilot glared at him impatiently as he hurried over to the debriefing room.

That was to be the last time we saw David Brown. After debriefing, a carmine red Aston-Martin whisked them over to the Wing Commander Flying's office, where Dave's sergeant instructor, his Fleet Air Arm examiner, the station commander and several civilians joined them for a mysterious and lengthy conference.

By the end of the week, everybody had taken their final handling checks and now only the written exams remained. After a weekend spent honing our aeronautical knowledge to a fine edge, we presented ourselves for examination. In the excitement, nobody noticed Dave Brown was missing.

Papers were set on meteorology, instruments, engines, airframes, aerodynamics, navigation, maps and charts, and aviation medicine. Most of the examinations went as we had anticipated, the only one to give anybody any problems was navigation plotting. Part of this exam consisted of what was called a 'dry swim', which is an imaginary flight as a navigator. We were each given a large Mercator chart of southern England, on which were printed a few airfields, beacons, coastlines but not much else. We set out from an airfield on our 'dry swim' and were given various courses and speeds to plot. After some time, we were given two or three radio bearings to fix our positions. After plotting the fix, we used the information to answer questions on track made good, ground speed, wind velocity and a few other points. The only way to answer these questions was to plot one's course on the chart, using protractor, divider and pencil, which we did.

Unfortunately for Big Dick, his plotted course took him off the edge of the chart and across the table top. At first he attempted to draw lines on the wooden surface below but when he began to run out of table top, he became concerned. By now he was practically on Lord Jim's chart on the next table. A quick glance by the examiner revealed Big Dick had plotted his departure point using west longitude instead of east. The matter was quickly resolved and Dick returned to his chart.

We received notification of the results before the weekend. Mike Parry had scored the overall top mark, Singer, Big Dick, Mlig and myself were equally spaced down the field. Switches Phipps had come last, a fact that worried nobody for we had all achieved the required pass mark. In our selfish excitement at passing, nobody had noticed one person's name was not on the list.

The end of course party was arranged for the weekend, to be followed by our passing out parade on Thursday and a dining-out night the same evening.

The week end party was an enormous success, Henry Bilek got filled-in by a concoction nicknamed 'car smash' because people invariably ended up smashing their cars after a glass of it. Lord Jim played the piano while assorted girl friends stood around decoratively and sang. Everybody got drunker and happier and bawdier. Finally, when the landlord closed the doors on the last of us at 3 a.m., I remember collapsing drunkenly into the back of the Pheasant Plucker and hearing some anonymous voice command, "Steer two six zero for base, pilot!"

Several people had noticed Dave Brown's absence and begun to wonder where he'd disappeared to. His instructor hadn't attended the party and none of the other instructors at the party knew his fate but when we cornered a drunken Henry Bilek in the car park, he twisted and squirmed like a hooked fish to avoid answering the question. Under pressure, he reluctantly informed us Dave hadn't passed his final handling check and had been chopped.

This didn't make sense to any of us; we recounted the details of Dave's final handling check, specially the loop and steep turns.

"Isn't he entitled to a flight commander's check?" Kiwi Green protested. Henry squirmed in acute embarrassment and mumbled something about 'political pressures'.

Monday was spent relearning drill for the passing out parade. Big Dick, being the tallest, was selected to be the marker and parade commander. He would be the person from whom everybody took their step and direction as we marched onto the square at the start of the parade.

For nine blissful months we had done little or no drill; a weekly parade was held every Saturday morning on the square but we were usually down at Flights catching up on flying hours. When we weren't flying, we were away on forty-eight hour passes, so our drilling ability was minimal.

By Monday afternoon, the Station Warrant Officer (SWO) had despaired of tomorrow's passing out parade bearing any semblance of military precision. We assured him dress rehearsals always went badly; tomorrow would be no problem at all. Unfortunately this was not so.

The format of the parade was that we, the passing out course, would march onto the square in front of other junior courses already paraded while the station band played 'The Royal Air Force March'. Having only heard them play one tune, 'Sussex by the Sea', I wondered if they knew any other tune.

An air vice-marshal arrived by Avro Anson to take the salute at the passing out parade.

We waited in the wings to march on. The Station Warrant Officer was giving Big Dick last minute instructions as the station band struck up the opening bars of 'Sussex by the Sea', which suddenly changed to the 'Royal Air Force March'. The air vice-marshal led the CO and assorted officers onto the saluting base while we snapped to attention and began to march to the front of the parade, as we had practised ad nauseam previously. Every one of us was conscious of the many pairs of eyes upon us.

As Dick passed the saluting base, he turned sharp left then left again after a few paces, to ensure that when he halted and turned a third time, he would be correctly placed in front of us to give the command to halt. Unfortunately the front row, comprised of Switches, Mlig and Lord Jim, forgot the reason for Dick's sharp left turn and followed him instead of continuing straight ahead! Dick saw what had happened, gawped at his unwanted followers and broke into a run while the SWO had a seizure on the edge of the square. The situation was saved by Mike Parry having the presence of mind to give the order to "Right Wheel" just before Big Dick panicked completely. Our course halted in an almost straight line and the air vice-marshal strode onto the podium. The day had been saved by some very quick thinking and initiative.

The band struck up 'The Royal Air Force March' again, the airmen presented arms, the air vice-marshal delivered the routine speech about old pilots and bold pilots but no old bold pilots, at which everybody chuckled politely, we marched past the saluting base and suddenly our passing out parade was over.

Lunchtime was spent shepherding parents, girlfriends, brothers and sisters round the station. After a half-hearted attempt to force my way into the crowded bar after lunch, I gave up and retired to my room to prepare for tonight's dining-out night. Singer, Mlig, Lord Jim, Kiwi Green and a few others came round a few minutes later and we persuaded one of our obliging batmen to make us a pot of tea while we discussed our immediate future.

The dining-out night contained a few unfortunate occurrences, but since our personal fitness reports had already been written and our personal files were on their way to our next station, everybody was confident any indiscretions would soon be forgotten.

Big Dick found himself seated opposite the CO's wife and their daughter Sonjah, who was dressed if not to kill, certainly to inflict serious injury. Her startlingly revealing dress was cut so low that she looked as if her delectable young breasts would spill out of it at any moment. She had lost most of her girlish puppy fat since the unfortunate incident with Big Dick and looked positively radiant now. Whenever she spoke to anybody, their gaze would fall first to her delicious bare shoulders before loitering at the top of her startlingly low cut gown. Thoughts would tend to wander to more erotic subjects than the small talk being exchanged under the stern glare of her crinkly-lipped mother. Sonjah knew full well the effect her décolletage was having upon those seated around her and revelled in the fact, despite her mother remarking many times that her dress was "quite unsuitable for the occasion".

Big Dick played it cool and conversed with her father. By the time dinner was over, he had persuaded the CO to recount some of his wartime experiences. One could feel the senior officer warming towards Big Dick and even the CO's wife relaxed her crinkly lips slightly after Dick insisted on ordering champagne for this auspicious occasion.

The champagne was Sonjah's undoing – literally, for as the evening wore on and more champagne was drunk, Sonjah began to get slightly bombed. This became apparent when she flirted with another APO in the hope of striking a spark of jealousy in Big Dick.

The ploy didn't work; Dick was the model of propriety, smiling politely at whatever Sonjah said or did. This only caused her to drink more than she could handle, despite the disapproving glances of her mother. Soon Sonjah's carefully coiffed hair had come apart and a long blonde tress hung over one eye. Her dress began to slip lower and lower despite mother's persistent instructions to "adjust your dress, dear".

Eventually the meal was over, and a few guests were finishing their coffees before the speeches started. Outside the dining room windows, the sun was setting, bathing the Mess lawn in a rosy glow while the batmen's dogs chased each other across the green turf. I gazed out the window pensively.

My thoughts were abruptly returned to the dining room by a gasp from the CO's wife, who was gazing horror-struck at Sonjah, whose beautiful firm young breasts had suddenly burst free from the confines of her dress and were protruding proudly forward like two puppy dogs' pink noses.

Sonjah seemed oblivious of her double exposure and was downing yet another glass of champagne while her mother made frantic attempts to cover her daughter's breasts with a table napkin. Unfortunately Mother's efforts knocked over several wine glasses, which attracted the attention of others further along the table, causing them to glance in her direction and seeing Sonjah's generous breasts on display, quietly nudge their neighbours and point.

While Mother tried desperately to think what to do next, Big Dick realized here was his chance to save the CO and his family from untold embarrassment. Leaping to his feet, he pointed out the dining room window, bellowing, "Look everybody, look out the window".

The thought was very ingenious, by distracting everybody's attention to something else, he would momentarily divert scrutiny away from the semi-naked Sonjah.

It was unfortunate for him that the batmen's dogs were copulating on the lawn at that precise moment.

After the last after-dinner speaker had sat down to muted applause, the CO and his entourage headed for the bar, which was the signal for everybody else to start the evening's celebrations.

Precisely at ten o'clock, the CO's staff car pulled up in front of the mess and a reluctant Sonjah was manoeuvred into the back. My last view of her was as she waved to somebody in the assembled group of officers before the vehicle started off abruptly, throwing her back into the comfortable padded back seat. I turned to go back inside and found myself face to face with the padré, who was still waving at the departing rear lights.

"Coming inside for a nightcap, padré?" I suggested conversationally. He stopped his waving and seemed to suddenly see me for the first time. With something resembling a guilty expression on his face, he accepted my invitation.

The evening turned into a splendid occasion with many hilarious antics. By midnight, a scene of carnage littered the bar and surrounding rooms. Somebody had suggested a bicycle race and the idea was enthusiastically accepted by eight or ten riders, who quickly procured mounts from the bicycle rack in front of the mess and waited for the 'off'. Nothing can describe the chaos caused by a large number of bikes racing down the mess corridor, through the crowded bar into the anteroom then back into the corridor for the second lap. Chaos was heaped upon pandemonium when somebody brought in the farmer's cart horse to share in the merrymaking. The docile animal either disapproved of our behaviour or, as Singer so succinctly put it, had a weak stomach, for after consuming several packets of cheese straws, it lifted its tail and expressed exactly what it thought of us!

The padré seemed anxious to leave about now. He approached each of us, shook our hands and wished us good luck in the future. Mike Parry, Big

Dick and I were at the far end of the bar so were the last he bade farewell.

"Better be off now, nice to have known you, good luck," he shook Dick's hand last.

"Got something special in your room, have you padré?" he suggested conspiratorially. This rather startled the cleric, who attempted to leave via a store cupboard before eventually finding the correct exit and hurrying away.

A little later I retired to my room to rest before starting to pack for the move to Oakington. Turning on the light, I surveyed the area that had been my sanctum sanctorum for nine very happy months. Tomorrow, everything would change, the model aeroplanes and photographs would come down, the cupboards and wardrobes would soon be empty until another young pupil pilot moved in and placed his personality on the room.

My thoughts were interrupted by a rustling in the ivy outside. A voice was calling "Good-night and good luck."

"Thanks, same to you – Sonjah."

We eventually learned David Brown's fate through the grape vine.

His father was determined to prevent his son and heir flying and had exerted every bit of political pressure on the Air Force to achieve his wish. All attempts at Air Ministry level had failed miserably, Dave was proving to be an enthusiastic and capable service pilot who the senior officers saw no reason to lose.

Sir David was a wily tactician, well versed in the ways of the world and accustomed to getting his own way. He approached his local Member of Parliament with an offer the politician couldn't afford to ignore in election year. The MP probed a bit deeper than Sir David and came up with a possible solution.

The reason the son found himself confronted by a non-Air Force officer for his Final Handling Check was because pleas for help had been directed towards the Lords of the Admiralty, who passed appropriate instructions to the examining officer, with promises of career advancement if he carried out the task to Sir David's satisfaction.

Dave's brilliant and lucky performance during his check should have earned him an 'above average' assessment. Instead it presented his examining officer with a dilemma, for when he reported it accurately to his senior officers, there seemed to be no reason to fail him. It was then he was reminded of one characteristic that could ground a pilot without question.

Ignoring any pangs of conscience in the interests of self advancement, the naval officer acted accordingly. Dave Brown, who would probably have ended up top of the course and become an exceptional pilot, was graded grossly over-confident at the end of his elementary flying training.

Dave was chopped and quickly returned to civilian life.

Chapter 25

Advanced Flying Training

We left Ternhill with high hopes the next day and headed south- east towards Oakington in Cambridgeshire. Nobody felt any nostalgia or regret at leaving our old station, we were like revellers moving from one party to another, confident the next nine months would be even more fun than we had enjoyed at Ternhill. None of us noticed how much change nine months' service life and 120 hours flying had wrought in us. Those of us who had survived the 50 per cent 'Chop' rate were competent piston-engined pilots, capable of aerobatics, instrument flying plus night and formation flying, but all at comparatively low speeds compared to the jet aeroplanes onto which we were about to transition.

We drove the 170 miles to Oakington in loose convoy, Lord Jim leading in a rather stylish Austin-Healey sports car that had been a nineteenth birthday present, Mike Parry, Big Dick, Tony Mlig and I in the Pheasant Plucker and Switches, Singer and Kiwi Green in a Citroen light fifteen which Singer had brought the day before with a loan from his generous bank manager, who had agreed that if his client was going to fly jet fighters, he could advance him the £150 required to buy a suitable motor vehicle.

Oakington lay on the other side of England from Ternhill, in an area called East Anglia. There was more social life here, plenty of good pubs and restaurants and more population to enjoy them with. It was different from our previous station in every way possible – firstly it was a lot closer to the 'bright lights', being only a few miles from the university city of

Cambridge with its wealth of social and cultural attractions, and for the really ambitious socialites, London lay seventy miles to the south-west.

The greatest difference was the flying, for now we would get our hands on high performance jet aircraft. Our instructors were mainly composed of young men only a few years older than us, taken from operational squadrons to instruct us. The aircraft were de Havilland Vampires, twin-boomed aircraft with the cockpit and engine in the wing centre section.

We would fly two types or marks of Vampire; our first few hours of initial training would be in the two-seat T-11 trainer, which had side by side seating for student and instructor in a rather cramped cockpit. We would do our first jet solo in this aircraft and after ten hours solo consolidation would be sent off in the Mark Five single-seat Vampire for all solo exercises. The Mark Five was a fighter bomber version of the Vampire, still in active squadron service with some Air Forces.

Soloing in the single seat Mark Five Vampire was the height of every course member's ambition for the aircraft represented everything that flying meant to us – it looked purposeful, even the name FB (for fighter bomber) Mark Five sounded war-like. Even more war-like were the gun ports, camouflage and previous squadron markings left over from earlier squadron service. Vampires had only recently been replaced by Venoms, a similar looking aircraft, and the future generation of supersonic fighters like the Hawker Hunter and Supermarine Swift were just entering squadron service with the élite squadrons of Fighter Command.

Unfortunately the Royal Air Force was rapidly shrinking in size at this time, due to the Tory government's Duncan Sandys' White Paper, which slashed defence expenditure drastically in an effort to stabilise the nation's economy. While I wasn't qualified to comment on the justification for such policy, I would have had to be both deaf and blind not to see the effect it was having on my future flying prospects. The most obvious was that no more national service pilots were following behind us. From now on, only permanent and short service commission officers would be trained as aircrew. The auxiliary fighter squadrons, the millionaire mob or weekend warriors who had performed so brilliantly during the second world war, had been grounded along with many other regular squadrons. Air Force morale was dropping to an all-time low, with too many pilots and not enough flying jobs.

Many of us national service pilots realized it would only take a stroke of an official pen somewhere in Whitehall, to terminate our training immediately. Fortunately for us, the official pen's owner hadn't been advised yet and we were determined to enjoy whatever flying we had left.

I have already remarked how different the flying was at Oakington – the aircraft were much higher performance, almost four times the speed of the piston-engined Provost, and flew over three times higher. We now wore yellow life jackets over our flying overalls, breathed oxygen through a mask and the two seater T-11 trainers were fitted with ejector seats to enable the pilots to 'bang out' in emergency. The earlier marks of Vampires had acquired an unenviable reputation for being difficult to bail out of without striking the tail, so de Havillands equipped the trainer version with bang 'ejector' seats.

Before embarking upon our advanced flying training, we first had to attend a five day ground school course on the aircraft and its systems for the Vampire had a retracting undercarriage, air brakes and an instrument called a Mach meter which indicated speed as a percentage of the speed of sound, Mach One being supersonic. This convinced us the Vampire was very different from the faithful Provost, not an aircraft you could just climb into and start to learn to fly. During these five days, our instructors went to great pains to emphasise things happened much faster in a high performance jet. One point constantly hammered home was if your instructor said "eject", don't ask him what he meant because you'd be talking to yourself! This point was a vital one, probably the most important item taught on the course, emphasising that unlike ships' captains, it was not considered cowardly for the instructor to be first to abandon the sinking ship.

Due to the many members who'd been chopped on our course, we were spliced onto the remnants of another one from Hullavington. The 'chop' and a few other reasons had reduced our number to less than fifty per cent of what we started with so it was common sense to merge the remnants of two courses to make up the numbers for a new one. The Hullavington contingent were a splendid team of fellows who'd suffered the same trials and tribulations as we had, so the merger took place painlessly.

Names I remember from Oakington were Melvin Evans, a small fat Welshman usually referred to as 'Blob Bottom' because most of his obesity was concentrated round that part of his anatomy, Jack Hennessey, an irrepressible Anglo-Frenchman (French father, English mother) who had done moderately well flying a Stampe biplane in international aerobatic competitions pilot before joining the RAF. His dual nationality seemed to bring out the best of both countries – he had the Frenchman's flair for life, being devastatingly charming, a gourmet where food and wine were available and he was one of the smartest dressers I have ever encountered; he could even look smart in stained flying overalls and life jacket! These Gallic traits were blended with the Englishman's penchant for understatement as evidenced by members of his course describing Jack's arrival at Hullavington nine months previously to commence his elementary flying training.

Jack had kept his private aircraft with him throughout the initial basic training and when the time came to travel to their new station, he chose not to accompany the other members of his course by surface transport.

There was no sign of Jack when they reported to 'Flights' on the first morning. The flight commander and several of the instructors were World War Two pilots who made no effort to hide their displeasure at a new pupil arriving late. Somebody did point out it wasn't eight thirty yet, the official reporting time, but the flight commander ignored the reminder as he turned to address the new course. Just as he started to speak, the sound of an aero engine at full power was heard. Students and their instructors followed the flight commander out onto the tarmac to watch a small orange and yellow biplane fly inverted down the runway at 100 feet. Having flown the length of the runway, the pilot performed an inverted 180 degree turn, still at low level, and flew down the runway again, interspersing his flight with an inverted snap roll at the mid-point. Considering how low the aircraft was and the difficulty of performing conventional snap rolls at a safer altitude, it was a masterful display of aerobatic flying. The pilot then crossed the airfield perimeter outbound, executed another inverted 180 degree turn and lined up on the grass runway – still inverted. Suddenly he closed the throttle and just as it seemed too late, he rolled the aircraft upright and the main wheels brushed the grass surface second later. This had all been witnessed by the assembled instructors and their pupils.

Once on the ground, the aircraft turned towards the dispersal area and taxied across the grass with the tail high in the air. Crossing the edge of the tarmac, the throttle was closed, ignition switches cut and the propellor jerked to a stop while the aircraft continued towards the on-lookers under its own momentum. At the last moment the rudder was kicked hard to the left, the nose swung round and the yellow and orange biplane stopped five feet from the open-mouthed pupils and instructors.

A cockpit side panel door opened, the pilot unstrapped himself, climbed out of the cockpit, retrieved his beret from inside the plane, placed it on his head and saluted the incredulous flight commander.

"My name is Acting Pilot Officer Hennessey, m'sieur," he announced to the silent audience. "I've come here to learn to fly."

The time was twenty nine minutes past eight . . .

A less enjoyable student from Hullavington was Ted Hannah, a rather bad-tempered second-hand car dealer from Southend. Perhaps because of his former civilian occupation, he tended to be somewhat shifty in appearance and rarely socialised with fellow members of his course. His nickname became 'Shy Ted' which quickly became 'Shit'ead'.

There were many more delightful characters on the new half of the course who soon settled down to enjoy the exhilaration of flying.

Our flight commander and most of our instructors were thoroughly likeable fellows, with only the odd exception. All had been plucked from operational jet squadrons, put through an instructor's course and posted to Oakington. Some had been in the Air Force less than four years themselves, so a spirit of camaraderie quickly bound everybody together.

My instructor was Bert Giles, a career Air Force officer, ex-Cranwell and a pleasant person to know. The majority of the instructors were on four, eight or twelve year short-service commissions, anxious to accumulate as many flying hours as possible before venturing out into the harsh environment of civil aviation. After the drastic reduction in operational strength of the Air Force, most of our instructors were delighted they still had flying jobs, for hundreds of pilots from disbanded squadrons were being given administrative ground jobs for lack of anything more suitable.

A Rose by Any Other Name

The nigger in the woodpile among our instructors was the squadron commander, Don Whittington, who in medical jargon was a complete c***. He was an elderly career officer of limited ability who hadn't quite cottoned on to the fact he'd been passed over for promotion to higher rank.

He possessed all the attributes of the most loathsome type of career officer, toadying to senior officers while never hesitating to humiliate more junior officers if it would show him up in a more favourable light. Add the fact that he was an incurable snob and you can judge his calibre. His main claim to fame was his descent from a past Lord Mayor of London, a fact which he never lost an opportunity to tell people ("My name's Whittington, descended from a Lord Mayor of London, you know.")

There were two things Whittington detested intensely, flying and national servicemen. During his first talk to us, he went to great lengths to emphasise his low opinion of those who "were only in the service for two years", referring to any one of us as "a rose by any other name". Fortunately his other hatred – flying – made our contacts with him infrequent.

Our first weekend on the new station confirmed our hopes that the next nine months were going to be very pleasant. Big Dick, Switches and I had planned a Saturday afternoon sortie into Cambridge, and enquired if anybody else wanted a lift. Shit'ead the shifty second-hand car dealer expressed interest and suggested we might like to meet some girlfriends of his sister, who were studying at Cambridge.

Cambridge proved to be a very happy hunting ground for the pursuit of pleasure and excitement at the weekends. Soon we had found our favourite haunts. A typical Saturday night would see several cars heading out of the officers' mess car park towards our favourite pub, the George and Dragon beside the river Cam. It was run by an ex-wartime pilot, George Trussler and his wife, whose name I never discovered because everybody referred to the hospitable couple as 'George and the Dragon', although George's wife looked less like a dragon than anybody else I can think of. Once inside their pub, we invariably met female students from one of the colleges, and the weekend had begun. Another favourite location was the Mill, another pub beside the Cam where you could take your drink outside in warm weather and sit on the wall of a bridge over the river while chatting up the female students. Socially Cambridge was even better than the rather limited social life at our previous station.

Chapter 26

First Jet Solos

If the social scene got off to a good start, the same could not be said of our flying training, which was marred by bad weather throughout December, January and February. The airfield was covered by snow for most of February and only the strenuous efforts of the ground crews kept the runways and taxiways clear. Pupils averaged two or three flights per month at the most. Ground school continued normally while we waited patiently for spring to bring better flying weather.

By the beginning of March the weather showed signs of improvement, the snow melted and conditions improved enough for us to achieve some continuity in our flying training. One of the problems with long intervals of time between training flights was the tendency to forget what we had learned previously, and time would have to be spent in revision. Because of this problem, everybody took longer than usual to reach solo standard in the T-11 two-seat trainer.

In contrast to the Provost, there was considerably less drama in reaching solo standard on the Vampire and it was rare for anybody to get chopped for failure to go solo. The speed of jets is considerably greater than piston-engined aircraft and at first the downwind speed of 180 knots, one and a half times the cruising speed of a Provost, seemed incredibly fast and new pilots had to work fast to accomplish the downwind checks in the shorter time available. Soon however, everybody on our course had gone solo.

Most of us did our solos fairly conventionally but Big Dick's was excitingly different.

Vampire T-11 dual trainer.

He had been airborne with his instructor for general handling practice on the first morning detail and was programmed to go solo just before lunch. One of the mandatory pre-solo exercises was spinning and stalling; Dick and his instructor were at high level, practising spin recovery when the aircraft became uncontrollable and refused to respond to the instructor's attempts to recover. The spin developed into a dreaded flat spin and they were falling out of the sky like the proverbial brick built house, the hands of the altimeter unwinding like a demented Catherine wheel and the needle of the vertical speed indicator pegged hard against the negative stop. The instructor gave the order to eject and, as had been stressed in ground school, then pulled the ejector seat handle above his head to 'bang out'

Big Dick reached up and pulled the yellow handle of the ejector seat forward and down. A green screen, designed to protect the pilot's face from injury by the slipstream, came down in front of Dick's face but the ejector seat's explosive charge failed to detonate. He quickly moved the blind aside, intending to jump over the side of the aircraft but then noticed it had begun to recover from the spin. The rapid rotation had stopped and gentle back pressure on the control column brought the nose back onto the horizon again. Despite the missing cockpit hood and a gaping hole in the aircraft floor where the explosive charges of the instructor's seat had fired, the aircraft was controllable. Dick applied power and flew it back to Oakington, where he carried out a very creditable emergency landing.

Subsequent investigation of the aircraft shortly afterwards revealed Dick had not pulled the handle of the ejector seat far enough to detonate the explosive charges in the seat. The reason was probably that Dick, being unusually tall, had long arms and legs. His arms, impeded by the life jacket, oxygen lead, parachute harness, buckles and webbing straps plus other pieces of equipment, had been constrained from moving far enough forward. Whatever the reason, another eighth of an inch of pull, and he would have been ejected.

While the engineering staff was investigating the causes of Dick's incident, frantic efforts were made to locate his instructor, the main concern being that a strong Westerly wind could have blown him out over the North Sea, where his chances of survival in winter would be poor. An air-sea rescue helicopter was despatched from Waterbeach to join several fixed wing aircraft in the search for the downed pilot.

There was no news of the missing instructor at lunch time; Big Dick had been taken to Station Sick Quarters where Flying Officer Jeckyll, the station medical officer, checked him over and prescribed a quick change of underpants before pronouncing him fit for further duty.

That afternoon while we were in ground school, waiting for an aerodynamics lecture to begin, Dick walked in looking very self-conscious. Just as we began to bombard him with question, the chief ground school instructor (CGI) hurried into the room, banged the door closed and spoke.

They had found the instructor, a few miles inland from Norwich, still in his seat with the parachute unopened. Nobody spoke for a minute.

"Dead?" somebody asked needlessly.

The CGI nodded his head. "Yes, I'm afraid so. The barometric release mechanism was probably mis-rigged and failed to free him from his seat automatically. There was no way he could have extricated himself from the seat and deployed his parachute manually in the short time available." We considered the dreadful prospect of falling through the air, fastened to several hundred pounds of metal, seeing the earth race towards you and knowing you only had seconds to live.

Our thoughts were interrupted by the CGI again, pointing at Dick. "And you, Howard, are the luckiest man alive. Your seat has been checked by engineering and your barometric release mechanism was also mis-rigged. If you had pulled the handle an extra eighth of an inch, you wouldn't be here now. You're a very lucky man; that fraction of an inch was the difference between life and death. Remind me never to play poker with you!" He left the room abruptly and the aerodynamics instructor took over. I don't think anybody learned much about aerodynamics that day; our thoughts were on Dick's incredible escape from death.

That evening Wing Commander Lyon, the OC Flying came into the mess and presented Dick with the handle from his ejector seat as a reminder of his incredible escape.

As if he could ever forget!

After going solo in the two-seater T-11 dual trainer, we all began casting covetous glances towards the single-seat Mark Five Vampire fighters. The normal procedure was for pupils to accumulate ten hours solo on the two-seater before being sent off in the Mark Five. Sometimes, at the discretion of their instructor, these ten hours might be extended. Inevitably something always seemed to happen to delay us getting the required ten hours – weather, aircraft unserviceability or the arrival of the weekend, forcing us to fret and fume impatiently until Monday, when either ground school, weather or something else might again contrive to keep us away from the single-seaters.

The first person to become eligible to fly the Mark Five single-seater unfortunately didn't! After accumulating the necessary ten hours solo in the two seat T-11 dual control trainer, Tony Mlig was authorized for a solo detail in a Mark Five on a clear frosty Monday morning.

Unfortunately for him, the compressor bearings on the Rolls Royce Goblin engine failed just after lift off from the westerly runway. Mlig had already selected the undercarriage up so he was left with no option but to dump the aircraft on its belly back onto the short length of remaining runway. The distance was insufficient for the aircraft to slide to a stop, causing it to continue off the end of the sealed surface across a grass area before passing between two elm trees which removed the outer wing panels. A tall hedge claimed the booms and tail surfaces, and other parts of the airframe fell off while traversing several adjacent frost covered fields. Eventually the remains, comprising the cockpit, engine and inner wing panels, slithered down a grassy bank and came to a stop in the middle of a roundabout on the main Huntingdonshire road.

By this time Mlig had shed every part of the aircraft except for the nose, cockpit and part of the centre section[1]. Fearful of the risk of being cremated

---

1. Mlig's subsequent accident report on the incident was a masterpiece of understatement. When describing the break up of the aircraft as it continued across the Cambridgeshire countryside, he wrote: "The trees removed the outer wing panels and undercarriage as I passed between them, and a substantial hedge removed the tail plane, fin, rudders and elevator while other parts of the airframe began to disintegrate and fall off. At about this point, I lost control of the aircraft."

alive if the aircraft's ruptured fuel tanks ignited, he struggled desperately to extricate himself from the narrow coffin.

He began performing the emergency actions:

Open canopy . . . er no, jettison it,
unfasten cockpit straps, stand up . . . oops,
undo parachute harness first,
don't forget R/T lead and oxygen tube . . .

The strong smell of jet fuel almost suffocated him as he became dimly aware of an immaculate brown-uniformed figure, in peaked cap, breeches and gaiters, standing close to the aircraft and peering inquisitively at the nose.

"Help me, for Chrissake," Mlig implored as he struggled desperately to extricate himself from probable cremation. The uniformed figure moved one foot closer but seemed reluctant to assist. "Give me a hand down," Mlig pleaded desperately. It could only be seconds before the jet fuel exploded but the uniformed figure regarded him suspiciously and still did nothing to assist. "Help me!" Mlig repeated.

This prompted the other to approach nearer, salute and enquire, "Are you a fully paid up member of the Automobile Association, sir?"

Eventually everybody got to fly the Mark Five. The feeling of being in a real fighter aeroplane was absolute. The cockpit was only half the size of the dual T-11 trainer but dials and switches were everywhere. The control column was the more glamorous 'spade grip' type, similar to Spitfires, and the sliding cockpit canopy, similar to Mustangs, Tempests and later marks of Spitfire, closed snugly round one's head. Most satisfying of all was the camouflage paint and squadron markings, very different from the silver and yellow paint schemes of the T-ll trainers.

At this stage in our training, we began to suffer severe attacks of over-confidence, probably as a result of having flown a single-seat front line fighter. This affliction was watched closely by our instructors, who realized that in its advanced form it could prove terminal, with the pupil usually writing off not only himself but a good aircraft in some hairy escapade. Just before our arrival at Oakington, a number of Iraqi pilots had died while low flying illegally. Their reasons for this breach of regulations would have been amusing if the results had not been so tragic.

When the weather was unsuitable for flying, pupils were often told to report to the ground school cinema to watch instructional films until either the weather improved or it was lunch or teatime. The supply of films was limited so after a few weeks we had seen every one many times. Most of them were rather dull with the exception of an American production containing some fantastic shots of pilots indulging in illegal activities like flying down roads and forcing oncoming vehicles to take to the scrub, flying through hangars and a final shot of a fighter pilot beating up his girlfriend's house and, in the words of the American commentator, "collecting the barn". I can't imagine how they did this shot for the aircraft just flew into the side of the barn whereupon both disintegrated.

The idea of that particular film was to deter student pilots from doing the same thing, which worked for Europeans, but the Middle Eastern nations viewed it differently and on their next solo details did all the things they'd seen on the screen. The result was two fatalities who 'collected the barn.' Despite the disastrous effect on our Middle Eastern allies, nobody thought to stop showing such films to succeeding courses of Middle Eastern students.

Another film, issued by the Royal Navy, had a rather negative effect on our morale for it showed endless sequences of aircraft crash-landing on carriers. It was captivating viewing, some of the crashes were unbelievable and nobody snoozed off when it was shown but the first time we saw it was shortly before we soloed on the T-11 and we were at the circuits and landings stage of our training. Just as the umpteenth aircraft had landed on the carrier, burst a tyre, collapsed the undercarriage, burst into flames and generally spoiled the pilot's day, the cinema lights came on and our instructor's voices called "OK, the weather's cleared, Clapshaw, Parry and Phipps report outside for circuits and landings." My first landing after seeing so many crashes was somewhat anti-climactic for I had expected a tyre to burst and the undercarriage to collapse, so I was delighted when it didn't happen.

After weeks of bad weather, we had seen every instructional film many times, so it was understandable for us to doze off during the umpteenth showing of 'How an Aeroplane Flies'. However, the corporal projectionist took his job very seriously and used his initiative to do something to retain our attention by borrowing some pornographic 'blue' films from the Sergeants' Mess. He interspersed these during the deadly boring training films. The effect was just what he wanted, people arrived early to get a 'ringside' seat, nobody dozed off in case they slept through the 'bluey' and nobody tried sneaking out when the lights were off.

Any over-confidence affecting us was snuffed out rather effectively by Bert Giles, my instructor.

Early one afternoon I reported to 'Flights' to find I was down for a solo general handling exercise. Flying conditions were perfect, with only a few patches of strato-cumulus in the lower layers. I noticed from the flight board that Switches and Singer were also down for solo details at the same time.

Our students' locker room was separated from the instructors' by a thin plywood wall, and while we were changing into our flying kit, I suggested to the other two that we rendezvous over the USAF base at Lakenheath and try our hands at a bit of dogfighting. The others jumped at this suggestion and we arranged to meet at high level, change to an unused radio channel and speak in phoney American drawls to avoid detection. We were so taken by the prospect of the mischief ahead that we were rather indiscreet in finalising the details.

Thirty minutes later I looked down from my cockpit at the concrete runways of the United States Air Force airbase five miles below. Changing to the out-of-use radio channel, I listened out for a few seconds to ensure there was no other traffic on the frequency. Feeling rather nervous, for to be caught illegally skylarking could result in considerable strife, I transmitted in my best American drawl.

"Er, thus zizz Ayer Fawce fower fye-eve niner," I announced.

"Hi thaar, thus zizz fower fye-eve eight," Singer's voice replied.

"An' er thus zizz fower fye-eve seven," Switches drawled. I looked around and picked up his aircraft turning towards me at the same altitude. This was going to be such fun.

Suddenly another voice was heard on the frequency.

"And this is flight lieutenant Giles. Return to Oakington immediately, Clapshaw, Singer and Phipps!"

Three very frightened acting pilot officers waited for more than an hour for flight lieutenant Giles to return to the crew room. While we waited, we agonised on his probable course of action. As a permanently commissioned career officer, he was strict on discipline and we feared that our tomfoolery would get us into serious trouble, possibly suspension and the dreaded 'chop'. To say we hadn't actually begun our illegal activities would be a rather weak defence, for it was obvious that the intention existed and only Bert Giles' intervention had stopped things going further. All three of us wondered how and why Bert happened to be airborne at the same time, listening out on that radio channel. We would have welcomed the professional services of Mike Parry to extricate us from this predicament but he was flying.

Finally, after an hour of unbearable tension and waiting, Bert strode jauntily into the crew room and eyed us three offenders. "Going to practise some dogfighting, were you?" he challenged Singer, who dropped his head ashamedly. "Collision practice would have been more like it! When we think you're ready for formation flying, we'll teach you. Right now, you're far from ready, you've only got a few hours on these aircraft so get that stuck into your thick heads!" He paused momentarily to regain his breath and composure. "In future, learn to obey orders," he continued. "When you're authorised for one exercise, don't go off and do something else that you fancy. Is that clear?"

We realized with tremendous relief that Bert wasn't going to take the matter any further. We murmured our understanding of his command.

"OK then, that's the end of the matter, the subject's closed," Bert strode from the room.

We were taking our first deep sighs of relief when he stuck his heads round the door again, this time with a smile on his face. "By the way, next time you're discussing something confidential, make sure there's nobody in the next room," he tapped the plywood wall partition of our crew room.

"These walls are terribly thin, you know."

He strode from the room and shortly afterwards we heard loud guffaws from the Instructors' crew room.

He was right, the walls were very thin!

Part of our flying course syllabus was initiative exercises. Periodically all members of a course would be taken up to Scotland for survival training, or to the Harz Mountains in Germany for very realistic escape and evasion practice. Another initiative exercise required the whole course to assemble outside the mess after Friday lunch, hand over all personal belongings except a handkerchief, Form 1250 identity card and a ten shilling note, then get as far from Oakington as possible, using only the ten shilling note and their wits, and return by 11 p.m. on Sunday night.

The instructors had also taken part in this exercise when it was first introduced, until six of them had hitched a ride aboard a USAF transport to the Cote d'Azur then made no attempt to return, preferring instead to spend two idyllic weeks as guests of the British Consul while Air Force red tape arranged their transport home again. After that, their participation was stopped.

When our turn came for this particular exercise, Switches, Blob Bottom and I got across the English Channel to Ostend, courtesy of Silver City Airways. We arrived back at home base confident of having travelled the furthest distance, but Mike Parry and Big Dick returned only minutes before the deadline, having conned their way to Munich and back. Details of their achievement were hard to obtain but we gathered Mike's persuasiveness and Big Dick's stature had worked wonders on two unnamed Lufthansa air hostesses. A member of a later course beat their distance by getting to Chicago and back within the allotted time! Some of the ruses thought up were extremely ingenious. Lord Jim borrowed a bed sheet and hitched a ride aboard a long distance lorry, telling the driver he'd bailed out of his aeroplane and had to get to Scotland to report back to his squadron. The driver obligingly gave him a lift to Glasgow and Jim, after thanking him, used the ten shillings to take a taxi to a relative's home for a rest. The next day he went to the lorry terminus and found the same driver for a lift back. When the driver questioned his rather thin story, Jim explained he was going back to collect a replacement aircraft. This seemed to satisfy the driver, and they headed south, stopping in Doncaster for James to buy them lunch at the best restaurant in town, with a fiver borrowed from his relatives in Glasgow. The sight of a Glaswegian lorry driver in bibbed dungarees, hobnailed boots and collarless shirt, and an Air Force officer with a bed sheet over one arm drinking Black Velvets together while debating whether to have the smoked salmon a l'Ecosse or the moules mariniere must have been unique. In best British tradition, nobody else in the restaurant paid them the slightest attention.

Dining-in nights were fewer at Oakington but much more happened at them. Members of operational fighter squadrons at nearby Waterbeach or Horsham St Faith often attended. We listened interestedly to their descriptions of squadron life but it escaped nobody's attention that they were the fortunate few still flying operationally in the rapidly shrinking Air Force. Hundreds of eager young RAF pilots were now grounded by Duncan Sandys' White Paper, with little prospect of another flying tour. Most national servicemen had civilian careers to return to at the conclusion of their military service and most of us tended to regard the two-year term as a wonderful paid holiday at the taxpayer's expense.

Chapter 27

The Black and White Minstrel Show

While the Royal Air Force was shrinking, other air forces were expanding, and the Oakington Mess began to fill with Iraqis, Egyptians, Nigerians, Jordanians, Lebanese and Indonesian student pilots. Different nationalities had different customs which were amusing to observe. During one dining-in night, the electric lights suddenly blacked everything out as the senior officer rose to propose the Royal toast. A main fuse had blown and it took the mess staff less then a couple of minutes to get everything working again. When the lights came on, the Iraqis were gathered with their backs against one wall with ceremonial daggers drawn, convinced the whole thing was an assassination attempt.

The differences in national temperament posed a real problem for the instructors. Sometimes a foreign student might temporarily lose control of the aircraft. The instructors would have already demonstrated the correct recovery technique to him and expected the student to use it. Sometimes however, the foreign student would cross his arms over his chest and announce "Allah has control". No amount of cajoling by the instructor would change the student's conviction and when, as sometimes happened, the aircraft eventually recovered by itself, they became even more convinced that Allah had indeed taken over control and saved them. Probably the best response to their attitude was the pragmatic approach of a rather unpleasant Southern Rhodesian instructor, who on first being told "Allah has control", replied: "Allah isn't in current flying practice, now you fly it, you little brown bastard." Rather interestingly, he had more success at instructing the foreigners than anybody else.

Inevitably these national differences led to a lot of foreign student pilots getting chopped, not through lack of flying skills but more through lack of airmanship. On one occasion while I waited at the runway holding point, a Mark Five Vampire approached with its undercarriage still retracted. Ignoring the warning of the tower, it skimmed half the length of the runway before touching down on its belly, coming to a stop on the grass overrun at the end.

There was no sign of the pilot when the fire trucks and ambulance arrived on the scene a few minutes later. His parachute was still in the seat so he hadn't bailed out. The damaged aircraft was taken away to the engineering section and a search began for the missing pilot. Examination of the flight authorisation sheet revealed he was a Jordanian student but no trace could be found of him. Eventually the search was abandoned and everybody returned to the business of flying.

At lunchtime the missing Jordanian pilot was found in the anteroom, dressed in a natty grey suit, nonchalantly reading the mess magazines. When other pupil pilots questioned him about his morning accident, he emphatically denied having flown that morning. Later his instructor confirmed he had been the pilot of the damaged aircraft but the Jordanian continued to deny it. Needless to say, he was quietly chopped for 'attitude'.

Details of some of the chop flights of foreign students were hilarious and it amazed us that some had survived the elementary flying training stage. One Libyan student, Ayonrinde, was probably the funniest of all. He had failed to reach solo standard after the usual time in the dual T-11 and had been given an extra five hours' instruction to attain the required standard. It was painfully obvious to everybody he wasn't improving with time. His approaches to the runway consisted of a series of swerves, sometimes resulting in the duty instructor in 'Chequers' beside the runway losing his nerve at the sight of a Vampire headed straight towards him and running out of his caravan.

When the extra five hours had wrought no further improvement in Ayonrinde's flying, he was put up for a chop flight. Unfortunately for the instructional staff, there were political implications involved when axing a foreign student and questions would inevitably be asked at higher diplomatic levels if too many pilots of a particular nationality were chopped. In typical Air Force fashion, the responsibility was passed down through diplomatic channels to the instructors. They tried to keep everything fair and even by keeping count of how many of each nationality had been chopped over so many months, so that if more Iraqis than Lebanese had been chopped this month, the pressure would be put on the Lebanese next month, in an effort to even out the scores. Meanwhile of course, a close eye was kept on Africa, Jordan, Indonesia and other races currently undergoing training.

The consequence of all this was that foreign pilots were usually given every possible opportunity to reach the required standard.

Ayonrinde failed the flight commander's check so was rostered to fly with his squadron commander, who had the good sense to go on leave. Ayonrinde was then farmed out to our squadron commander, Don Whittington, who quickly realized his career was on the firing line if he chopped him. Don embarked upon a propaganda campaign to raise Ayonrinde's hopes and morale, loudly reassuring everybody in the mess the night before, where he was determinedly getting drunk at the thought of flying next day, that he hadn't chopped a student in two years. He conveniently ignored several instructors who muttered he hadn't flown much in two years either. As the evening wore on, Don Whittington became more and more expansive in his prediction of how tomorrow's flight with Ayonrinde would go.

"We'll go out to the aircraft when you're ready," he told the hapless pupil. "And I want you to forget I'm there, just go through your pre-flight checks, start up and away we'll go. Then if everything goes well, we'll have you off solo before lunchtime. How does that sound, eh?" Don smirked contentedly, confident that in one swift rather clever move, he was going to enhance his promotion prospects thanks to this Libyan student.

Next morning, quite a crowd had gathered on the dispersal area outside Don Whittington's office. After a short but comprehensive briefing, both aviators emerged from Don's office and strode to the waiting aircraft. Whittington certainly looked very white this morning, the combined effects of last night's drinking and today's prospect of flying made him look an old man.

He stood back from the aircraft, expecting Ayonrinde to do a walk around inspection before climbing into the cockpit, but he had forgotten such trivia and proceeded to scramble up into the cockpit, encumbered by his heavy flying gear. Somehow or other, he managed to make a complete mess up of the simple task of getting into the aircraft and ended up standing on the seat facing the tail. After acknowledging a round of applause from the spectators, he turned the correct way and sat himself in the seat, where he began to weave fantastic webs of confusion with the many straps, oxygen tube, electrical lead and other gadgets.

Whittington meanwhile had tactfully overlooked Ayonrinde's failure to carry out the external checks and walked round the aeroplane, checking flying surfaces, condition of the undercarriage, oleo struts, tyres, flaps, removable panels, airbrakes and the hundred or so important items that had to be checked to ensure the aircraft was fully serviceable and safe for flight. Having satisfied himself on these points, he removed the pitot cover and mounted the few short steps to the cockpit.

Even Don Whittington couldn't suppress a snigger of amusement at the sight of his student struggling to achieve some semblance of order out of the parachute straps, various buckles, belts, ejection seat straps, tubes and leads belonging to his flying equipment. Ayonrinde's white eyes rolling anxiousluy in his black face completed the already hilariously funny scene. Don spent the next five minutes extricating his student from his imprisoned state. Snippets of conversation like "No, those are my straps, that's why they won't reach" and "the helmet goes on the other way, that's why you can't see . . . " reached us and fuelled our mirth.

When the student was satisfactorily trussed, Whittington strapped himself in and suggested to him he might like to run through the pre-starting checks. Ayonrinde seemed to have never heard of such niceties, so Whittington performed them while the crowd outside his office waited for the next morsel of fun to be tossed their way.

They didn't have to wait very long!

I'm not sure whether Whittington or his pupil started the aircraft's Goblin engine but as soon as it was running satisfactorily, Ayonrinde increased power to commence moving. To his annoyance, the aircraft failed to budge an inch, despite him increasing the power to maximum. Behind the aircraft, various chocks, ladders, battery carts and other pieces of ground equipment were blown across the tarmac by the jet blast from the Vampire's engine. The crowd placed their hands over their ears as some form of protection against the incredible noise level.

The reason for the aircraft not moving was readily apparent to all of us. The wheel brakes were firmly parked and even if they hadn't been, the substantial metal chocks under each main-wheel would have prevented forward motion. Two airmen ground crew members waited patiently at each wing tip for the 'chocks away' signal. In the cockpit, Whittington's head could be seen bobbing vigorously as he issued instructions to his student.Ayonrinde suddenly got the message and waved his hands in front of his face as the signal to take the 'chocks away'. The airmen tugged hard on the ropes attached to the chocks, which slid out from their position in front of the main wheels.

He also remembered the brakes were on, and simultaneously released them. The aircraft, now unrestrained and with the engine developing full power, leaped forward from the line of parked aircraft and headed towards the assembled crowd, who sensing real and imminent danger, scrambled for cover behind convenient structures.

Don Whittington had placed his hands on the cockpit coaming above the instrument panel as a reassuring sign to Ayonrinde that he was 'just along for the ride'. As the aircraft began making for the buildings, Don's hands flashed down onto the controls at a speed that would have left any Western gunslinger still reaching for his weapon. The incredible noise from the engine died to the quieter whine of idle power, and an up and down porpoising motion of the nose indicated the instructor was applying heavy braking to bring the aircraft to a halt. A snarl could be discerned on Don's face as he turned onto the taxiway and passed the crowd of frightened spectators emerging from their funk holes. Ayonrinde's rolling white eyes could be seen staring out the cockpit side window as they proceeded to the main runway and were cleared for immediate take-off. The take-off appeared to be normal except the undercarriage was left down for longer than usual.

As the dreadful duo left the circuit for 'upper air work', everybody began to drift back to their 'Flights' and classrooms. As I wasn't flying until the second detail, I was in our pupils' crew room when the word was passed round that Ayonrinde was returning to the circuit.

It wasn't difficult to detect which aircraft was his. Four other Vampires were slowing down to the standard downwind circuit speed of 180 knots, except one which could be seen racing downwind at probably more than 250 knots. As it turned onto base leg, using almost ninety degrees of bank to get round in a reasonable distance, we could hear the power reducing and observe the speed decreasing. By the time the aircraft had settled into a zigzag final approach, the wheels and flaps were extending and they appeared to be on a more or less correct glide path for the runway.

Fortunately for us, but not for the duty instructor in the Chequers caravan, we weren't in a position to discern the aircraft was never aligned with the runway for more than a second at a time. As Ayonrinde zigged and zagged either side of the extended centre line, we saw the duty instructor's head weaving like a boxer's as he tried to determine which side of his caravan the aircraft was going to pass.

As they neared the runway threshold, the aircraft appeared to develop a slight left bias, keeping about ten yards to the left of the centre line and showing no tendency to return to the correct approach path. As the jet rapidly approached the airfield at 120 knots or more, it became obvious to us that unless he regained the centre line immediately, he was going to pass either perilously close to, or through, Chequers!

The same thought had occurred to the weaving duty instructor inside, and he directed a red Aldis lamp at the aircraft. When this failed to achieve any form of corrective action by the pilot, Chequers fired a red Very flare, which didn't seem to have any effect either. By this time the Vampire was less than five seconds away.

Another Very light arced skyward and simultaneously the door in the side of Chequers flew open and a white-faced instructor emerged at a fast clip.

The second Very flare had the desired effect; the aircraft's engine note rose as Whittington initiated overshoot action. We were left with a vivid recollection of a Vampire flying under the smoke trail of the arcing Very flare while a white-faced duty instructor ran for his life.

The aircraft climbed away to commence another circuit. Behind me I overheard a sympathetic instructor remark, "Crikey, has he got to go through that again?" Out on the airfield, two technicians were escorting the reluctant duty instructor back to his caravan.

Don Whittington confided afterwards it was this second circuit which finally convinced him this student could never be taught to fly. After turning left and settling at circuit height again, Ayonrinde forgot to reduce power. The airspeed began increasing rapidly at a time when it should have been decreasing to permit undercarriage and flaps to be extended. Don drew his pupil's attention to the airspeed excursion. The observation was acknowledged but no effort was made to correct it, either by reducing power or deploying airbrakes. The instructor repeated the information and Ayonrinde nodded again.

Don then noticed the needles of the pneumatic brake pressure gauge fluctuating. He looked round curiously and saw Ayonrinde squeezing the bicycle type brake handle on the control column to slow them down, ignoring the fact they were a thousand feet above the ground with the wheels still tucked up in the underside of the aircraft. Whittington sighed resignedly, informed the pupil he was taking over control, completed the circuit and landed normally.

Turning off the main runway onto the taxi track, he proceeded back to the dispersal area. The same two ground crew airmen chocked the wheels, the engine's whine died and the cockpit canopy opened like an alligator's jaw bone.

Now that all immediate danger was over, a few braver ones strode over to the aircraft to help Ayonrinde unstrap himself. They were in time to hear his last remark. "Can I go solo now, Sir?" he enquired hopefully.

Don Whittington beat his gloved hand on the windscreen frame in total frustration. He might just as well have been driving a nail into his career coffin.

By the middle of March., a spell of decent flying weather arrived and we began to catch up on our flying hours. Navigation exercises were interspersed with aerobatics and various emergency manoeuvres including flameouts, a situation where the jet engine stops and the pilot calls ground control to guide him to a suitable airfield. The Vampire was a much cleaner aircraft aerodynamically than the Provost and flew over three times higher so consequently it could glide further. However, unlike the piston-engined aircraft, it couldn't be landed in a farmer's field successfully, so a flameout was followed fairly rapidly by either a 'Pan' or 'Mayday' distress call to seek directions to the nearest suitable airfield. There were many such airfields over eastern and southern England and it never proved a problem to find a bolt hole to glide to – on the only occasion that a student on our course had a genuine flameout, he was directed to Oakington.

Instrument flying training, the dreaded IF of earlier days, began earlier during the jet stage. I was rather apprehensive about it at first but found the Vampire easier to fly on instruments than the Provost. It was smoother than a propellor driven aircraft but when it did diverge from the required flight path, it did so much faster. A jet aircraft could lose 20,000 feet in a minute so it isn't difficult to understand that when a pilot is endeavouring to maintain a height tolerance of plus or minus 100 feet, a second or two of inattention can take him outside tolerances.

The most important facets of instrument flying were approaches or let-downs. At the advanced (jet) stage they consisted of QGH controlled descents through cloud, as previously learned at Ternhill, ACR7 stepped down approaches and GCA (ground controlled approaches). There was also a fourth, called a 'Martin Baker' let-down, named after the manufacturer of the ejection seats, which I never had to use!

ACR-7 (Aircraft Control Radar) was a poor man's G.C.A. It provided azimuth (plan view) information to a ground controller who could direct the pilot onto the approach centre line while advising him what height he should be at. A typical ACR spiel would be "Come right four degrees onto 223, you are four miles from touch down and should now be passing through 1,200 feet, turn left now onto 220 to maintain centre line . . . "

Break off height was supposed to be 400 feet, higher than GCA which was 200 feet, but the approach could be continued below this height if necessity dictated.

The most accurate of these approaches was the Ground Controlled Approach (GCA) where a radar operator on the ground directed the aircraft on to the extended approach centre line of the runway, told the pilot when to perform cockpit checks, start his descent and even reminded him to check his wheels were down and locked. Radar enabled the ground operator to monitor your approach and advise of any deviation from the correct approach path. Although the GCA system was only supposed to be used down to a minimum altitude of 200 feet, in actual conditions it was not unusual for the operator to continue a practice talk down to ground level and every member of our course recalled at some time hearing the reassuring voice of the controller telling him "You're on centre line, on glide path, crossing the airfield boundary now, nicely on centre line, on glide path, passing through fifty feet on course, on glide path, passing ten feet, start your round out now – five feet – wheels should be touching now – approach complete. Cheerio!"

It was nice to know such skill was available to rescue us if we ever needed it.

Martin Baker let downs were not taught because it was hard on aircraft and too cold and draughty for the instructor left in the cockpit.

We also learned other instrument flying techniques, including one for alerting those on the ground that our radio was useless and we required assistance to descend through cloud. The approved technique was to fly a left handed triangular pattern for one minute, and hope some alert radar operator would notice the triangular pattern on his screen before your fuel got too low. If time permitted, the operator would then alert the nearest suitable squadron to scramble a similar performance aircraft to intercept and guide you down through cloud. Such an aircraft was called a 'Shepherd' for obvious reasons. Learning this inspired a member of a more senior course to write a short novel on the subject, entitled 'The Shepherd'. Unfortunately fuel endurance in the Vampire was always a problem, our sorties were usually planned for fifty minute to provide us with a safety margin when we returned for an approach and landing. The Goblin engine was notoriously thirstier at low level than high altitude, so most nav-exes were planned at the higher levels. Jet engines are more efficient at higher altitudes, so by keeping high, we burned less fuel and increased our endurance, enabling us to fly further.

If the fuel state was insufficient to keep the engine running while a shepherd aircraft was scrambled to intercept and guide you down, the only remaining course of action was to carry out a Martin Baker let-down. The only time that most of us got close to performing this let-down was on a ground rig which toured the various advanced flying training stations to provide students with the opportunity to practise ejecting. Only the T-11 dual trainers were equipped with bang seats, the FB-5 single seat fighter had to be abandoned by stepping over the side, a hazardous pastime since the pilot was likely to be decapitated by the double tail!

The most frequently used let-down at Oakington was the QGH. The advantage of this type of approach was that it required less specialized equipment than the GCA and the air traffic controller in the tower could run the procedure. The basic procedure was to bring the aircraft over the airfield at a predetermined altitude and speed. Once overhead, it was given a heading and airspeed at which to descend. After an appropriate time on the outbound heading, the aircraft was told to turn inbound back towards the airfield while continuing its descent. It was now approximately aligned in the approach lane of the duty runway and by means of cathode ray direction finding, the ground controller could guide the aircraft into the middle of the ideal approach path.

Nowadays, approach aids have tended to become pilot interpreted rather than by an operator on the ground, the rationale being that the person flying the aircraft has more interest in the safe completion of the approach. A contrary argument could be that the pilot has to concentrate on two difficult tasks at a critical phase of the flight, when he could be assisted with one of them. Because of pilots' preference for pilot-interpreted aids, most let-downs today are Instrument Landing System (ILS), Very High Frequency Omni-Range (VOR) or Automatic Direction Finding (ADF). GCA is still in use at some airfields but ILS is the preferred aid in civil flying.

Our flying training continued at a fairly swift pace, while the social scene also began to develop nicely. I have already mentioned our favourite pubs, The Mill in the centre of Cambridge and the George and Dragon, kept by an ex-second world war fighter pilot, further out of the city.

Saturday afternoons were devoted to sport for those wishing to play cricket, tennis or any other British weekend pastime. Interest in the various activities seemed to wax and wane among our fellow course members, with the exception of beer drinking and the pursuit of females, which was, is and always will be the number one Saturday sport. Motor rallies were popular in the winter months, mainly because they provided everybody with an excuse to end up in front of a blazing fire in a comfortable pub. Now in the summer months, interest was equally divided between cricket and sailing, with a few preferring tennis.

I was one whose interest lay in tennis.

I had begun to achieve a small degree of success in station tournaments fairly early in the season. Although this was not my main reason for playing tennis, success engendered additional enthusiasm for the game.

One evening I was recounting the details of the day's play to a few other members of the club, one of whom was a stunningly attractive brunette with a mischievous twinkle in her eyes, which always left me wondering what she was thinking about. During the course of this conversation, I mentioned I was looking for a partner for the forthcoming mixed doubles tournament.

Natalie, that was her name, immediately volunteered to partner me, adding that she had played a considerable amount of competition tennis and would like to resume playing.

Next Saturday afternoon we entered the station mixed doubles tournament and won convincingly. After the victory, I congratulated her on her performance and escorted her to her car. While walking, she asked me what I was doing that night and I told her a gang of us were going in to Cambridge. I remember her saying what fun that would be.

I bade her good evening and returned to my room to shower and change for the evening's happenings.

I felt rather strange; I would like to have invited Natalie into Cambridge that night and I sensed she would like to have come. Unfortunately I also knew she was the wife of a fellow officer on the station – Wing Commander Lyon, the Officer Commanding the Flying wing!

Chapter 28

Open the Door (Sir) Richard

Suddenly it was Monday morning again but this time with a big difference, for next Friday was the Air Officer Commanding's (AOC's) inspection.

AOC's inspections usually consisted of some air marshal arriving in an antiquated Avro Anson to take the salute at the parade held specially in his honour, after which he would inspect the airmen on parade, make a speech, go on a conducted tour of the station and attend a guest night in his honour that evening.

During our time in the Royal Air Force however, the AOC Flying Training Command was the legendary Batchy Atcherley, one of the famous Atcherley twins. He had achieved fame before World War Two as one of the pilots of the Supermarine S6B Seaplane that won the Schneider Trophy for Great Britain. Every aviation enthusiast knew how the experience and knowledge gained from designing the high speed seaplane enabled Supermarines and Rolls Royce to produce the immortal Spitfire.

More than twenty years and a world war had passed since those days and Flight Lieutenant Atcherley was now Air Marshal Sir Richard Atcherley, KCVO, AFC, AOC Flying Training Command. In characteristic fashion, Batchy (for everybody called Sir Richard that out of earshot) liked to conduct his inspections differently from everybody else.

The Oakington drill instructors (DIs) spent the first four days of the week trying to retrain the officers and airmen to drill. Since none of us were particularly interested in learning, the teaching process was heartbreaking for the DIs and rather boring for us. By Thursday they had almost given up hope of holding any semblance of a parade. After a severe lecture from the Station Warrant officer, we were told to buck up our ideas for the parade the next day.

The AOC was scheduled to arrive at eleven o'clock on Friday. In typical Batchy fashion, he landed in his Anson just after eight thirty. It was a foggy morning and we were still in met briefing as he taxied in through the swirling mist and parked his aircraft. Striding into the tower, he demanded to know where everybody was. The duty air traffic controller tried unsuccessfully to explain to the air marshal he wasn't expected until eleven o'clock.

"Caught 'em all on the hop, have I?" Batchy's eyes gleamed as he spoke. The duty ATCO failed to mollify him, so Batchy picked up the phone and demanded to be put through to the station commander. When the CO couldn't be found, he asked for the Wing Commander Flying.

The Wing Co. Flying was also missing from his office so Batchy told the operator to phone round flights. The first call was to us in 'A' Flight. Usually at this time of day it was a wrong number or members of another course phoning us. Because of this, we had developed our own unique telephone answering technique:

"Good morning, station sick quarters?""Yes."

"Can I speak to Dr Jeckyll please?[1]"

"I'm sorry, Dr Jeckyll is changing – this is Mr Hyde, can I help?"

Or:

"Station farm?"

"Yes, this is the duty hog speaking."

It was bad luck that the phone rang as we were strolling back from met briefing. Singer, nearest the phone, answered.

---

1. Incredibly, the station medical officer was Dr Jeckyll and his administrative assistant was Warrant Officer (Mr) Hyde!

Air Marshal Atcherley.

"Good morning, we're not on the phone," he began. After a longish pause to digest this improbable piece of information, Batchy spoke:

"Who is this speaking?"

"You are!" Singer replied. In the background we laughed.

"Do you know who this is?" Batchy demanded. Before Singer could reply, he told him. "This is Air Marshal Sir Richard Atcherley, AOC Flying Training Command . . . "

Singer turned several shades paler and turned to us. "It's the AOC," he hissed, holding one hand over the mouthpiece.

Mike took the telephone from him. "Do you know who this is, Sir Richard?" he enquired very matter of factly. The AOC admitted he didn't.

"Thank Christ for that then, good morning to you, sir!" Mike replaced the receiver and everybody resumed breathing normally. Initiative had won the day once again.

The same could unfortunately not be said of the audience in the ground school cinema, who because of the fog, had been sent there to watch innumerable instructional films for the umpteenth time.

During a self-conducted tour of the ground school Batchy let himself into the cinema and sat at the back, watching the film. He was gratified to see nobody leave at the start of each new one.

When the next film came on, it was *Penelope's Playtime*, one of the 'blueys' brought in from the sergeants' mess by the enterprising projectionist. It achieved its purpose of holding the audience's attention that foggy morning – they watched the antics of two elegantly dressed oriental ladies as they slowly disrobed in front of a male European. As each item of their clothing came off, they also removed an item of his clothing.

It took Batchy half a minute or so to realize what he was watching. Perhaps the old Schneider Trophy pilot's eyes weren't as sharp as the audience's or maybe he wasn't paying as much attention to the screen but by the time he'd cottoned on to what was being screened, an atmosphere of intense concentration prevailed. Fifteen or twenty pairs of eyes watched the first oriental lady remove the gentleman's last item of apparel then sit astride his chest, lowering her white breasts onto his ecstatic features while her colleague concentrated on his nether regions, her glossy lips raising him to incredible heights of ecstasy.

Anybody dropping a pin at that moment would have been expelled for making excessive noise!

Batchy Atcherley turned a deep shade of purple when he realized what he was watching. Recovering from the initial shock, he called out for the film to be stopped. Angry voices from the audience told him to shut up, which further infuriated the air marshal, who demanded to know which of the darkened figures had insulted him. More people gave him advice, ranging from instructions to "Shadddup or ship out", to "Go pull yerself" to finally "Fuck off fer Chris' sake."

On the screen, the oriental ladies were changing positions while the male actor, resembling a three legged stool, arranged himself between the white buttocks of the second lady, while her companion suckled him from a stooping position.

Batchy continued to scream for the film to be stopped, all the time searching for the light switch. His efforts were accompanied by catcalls and jeers from the audience who were incensed at having their entertainment spoiled. Finally the air marshal found the door to the projection room and stormed in on the unsuspecting corporal projectionist.

This worthy servant spotted the air marshal's bands on Batchy's uniform and recognized doom staring him in the face. Terrified, he stopped the projector and turned on the cinema lights. Groans of angry disappointment from the audience quickly subsided when they spotted the air marshal. In twos and threes they began to sneak out through a side door while Batchy lambasted the unfortunate projectionist. On the screen, the two Oriental ladies remained frozen in position. The object of their attention would now suffer unendurable ecstasy, indefinitely prolonged!

By the time Batchy had finished with the projectionist and returned to the viewing pit, every APO had shot away, leaving only the sleeping padré and the leadership training officer for him to vent his wrath upon.

Sadly, somebody's head had to roll to appease Sir Richard's wrath and it was the enterprising corporal projectionist's. He was arraigned on several charges and eventually dismissed from the service for disgraceful conduct. Instructional films at Oakington then returned to their former deadly dull format.

The remainder of the AOC's inspection passed without disciplinary action being taken against anybody else. The parade was held, Batchy took the salute, made a rather long-winded speech which nobody heard above the noise of a jet engine being run up in the test bay, then everybody went to lunch.

Lunch in the officers' mess was slightly more formal than usual. A carefully chosen cross section of pupils and instructors were told to assemble in the bar before lunch to engage Sir Richard in interesting conversation. Among those chosen were Lord Jim, Kiwi Green, Flying Officer Jeckyll the Station Medical Officer, and various instructors and flight commanders. The intention was to soften the air marshal up with a few drinks before steering him into the dining room for a specially prepared lunch of his favourite dishes. In best service tradition, the scheme misfired badly. Some of the pupils got Sir Richard onto the subject of flying before the Second World War and soon the air was thick with "Gloster Grebe, now there was an interesting aircraft – better than the Gladiator that came later – Hawker Hinds, Rolls Royce Kestrels, Bristol Bulldog, Comper Swift etc." The station hierarchy smiled benignly as the talk ranged from the Hendon air shows, through the Mediterranean campaign to modern aerial warfare. They hoped alcohol and time would purge Sir Richard's memory of the unfortunate events earlier that morning.

But while the hierarchy were smiling benignly at Batchy and his new-found friends, Big Dick and a knot of hard drinkers in a corner of the bar were busily getting themselves bombed on too many glasses of cream sherry. By the time the air marshal rose to lead everybody in to lunch, the hard drinkers were in riotous form, shouting and laughing in their corner. Only a terse reminder from a senior officer persuaded them to leave the bar and follow the air marshal's entourage into the dining room.

Once assembled in the Number One Mess dining room, the padré said grace and we all sat down. The tables had been arranged in the shape of a letter 'U', with Sir Richard at the head of the centre table. To his left and right sat the Station Commander, the Wing Commanders Flying, Technical and Admin whilst a little further away sat squadron commanders, accounts officers and myriad other trades and professions ranging from the station photographic officer to 'Cu Nim Jim' the resident met man.

While we waited impatiently for the food to arrive, Big Dick and his knot of drunken friends continued to frolic at their end of the table. At first their playfulness took the form of flicking pieces of bread roll across the table at each other, while the senior officers at the top of the table endeavoured to distract Sir Richard's attention away from the noise.

Bread rolls, then table mats and larger items on the table were thrown by the intoxicated participants. Things came to a head when Big Dick somehow flicked a wine glass with his fingers, which caused it to fly across the room and land in front of Sir Richard.

The air marshal looked enquiringly towards the source of the missile and asked the Station Commander the name of the officer who had just thrown the wine glass across the room. The CO glared at Big Dick and in the silence that now reigned, ordered Jack Hennessey to "escort Pilot Officer Howard from the dining room, please". All eyes were upon Big Dick; Jack Hennessey looked at him embarrassedly then the pair rose to their feet and exited together, leaving behind an awed silence. Behaviour like this was fairly certain to result in the perpetrator being chopped for OQs.

Conversation gradually resumed again but at a greatly reduced volume, especially at the end of the table where two empty seats testified to the recent sudden departure of Big Dick and Jack. At the top table, Batchy Atcherley resumed swapping reminiscences with his senior officers.

After what was less than ten minutes but seemed infinitely longer, Jack returned to the dining room but instead of going to his seat, he spoke briefly to the CO then walked over to the Medical Officer. After a brief discussion, the MO followed Jack from the dining room, leaving everybody wondering what was happening.

After a further ten minutes, they returned. Even Batchy Atcherley was curious to know what was going on. Jack provided the details: "Sunstroke, I'm afraid, Sir. One of the worst cases the MO's seen. Probably happened during the long hours of practice on the drill square these last few days."

"Combined with even the slightest amount of alcohol makes the patient undergo severe personality changes, sometimes to the point of becoming quite irrational and behaving in a quite uncharacteristic way," the MO added. "The best cure is complete rest for a day or two. After that, the patient should effect a complete recovery."

Batchy pursed his lips sympathetically. "Poor chap," he murmured. "As a matter of fact, I recall a similar incident to one of my best chaps in Iraq during the war. Well, look after him, Doc, and tell him the AOC says he's to get well and resume his flying duties when you think he's recovered." The MO assured the air marshal he would do just that. Conversation then resumed its normal volume and Batchy began recounting an anecdote that occurred to him in the Middle East. I glanced across at the MO and caught him exchanging a conspiratorial wink with Jack Hennessey.

The AOC spent the afternoon touring the rest of the station, calling in on the airmen's mess, where everybody had been cautioned to reply "None Sir", to the air marshal's calls for "Any complaints?" He then drove round the married patch, back to the station to inspect the engineering and admin sections before finally returning to the mess to prepare for the forthcoming guest night.

Naturally, every member of the mess was on their best behaviour. Those with a reputation for bawdy conduct were dissuaded from using the bar and again, as at lunch time, a courteous mob of hangers-on were in attendance to engage the AOC in conversation.

By the time dinner was over and the port decanter passed from left to right, coffee drunk and speeches made, Batchy looked bored out of his mind. As he was leaving the dining room for the bar, he collared a few of the younger officers to vent his displeasure on. "When I was a young officer, we really knew how to enjoy mess life," he challenged one of them. "Wining and dining, then into the bar for a game of mess rugby or high cockalorum. I'm afraid there's none of that spirit in today's Air Force."

The object of these remarks bristled indignantly. "Oh, I don't know about that, Sir. We still have plenty of fun, there's the skiffle group and the Air Force still plays mess games."

Batchy's face brightened immeasurably. "Really? Well let's have a game of mess rugby then!" he suggested. "You captain one side, I'll captain the other. Now then, where's a waste-paper basket we can use as a ball . . . ?"

Before a senior officer could flinch, the anteroom carpets were moved aside and a hectic game of mess rugby began. The station commander and his three wing commanders looked on helplessly. Strict instructions had been issued that no riotous behaviour would take place during the AOC's visit and now the AOC himself was the prime instigator. Senior officers looked on anxiously as the evening's tempo began to increase.

Apart from a few broken pieces of furniture which could have been written off to the Mess Guests' account, the evening would probably have run down to a safe conclusion if Switches Phipps hadn't suggested a bicycle race through the mess. Of all mess games, this was by far the most hazardous, which was probably why it was the most popular!

Batchy led the scramble outside to the front of the mess, where a number of regulation issue Air Force bicycles waited patiently for the morning. The standard Air Force issue bicycle is a large upright machine of incredible strength and weight, not at all suitable for indoor use.

While mounts were being obtained, other members of the mess laid out the course. The starting and finishing posts were in the entrance foyer, then the course ran down the passageway to the bar, through into the anteroom then back into the passageway and out through a pair of French windows opening out to the car park, thence along the front of the mess and up the steps back in to the finishing post in the foyer.

The field for the first race comprised Batchy Atcherley, Blob Bottom, Big Dick and Shit'ead. I was appointed official judge and starter, while Lord Jim became clerk of the course. The course bookmaker began quoting odds on the four runners: Shit'ead was favourite at two to one on, Batchy was second at even money, Big Dick was third favourite at five to one and Blob Bottom was the rank outsider, probably because of his obesity, at a hundred to eight.

By the time the flag was up to bring the field under starter's orders, there was almost twenty-five pounds field money in the kitty.

They got away to a good start, Batchy led into the first bend with Big Dick a close second and Shit'ead coming up in third place. Blob Bottom had technical trouble with the chain on his mount and got away late.

As they entered the bar, Big Dick challenged on the outside, leaving Batchy Atcherley in second place and Shit'ead a close third. Taking the turn into the anteroom, it became obvious to the cheering crowd that Big Dick wasn't going to make it. He struck his head on the top of the doorway and fell in front of Batchy. Shit'ead swerved to avoid both fallen riders and rocketed through into the anteroom as Blob Bottom pedaled into the bar.

It was unfortunate nobody had thought to suggest to the station skiffle group that they might like to move from their position in the centre of the room, because Shit'ead's machine scooped up their washboard player as he passed through. The extra drag slowed him down somewhat, enabling Blob

Bottom to challenge on the outside of the next turn as they raced into the passageway. Behind them, Big Dick was holding onto third place and Batchy Atcherley could be seen pushing his bike along in fourth.

As the leaders shot through the French doors out into the car park, it was Blob Bottom leading Shit'ead and Big Dick in third place. Batchy was remounting as they turned into the car park straight. It looked like certain victory for the rank outsider as they crossed the darkened car park, but unfortunately none of the riders had remembered the dozen or so bicycles parked outside the entrance to the mess.

Blinded by the glare of the bright lights from within as they took the final turn, Blob Bottom failed to see the bikes and collided with them, falling in front of Shit'ead. This was all too much for the washboard player impaled on the front of Shit'ead's machine, and he began struggling to wrest control from the rider. Batchy had been waiting for an opportunity like this and took the final turn wide to cross the finishing post the winner. Blob Bottom was first to recover from the multi-bike pile up and came in second. The other two mounts had sustained more serious injuries and were led away to the motor transport section for treatment.

I pronounced Air Marshal Sir Richard Atcherley the winner of the first Oakington Gold Cup; Lord Jim congratulated him and presented him with the winner's trophy, a large cracked china po, which Batchy accepted gleefully and handed to the barman to fill with beer. Everybody then toasted the winner.

It was only after the course bookmaker had paid out all winnings that somebody noticed Batchy was injured. His mouth and lower jaw were bloodied and several teeth appeared to be missing. Two course officials later found them at the first crash site between the bar and anteroom. In the crash, the poor old flier must have collected a pedal or handlebar in the mouth. 'Fangs' the station dentist examined the injury and suggested the air marshal accompany him down to sick quarters for a bit of patching up. The poor old flier was beginning to look distinctly pale and fragile now, which considering he had challenged and beaten young men forty years his junior was quite allowable and understandable.

He was led away with only minimal protest, given a sedative and tucked up in station sick quarters for the night.

The moment the AOC left the scene, things changed dramatically. The station commander gave the order for all unruly behaviour to stop immediately, the carpets and furniture were put back in position and any officer stupid enough to have suggested further mess games would have been charged. The CO stormed from the mess, leaving the President of the Mess Committee (PMC) to deal with the offenders.

It was our bad luck that the PMC was none other than our arch-enemy and squadron commander – Don Whittington! Next morning immediately after breakfast, Lord Jim the clerk of the course, the three riders, the washboard player and myself were summoned to Whittington's office, and subjected to a fifteen-minute lecture on our behaviour the previous evening.

As official starter, I was blamed for inciting riotous behaviour, causing damage to government property and, most serious of all, injury to an officer of air rank. We remained silent as Whittington finished his tirade. I stole a sideways glance to see if any of the others were preparing any defence but I think they realized the squadron commander had it all his way today. To have attempted to discuss the matter with him would have been foolhardy in the extreme. We hung our heads in silent shame and waited for the end.

"All of you will all pay for last night's damage," Don pronounced. "And you are prohibited from using the bar or mess public rooms for fourteen days." I began to see a glimmer of light – if he was banning us from the bar area for fourteen days, he obviously wasn't going to chop us. "If there is any repetition of this kind of insubordination, I will recommend you for the chop. It now remains to be seen what action the AOC will be taking against you," he concluded.

This last remark was accompanied by a long, cold, hard stare at each of us in turn. I had no doubt that if prime culprits had to be found, Don would nominate us. It would have been foolhardy and naïve to have expected much allegiance from the AOC either. Prominent people tend to slam the door in your face when you need their help and support, for events of the night before don't look quite so funny the morning after, especially when you're nursing a broken jaw and missing two front teeth.

Chapter 29

Don't Shut the Door on Me, Dick!

The weekend after the AOC's inspection, those of us banned from using the mess facilities decided to motor down to London. A few others heard of our plans and decided to join us, so a small formation of ancient motor vehicles headed out of the station gates on Saturday morning. The Pheasant Plucker was going really well now after a bit of remedial work, as was her stable companion, Lady Chatterley's Lover, so sixteen APOs crammed into the two stately vehicles and accompanied by two other vehicles, set course south.

Don Reid, one member of the Pheasant Plucker's crew, had been a mining engineer in civilian life and was the only married student on the course. Because the Air Force frowned officially on officers marrying before the age of 25, he was ineligible for either an Air Force married quarter or even a marriage allowance, which forced him to live with his wife in a small flat in Cottenham. He possessed a devilish sense of humour which frequently provided us with much amusement.

During the long drive south, Don mentioned that Shit'ead, our rather bad-tempered member, had asked to borrow his tiny flat for the weekend. There were strict rules against entertaining female guests in our rooms, so finding somewhere to take a willing partner was always a problem. Hotels were expensive and usually asked for some form of identity, motels were rare and the only other location for an eager young couple to vent their lust was in a motor car in some remote location. This idea had lost a lot of its attraction for us since Little Dick's episode atop the Wrekin.

A fourth alternative was to borrow somebody's home, which Shit'ead had done. Somebody remarked what a cheek he had in asking such a favour, to which Don agreed, adding he felt sure Shit'ead and his lady friend wouldn't be deterred from their lustful pursuits by the tape recorder Don had left turned on under the bed!

We chuckled at the thought of listening to the tape on our return.

That evening we toured most of the night spots frequented by Air Force officers – the Captain's Cabin off Leicester Square, the Denmark in Old Brompton Road, the Grenadier between Wilton Place and Knightsbridge and finally the Air Force Club across the road at Hyde Park Corner.

Sunday morning was spent trying to recover from the previous night's excesses, after which we drove down to the Thames embankment for a 'hair of the dog' at a delightful pub in Cheyne Walk. Leaving London in the late evening, we headed back home and turned into the Oakington Officers' Mess car park shortly after midnight. The next day started with ground school in the morning, so any fatigue would be assuaged by the time we started flying after lunch.

Lunchtime brought a pleasant surprise in the form of a letter to all members of the mess from Air Marshal Sir Richard Atcherley, which read:

Air Ministry,
Theobalds Road,
London WC1

28th July, 1957

Dear Sirs,
I would like to express my appreciation of the hospitality extended to me recently by the members of the Oakington Officers' Mess.

At a time when people complain the morale and esprit de corps of the Royal Air Force are sinking low, it is gratifying to me, as your Air Officer Commanding, Flying Training Command, to find one station where this is definitely not the case.

I would particularly like to thank those officers who participated so fully in the evening's after dinner activities and to assure them I haven't had so much fun in years!

Yours faithfully,
Richard Atcherley,
Air Marshal KCVO

P.S: If anybody happens to find a lower plate containing two dentures, it's mine!

A member of the Mess Committee had pinned it to the notice board for all to see. It remained there for several days before Don Whittington caught sight of it and angrily tore it down. By then it had said all there was to say on the matter.

"Good old Batchy," Blob Bottom commented. "He didn't slam the door and forget us after all."

That afternoon I was down for a dual detail with Bert my instructor. He enquired how the week end had gone then briefed me for the forthcoming dual flight.

We would be climbing to high level, forty thousand feet or even higher if conditions were cold enough, where he would demonstrate high Mach number runs. The purpose of this exercise was to show the student the effect on the aircraft as the airflow over the wings approached supersonic speed. This usually started as a gentle rumble at about Mach 0.74 (74% of the speed of sound) and by Mach 0.80 the rumble had increased to buffet the whole aircraft. Mach .80 was an incredible speed in the late 1950s, although nowadays modern jet airliners cruise above that speed, and compressibility begins much later.

The afternoon weather was overcast with a cloud base of around 800 feet with stratified layers up to 10,000. Above that height the sky was forecast to be generally clear apart from a few local areas of high cloud.

I remember thinking as we taxied out that we would almost certainly have to carry out a QGH (controlled descent through cloud) approach on our return. As we neared the holding point of the duty runway, Singer was cleared to take off ahead of us. The tower cleared us to line up and hold our position as he lifted off the runway and disappeared into the overcast.

Mach runs were exciting because the pilot felt close to a frontier of science. The sound barrier had only been exceeded a few years previously and until then had been regarded as an impenetrable barrier that tore aircraft apart as they neared it. This myth was destroyed by an American test pilot, Chuck Yeager, going supersonic in the Bell X15 rocket powered research aircraft. A short time later, John Derry became the first Englishman to fly supersonic, in the de Havilland de H.108 'Swallow'. Our single-seat Vampires bore close similarities to the 'Swallow' and this further contributed to the excitement of flying near the speed of sound. Another exciting thing about flying at high Mach numbers in the Vampire was that you couldn't always predict precisely how the aeroplane would react at the onset of buffeting.

To cap the whole business, a film had recently been made entitled

The Sound Barrier which highlighted the danger and glamour of supersonic flight.

Our Mach runs went routinely that day. While Bert flew the aeroplane to 40,000 feet, the Mach indicator's needle gradually crept round to higher numbers as we climbed, while the airspeed indicator (ASI) became increasingly sluggish and unreliable. This was perfectly normal, in fact the inaccuracy of the ASI at high altitudes and speeds was the reason for the introduction of the Mach meter to replace it. The speed of sound, usually referred to as Mach One, was the most convenient datum with which to work at speeds approaching or exceeding supersonic (MACH 1.0).

Bert left full power on while entering a gentle descent to accelerate.. As the speed or Mach number increased past .75, mild vibration started, which increased in amplitude with the slightest back pressure on the control column. It became quite violent above Mach 0.80. Bert closed the power at .81, selected air brakes to slow us to a slower speed before pulling back gently on the control column to raise the nose back onto the horizon. He then re-applied power, retracted the airbrakes and told me to repeat what he had just demonstrated.

By the end of the detail, the weather had deteriorated as a frontal system crossed southern and central England, and QGH approaches were in progress. We joined number three in the approach sequence and completed our approach without incident, breaking out of the cloud base at 500 feet. The runway lights had been turned on to help approaching aircraft discern the runway when they first broke out of the bottom of the overcast.

As we walked away from our aircraft towards the 'Flight' hut, I noticed the weather was deteriorating rapidly as the frontal system swept across East Anglia. Soon heavy rain began falling and cloud base and visibility were too low for any type of flying. The inevitable card games had soon started in the various other crew rooms to while away the rest of the afternoon.

The afternoon's atmosphere of gloom and boredom didn't last very long in our crew room, for Don Reid arrived with an enormous grin on his face, carrying the ancient tape recorder which he had retrieved from beneath the bed in his flat. Now he was about to play back the contents to us.

After carefully checking that Shit'ead, one of the star performers, wasn't around, we phoned round to a few other 'Flights' and invited them to "come and hear something different." We didn't tell them more than that, because the crew room wasn't capable of holding more than twenty people and if word had got round that we were about to play a 'blue' tape recording, a hundred or more would have tried to pack into the small room.

We began listening to the tape with gleeful anticipation. Unfortunately the various control buttons on the dilapidated machine were very worn, which had caused the record button to stop intermittently, and a previously recorded passage would suddenly be heard. Then just as abruptly, the recording would resume again. Despite this, the tape was intelligible.

The recording started with sounds of a key turning in the lock as *the cast* arrived. Everybody stifled anticipatory giggles in anticipation of what lay ahead. It certainly beat the hell out of Mrs Dale's Diary for entertainment value, and as events progressed, guffaws of delight rose from the listening audience. This aroused the curiosity of passers by and soon the crew room was crowded with more and more enthralled listeners.

After one particularly hilarious part, while everybody else was rolling around with laughter, I glanced round at the back of the room and was horrified to see Shit'ead in the audience. Even more surprising, he was laughing as much as, possibly more, than anybody else in the room. I watched him curiously, for such sporting behaviour was completely out of character for him, for he detested any form of joke at his expense and his sex life was a serious matter which he pursued with relentless determination.

I suddenly realized the answer. Tape recorders were pretty rare in those days and few people had ever heard their own voices. Those who had, were invariably surprised at how different they sounded.

Shit'ead didn't realize he was the star of the show!

I tried to catch Don Reid's attention before it was too late but he was listening intently to the recording, and I was too far away to turn the machine off. Even if I had been able, I would have probably been overpowered by the excited audience.

The plot was nearing its climax – literally! The girlfriend's voice could be heard above an accompaniment of creaking bed springs, ecstatic groans and murmurs to "Promise me, Ted. Promise me . . . " Porcine grunts and puffing from her co-star added to the hilarity of the situation. The girl's voice continued to exhort Shit'ead to "Promise me, promise me, Ted" and the listening audience joined in with advice like "Don't promise her a bloody thing, Ted!"

Suddenly the female voice underwent a change of heart and she began telling Ted to "Stop Ted, stop. We mustn't . . . "

Her protests were obliterated by the gruff voice of Shit'ead gasping "I've waited two weeks for this, I'm not stopping now!"

This last bit of dialogue must have sounded familiar to the ill-tempered Shit'ead at the back of the audience, and he abruptly stopped laughing and listened carefully. Slowly, recognition of the truth dawned on his face. He turned an angry shade of livid red and shouted for the machine to be turned off. Those capable of speech told him to keep quiet, they wanted to hear what came next.

This was too much for Shit'ead. He became almost apoplectic with rage and threw people aside as he strove to get to the tape machine. Don Reid and a few others recognized the imminent danger and forcibly restrained him from smashing the recorder. Somebody else turned the machine off and quickly packed it away.

People began drifting away when tempers had quietened, leaving us to keep an eye on Shit'ead, the star.

I glanced at my watch and was surprised to see the time was nearly five o'clock – afternoon tea time. We called into the instructor's room to get their OK to leave for the day but, rather strangely, it was empty. A similar check of the Flight Commander's office also proved futile so without giving the matter any further thought, we headed back to the mess.

The reason for our instructors' absence was soon revealed when we entered the anteroom for afternoon tea and found it empty. An aircraft had crashed during an instrument approach. Details were sketchy at this stage; all we could learn was that the pilot, a student, had been carrying out a perfectly routine QGH approach when radio contact was lost halfway through the procedure. No contact was made on another frequency, he hadn't carried out the radio failure procedure and the police were at this moment investigating a report of a crashed aircraft in an area south of Great Yarmouth.

A quick check of numbers revealed one member of our course was missing.

Later that evening, Wing Commander Lyon returned from the accident site and confirmed the crashed aircraft had been one of ours. After first confirming that the dead pilot's next of kin had been notified, he announced the name.

As we had already begun to dread and suspect, it was a member of our course – Singer.

Next morning, both Wing Commanders Flying and Technical stood up after met briefing and told us what they knew so far about the possible causes of the accident. Usually when an aircraft crashes for no apparent reason, the first thought is that the pilot's oxygen supply must have stopped, causing him to pass out from the effects of anoxia. This was unlikely in Singer's case, since he was descending to a lower altitude when contact was lost. He would have been below 10,000 feet and able to function without aircraft oxygen.

A team from the Accident Investigations Branch, Farnborough, arrived at the crash site to examine the wreckage for clues. In the meantime, we were to continue our flying training.

Although everybody pretended very convincingly to carry on normally, there were a few rather prosaic arrangements to be made. Don Whittington, in his official position of squadron commander, appointed me officer in charge of funeral arrangements. Singer would be given a full military funeral before being buried in the local village churchyard.

I arranged with the commanding officer of the RAF Regiment contingent, colloquially known as the 'Rock Apes', for a platoon of airmen to perform funeral drill at the graveside. As there were several items of funeral drill that were seldom practised except on these solemn occasions, two drill instructors spent several mornings teaching the Rock Apes how to 'rest on their arms reversed' and other funeral drills. Normally an intense rivalry existed between the Rock Apes and the General Duties (GD) branch but on sad occasions like this, everybody worked together to ensure everything proceeded smoothly.

The padré would conduct the service in the station chapel next Thursday morning, then the funeral procession would head to the village churchyard for the interment. Members of our course would act as Singer's pall-bearers.

I took these responsibilities very seriously and by the time the date for the service came, was reasonably confident I had made all the necessary arrangements. Whittington had been quite impossible during this time, often summoning me to his office when I was in consultation with the padré or the Rock Apes, only to enquire whether I had begun the arrangements yet. I think he realized that, as Singer's commanding officer, he was going to be in the limelight so wanted to come out of the whole thing looking good.

On the day of the funeral, the parents and relatives arrived outside the mess at 10 a.m. Whittington ushered them in and introduced them to the padré and one or two assembled officers.

I had been double-checking everything since dawn. The pall-bearers were briefed to be in the chapel half an hour before the service was due to start. The padré would accompany the relatives on the short journey to the chapel, and a member of a senior course, a Cambridge organ scholar, had offered to play the organ at the service. The officer in charge of the Rock Apes had assured me the funeral platoon would be waiting at the graveside when the burial party arrived.

Afterwards, the parents and other relatives would be taken to a nearby hotel for lunch.

Despite Whittington's fears to the contrary, I was confident everything was under control.

I had arranged for the parents to be seated in the chapel at ten fifteen. I frowned slightly when the appointed time came and went. At twenty past ten, I sidled up to where Whittington was conversing with Singer's parents and muttered out of the corner of my mouth that it was "twenty minutes past ten, Sir."

This elicited an instruction from Whittington to "go away and don't be a pest".

At twenty five past ten, I avoided the questioning glances of the padré and tried to gain the squadron commander's attention. He pointedly ignored me and continued chatting with Singer's mother and father.

When ten thirty came, I threw discretion to the wind and reminded him in a loud clear voice that everybody was waiting to go. He turned irritably and ordered me from the room, an order I had no choice but to obey. I waited in the foyer while everybody else was in the anteroom, taking very little notice of a young corporal Rock Ape nervously twiddling his cap his hands, until he approached me. "Er sorry to trouble you, Sir . . . "

"What do you want?" I demanded abruptly.

"I've got a message for one of the officers, Sir."

I clicked my tongue irritably and told him to leave it in the officer's mail slot. He hesitated. "It's rather urgent, Sir," he persisted. "Perhaps you could tell me if the officer's in the mess?" I looked at the individual, he probably had some trifling message for somebody, just when I was trying to get the funeral under way. "Look, I'm dreadfully busy right now, leave the message in the mail rack and the officer concerned will pick it up at lunch time," I gestured in the direction of the anteroom, from where one or two members of the funeral were starting to emerge. The young Rock Ape looked at me concernedly.

"It's very important, Sir, too important to leave. It's for a Pilot Officer Clapshaw, Sir, do you know whether he's in the mess? I couldn't find anybody else to ask."

Warning bells began to sound in my head. I held my hand out for the message as more people began to congregate in the foyer. Realizing we were about to leave for the service, I hurriedly stuffed the note in my pocket.

"I'll see to it once all this is over," I assured him, pointing at the assembled cortège.

The young Rock Ape thought for a moment a moment but didn't move. I took this opportunity to dismiss him.

"Look, buzz off for Heaven's sake, can't you?" I implored. "We're just about to start a funeral . . . " Out of the corner of one eye I saw two or three more people emerge from the ante-room. I moved to open the front door of the mess when the young Rock Ape spoke, in a nervous tremolo.

"The warrant officer said to tell you the grave hasn't been dug!" he blurted out.

I stopped in mid-stride and gazed at the speaker, which made him even more nervous. He twisted his cap in his nervous hands.

"What did you say?" my voice quivered disbelievingly, hoping this was all a nightmare from which I'd soon wake.

"The warrant officer says there's no grave dug yet, Sir. He thought you'd like to know, seeing as how you're in charge of all that . . . "

I groaned; I had tried to think of everything, the catering, the undertaker, the plot, the padré, the funeral service but had missed one vital thing. It was unfortunately probably the most important. I looked around in blind panic. More people were filing into the foyer towards the front door. One or two had even begun to leave for the chapel.

"What's he done about it?" I demanded.

"Fuck all . . . er nothing, Sir," he informed me helpfully. "He said he'd leave it to you to sort out. The men are waiting at the church."

In the anteroom I could still see Whittington conversing with the bereaved parents. As long as he stayed there, the funeral wouldn't start. I hurried over to him and waited for a pause in the conversation. He rambled on for two more agonizing minutes, describing the part he had played as a junior officer attending the funeral of the late King George the Sixth. I realized I would have to break into the conversation.

"Er . . . hrmm, excuse me Squadron Leader Whittington, Sir."

He turned towards me, disfavour written all over his face. "I told you to wait outside," he reminded me quietly before returning to the unhappy parents.

"Yes, I know Sir, but his is important . . . " I insisted, tugging at his sleeve to ensure his undivided attention.

Whittington turned again. "I told you to wait outside," he reminded me threateningly.

"I can't, Sir. There's something terribly important . . . " I began. Whittington pulled himself up to his full height as my popularity rating with him dropped to an all-time low.

"Pilot officer Clapshaw," he began threateningly "I order you from the mess." We were both conversing in low voices, anxious not to arouse the curiosity of the parents or guests. I stood rooted to the spot while Whittington caught the attention of two flight lieutenant instructors. He was going to order them to forcibly remove me from the premises. I had the horrible sickly taste of fear in my throat as I imagined the funeral party arriving at the grave yard with the coffin and having no place to lower it. They could spend all afternoon wandering among the gravestones!

The two flight lieutenants converged on my left and right arms as I threw discretion to the wind. Whittington had returned to Singer's parents. "They haven't dug the grave yet!" I blurted out. Whittington flinched as if struck by a heavy blunt instrument from behind, then turned. The sickly expression on his face told me he had received my message loud and clear. My popularity rating dropped even lower, it was now in negative numbers, equivalent to a pork pie in a synagogue. "I put you in charge of everything," he accused as the two flight lieutenant instructors took hold of my left and right arms.

"Yes, I know, its my fault right now but we both have a problem," I urged. The flight lieutenants began escorting me from the anteroom as an expression of utter hopelessness crossed Whittington's face. He passed a nervous hand across his sweaty face and I heard him mutter, "Oh Christ!" softly.

"Give me an hour before the funeral gets to the graveyard," I implored. The two flight lieutenants sensed something important had occurred and relaxed their grip on me.

"How can we do that?" Whittington snarled.

"Tell the padré to delay the start of the service, throw in a few extra hymns, maybe a sermon but give me time, Sir, just give me time."

Don Whittington nodded quickly and I fled from the mess. Minutes later an Air Force Land Rover full of Rock Apes and shovels sped through the guard room gates towards the church.

Forty-three minutes later, a six-foot hole had been dug, and the local vicar had provided planks over the muddied surface for the mourners to walk on. As the Rock Apes' Land Rover drove away from the graveyard, the hearse containing Singer's coffin drew up outside the church. In one of the following cars I saw Whittington's worried face gazing out anxiously. I gave him the 'thumbs up' sign to put him out of his misery.

The rest of the arrangements proceeded satisfactorily. The coffin, containing mostly sand, was lowered reverentially to its final resting place, the funeral platoon fired a Last Salute then rested on their reversed arms, a few final words were spoken at the graveside and everybody departed.

As Whittington and I left the church yard simultaneously, I paused to note the inscription above the west door of the church:"Forsan et haec olim meminisse invabit". *Perhaps one day this will be pleasant to remember.*

Next morning we returned to the business of learning to fly.

Whittington summoned me to his office only minutes after Met briefing and delivered the most resounding rocket it had ever been my misfortune to be on the receiving end of. I stood before him, eyes lowered and head hung in shame. I recognized I had erred badly in yesterday's unhappy sequence of events and Whittington was now justifiably castigating me.

He dismissed me at the end of the tirade. I turned to him before I left this office and apologized unreservedly for my oversight. Whittington regarded me disdainfully before replying. "I've had about enough of you and your sort," he fumed. "A rose by any other name, that's you – you come into the service, we train you then just when you're ready to contribute something, you leave." He glared at me sardonically. "Now get out!"

I left this office with my tail between my legs; he never forgave me for the irreparable damage I had nearly done to his career and grasped every opportunity to gain revenge.

Maybe the Air Force knew a lot more about learning to fly than we gave it credit for, or maybe it was just pure luck that I wasn't down to fly that morning. After the previous morning's nerve racking experience then the half-hour bollocking from Whittington, I wasn't in the right frame of mind to pilot a jet aircraft at 500 mph. After attending ground school in the afternoon, we made plans for the weekend.

OQs could be the downfall of anybody, and unlike 'The Chop', you didn't get a second chance with another instructor before heading through the guardroom gates back to civilian life. Singer's funeral was the closest I ever wanted to come to getting clobbered by OQs, so I decided to head south to stay with Mum and Dad for a few days to try and forget the whole episode. Dairy farming is a 365 days a year business where the workers (the cattle) don't take a break at weekends or public holidays, so Mum and Dad would be home.

I arrived in the mid-afternoon to find a large pink American Ford Thunderbird motor car on the drive in front of the house, and Mum making tea for a rather spectacular young blonde with bouffant hair, pouting lips and the kind of breasts men kill for. She looked about six or seven years older than me and her name was Diana. The reason for her visit was her sheep, or to be more precise, their tendency to find gaps in the fence and wander through into our fields and garden.

I listened to their conversation bemusedly, for Diana was definitely the most desirable woman I had ever set eyes upon. Something in the back of my mind told me I'd seen her before but I couldn't think where – certainly not at any local dance or the annual Hunt Ball.

Diana suddenly interrupted my furtive admiration of her breasts with a question. "And what do you do, Guy?" the words issued from her beautiful glossy pink lips like soft music.

"Oh, I er . . . " I abruptly ceased my contemplation of imagining how she would look with nothing on, and returned to the present.

"Guy's in the Air Force," Mum replied for me.

"Oh really?" Diana enquired rather disinterestedly, for many young men were trapped by National Service for two years. "Doing what?"

"Flying," I replied. "I'm a pilot at Oakington."

"Not Oakington in Huntingdonshire?" Diana enquired suddenly interested.

"Er yes, just a few miles north of Cambridge. Why, do you know it?" I suddenly realized where I and the rest of the world had seen Diana; she was Diana Dors, the star of *Oliver Twist*, *A Kid for Two Farthings*, *Holiday Camp* and *The Shop at Sly Corner*. Britain's answer to Marilyn Monroe, Mae West and Jayne Mansfield all rolled up into one incredibly desirable curvaceous blonde body.

"Yes," she pouted. "By a strange coincidence we're filming location shots near there next week."

She was obviously an aviation fan, for she then asked me all sorts of questions about flying – how fit do you have to be (I immodestly told her 'incredibly'), educational and physical requirements (rocket scientist or better) and how long it took to learn to fly. Time stood still while this goddess listened with unconcealed admiration to my tales of daring-do in the air – all highly exaggerated, I'm ashamed to say.

After more than an hour, which seemed like five minutes, Mum apologized to Diana for keeping her so long and assured her the wandering sheep weren't a problem. We escorted Diana back to her pink Thunderbird, the colour of which matched her lip gloss perfectly, and she thanked us for the tea.

"Call round and visit me on location next week if you're not too busy flying," she handed me her card printed in the same colour as her glossy pink lips and shiny American car. I was so enwrapped in gazing at her that I didn't look at it, for an incredible idea had suddenly occurred to me.

"Er, I don't suppose you'd like to . . . " the idea was so preposterous that I didn't even finish my sentence. "No sorry, of course you wouldn't. Sorry, silly of me to even ask . . . "

"Like to do what?" Diana Dors pouted while half way into her pink Thunderbird. "You haven't even asked me yet." She paused halfway into getting into her vehicle, revealing long lengths of exquisitely shaped legs and delectable creamy breasts in danger of tumbling out of her sweater.

"Well, there's a guest night in the officers' mess next Tuesday, when everybody brings wives, or girlfriends or guests, and I er, that is, I wondered whether you'd maybe like . . . but no, you're probably far too busy filming that day and . . . er"

"Guy, if you're inviting me to a ball in your officers' mess, where there'll be handsome young RAF fighter pilots in attendance, my answer is a definite 'Yes'," Diana assured me. "Did you say next Tuesday?"

"Er yes, Tuesday next week, the 14th. You mean you'll come?" I thought I was dreaming.

"You bet I will. What time do you want me there?"

"Seven o'clock for seven thirty. I'll wait for you outside the officers' mess."

"See you there then," and with a beautiful smile, she swung her long legs into the car, pulled her sweater up above her delectable breasts and disappeared down our drive.

By Monday morning, things had returned to normal at Oakington. Singer's room had been allocated to a member of a junior course and all that remained of its previous occupant were a few joyous memories of happy occasions spent in his company and a nagging desire to know what the devil had happened to him.

Chapter 30

Tea for Two

I found it impossible to concentrate on anything else on Tuesday. Ground school was a blank recollection for I took no notes; fortunately the afternoon's flying wasn't too demanding but I was glad when the days' work was over and everybody had gone to prepare for tonight's Guest Night.

Whittington was the duty squadron commander, which meant he had to act as mess president and announce the usually boring collection of school teachers, politicians, businessmen, clergy and local land owners on arrival, the first of which had begun to arrive when I positioned myself on the mess steps to await Diana Dors' arrival.

In best military tradition, the pink Thunderbird drew up outside the mess at 7 p.m. precisely. Diana wiggled out wearing a spectacularly low cut tight pink diamante dress trimmed with fur; her bouffant blonde hair, bare shoulders and pouting pink lips complemented the rather adventurous expectant look in her eyes.

"Do I look OK?" she enquired concernedly as she attached herself to my right arm and gazed up at me enquiringly. I couldn't keep my eyes off her spectacular figure bulging out of her dress.

"You look like a film star!" I assured her. "Now come with me and I'll introduce you to tonight's president." I manoeuvred her sideways through the glass doors of the mess where her effect on everybody was dramatic. Waiters carrying trays of drinks dropped them and stared unashamedly at the apparition before them. Officers and other male guests attending the guest night eyed her with stallions' eyes and either walked into walls or collided with each other.

Diana Dors.

We joined a short queue of officers and their guests waiting to be greeted by Whittington.

The usual protocol was for each officer to hand the guest- night president a card bearing the name of his guest. The president would then read it and announce the names of the officer and his guest; a typical greeting might be "Pilot officer Smith and Miss Janet Jones" followed by a handshake and a smile before the couple joined everybody else for pre-dinner drinks in the anteroom. The background noise level in the anteroom required Whittington to raise his voice to be heard.

He had just finished introducing the Bishop of Salisbury and his wife when Diana Dors and I reached the front of the queue behind the clerical couple. I handed Don the visiting card which Diana had given me a few days earlier and waited for him to announce us. Diana Dors' arrival had stopped all movement and conversation among the other assembled male guests, who all gawped at her unashamedly. You could have heard a pin drop as Whittington took the card while staring furtively at her spectacular cleavage, and announced our names in a loud clear voice.

"Acting Pilot Officer Clapshaw and Miss Diana Fluck."

The effect of the announcement was instant, the room exploded with male laughter at what they thought they had heard – and were certainly thinking. Only Whittington failed to be amused, he glared at me with fury in his eyes and announced in a whisper, "I'll see you in my office tomorrow morning . . . "

I was as perplexed as anybody else as to the reason why he had announced Diana Dors as Diana Fluck but my beautiful guest supplied the answer.

"Diana Dors is my stage name," she explained to the swarm of slobbering male admirers clustered round her. "My correct name's Diana Fluck but my agent made me change it to Diana Dors. He said it would look better on bill boards and screen credits. Personally I prefer Fluck 'cause it rhymes with . . . "

"Luck," I completed the sentence for her.

The evening was sensational; Diana and I were invited to sit at the top table between the station commander and a very angry Whittington. Fortunately for me, the CO spent most of the dinner with his mouth wide open like a whale trawling for krill, ravishing Diana with his eyes while telling her what a great fan of hers he was. They conversed animatedly together throughout dinner, in contrast to Whittington, who hardly said a word during the whole meal, convinced I'd set him up.

After-dinner speeches were kept short, for everybody wanted to meet Diana Dors. Whittington had slunk away at the earliest opportunity along with the station commander who'd received a sharp tug on the wrist from his wife. "Good night Miss Fluck," he'd caressed Diana's hand in his. "May I call you Diana?" They conversed together for a minute or more before his crinkly-lipped wife gave him another tug on the wrist to advise him it was time to leave.

Next morning I was summoned out of ground school to appear before a glowering Whittington, who announced that after reviewing events of previous months, including last night's, he had decided to recommend to the Wing Commander Flying that my flying training be terminated immediately. I was going to be chopped.

"Publicly humiliating a senior officer in the way you did last night is a blatant act of insubordination," he pronounced slowly. "For which there is no place in today's Air Force. That is all, you are dismissed."

I tried to plead that my guest's name had been genuine but he angrily gestured me out of his office. I slunk out like a whipped dog, devastated that my flying career appeared to be over. Feeling stunned, I had to pause momentarily in the outer office to regain my composure.

It was the station commander who saved my bacon by arriving unexpectedly on the scene only seconds after my abrupt dismissal.

"Wonderful evening last night, Don," I heard him enthuse. "You ran a good show, bloody wonderful in fact; I can't remember when I've enjoyed myself more. Good food, excellent service, no long speeches . . . Wish I could have stayed longer but the wife suddenly decided she wanted to leave. Pity really, I bet everybody had a lot of fun afterwards, I've just had a thirty-minute phone conversation with the headmaster of Repton who was there, he told me what a wonderful career he thought the Air Force would be for a young man today. Dunno how you did it but you provided a wonderful boost to morale last night. Well done!"

He didn't heed Don Whittington muttering something about disciplining the offender severely. "Gotta go, late for a meeting with the Wing Commander Admin," he apologized as he exited into the outer office where he found me skulking and listening.

"Aah, Diana Fluck's companion," he greeted me enthusiastically. "You're a lucky young fellow, how did you get to meet her?"

When I explained she was a neighbour, he beamed with anticipatory pleasure. "So that means you might bring her here again?" he suggested hopefully.

"Er apparently not, sir," I mumbled something about humiliation and blatant insubordination.

"Nonsense!" he turned as he bellowed. "Don, make sure Diana Fluck's invited to the next guest night, will you?" Don Whittington was smart enough to recognize praise when it was heaped upon him and gave me a sickly sweet smile while assuring his commanding officer he'd certainly obey his instruction.

Having nothing better to do, I returned to ground school to listen to the station medical officer lecture us on the symptoms and effects of high altitude anoxia. After lunch I attended met briefing and on reporting to 'Flights' was immensely relieved to see my name included in the afternoon's flying programme. Whittington never advised me of his later decision not to terminate my training and I never mentioned the subject, believing that some things are best left alone.

Circumstances never conspired together again to enable me to invite Diana back to another Oakington guest night, which was a pity for everybody.

Time flies when you're having fun and suddenly we were the senior course on the station. Apart from having to provide somebody as Mr Vice-President at dining-in nights, it didn't entail any additional duties. It did however sometimes require one or more of us to act as 'suitable male escorts' to the daughters of visiting guests – usually high ranking military officers, headmasters of famous English public schools or members of the House of Commons.

These daughters were almost invariably plain and unattractive, which coupled with a stern warning that they were not to be 'bedded down' regardless of whether they were agreeable to the idea or not, made them in Shit'ead's words "worse than effing useless".

It was unfortunate for those forcibly 'volunteered' for escort duty that having carried out their task conscientiously and correctly, they were invariably chosen for similar tasks on subsequent occasions. This suited the rest of us admirably and we made a great pretence of getting rather the worse for drink before the disapproving glances of senior members of the mess, to ensure we were never numbered among the chosen few. Although this removed the 'burden of responsibility' from us, it was tiresome for the chosen few and detracted from their enjoyment of guest nights.

To rectify this unjust situation, the course bookmaker suggested holding a competition for the ugliest woman at the next guest night. Everybody accepted this suggestion enthusiastically when the prize for the 'grimmest grim' was announced as a case of liquor of the winner's choice – beer, whisky, gin, champagne – the choice was ours.

The night of the first grim competition was a tremendous success; the result was a dead heat between an eminent cabinet minister's spotty cross-eyed daughter and an incredibly plain schoolteacher with protruding teeth that could have consumed apples through a tennis racquet. Everybody enjoyed themselves, a lot of plain girls were invited out when they had expected to be left at home in favour of their more attractive sisters and two APOs were better off by half a crate of booze each.

The most vivid recollection of the evening was an inebriated cross-eyed bus conductress confiding to Big Dick that she "coon't onderstund ye takin' me when there's s-o-oo many other girls ye cood a taken".

None of the grimmies ever discovered the reason for their popularity and in the words of parish magazines, 'a good time was had by all'.

Tea for Two

I found myself escorting Natalie to that particular guest night due to a misunderstanding between us. When I had mentioned to her that the forthcoming guest night should be rather amusing, she had assured me she was coming, and I had assumed she would accompany her husband, the Wing Commander Flying. I therefore got quite a surprise when, holding a regulation glass of sherry in my hand and watching the guests arrive, I saw the Wing Commander's car pull up and Natalie get out – alone. I assumed her husband must be somewhere in the mess and set out to find him. When it became obvious he wasn't around, I went to meet Natalie in the foyer. She looked absolutely stunning; her dark eyes were set off by her smooth sunburned skin, and dark hair. Her bare arms and shoulders were shown off to perfection by a form-fitting black cocktail dress. As she took both my hands in her's, I detected the exciting aroma of her perfume.

After a brief exchange of small talk, I commented on her husband's absence, assuring her we'd soon find him. She looked at me very directly.

"Why would we want to do that?"

"Er well, he's around here somewhere, isn't he?" I stammered.

"No, of course he's not, he's away on his annual instructor's refresher course at Little Rissington. He'll be away for another ten days . . . " this information was delivered with a subtle innuendo.

"B-but you said you were coming when I spoke to you at tennis on Sunday . . ." I reminded her. Natalie gave me that direct look again.

"And here I am, Guy. What are we going to do together tonight?" I blushed as only an inexperienced nineteen-year-old can; I was in a tricky situation and unsure of the best course of action.

After she had deposited her wrap in the cloakroom, I ushered her into the ante-room and introduced her to my fellow course members, trying unsuccessfully to avoid the curious glances of the instructors and their wives. The evening proceeded in better than usual fashion, probably because of the 'grim' competition. When the after- dinner speeches were finished, everybody headed for the bar while the mess staff moved the tables aside for dancing in the dining room later. Natalie was delightful company and fitted in easily with the carefree mood of gaiety that evening. Unfortunately I was completely out of my depth with this beautiful married woman, and drank considerably more than I could handle. As the hours and minutes ticked away, Natalie and I danced until the combination of alcohol and her persuasive good looks persuaded me to throw caution to the wind and enjoy the evening.

By the time the winners of the 'Grimmy' competition had been announced, my arm was firmly entwined around Natalie.

Next morning I awoke with a screaming headache. A quick glance to my right told me I had overslept, the time was now eight o'clock, met briefing was in thirty minutes' time. I made a mental note to rebuke my batman for not waking me.

A glance to my left told me the situation was worse than I had first imagined: beside me, still sound asleep, lay Natalie. Her black dress, stockings and lingerie hung neatly on a chair. I gazed at her in horror.

"What the hell are you doing here?" I demanded, waking her up. She murmured something sleepily in reply, turned over and snuggled up to me. "You can't stay here," I pleaded, wishing that I could. Her long legs brushed against me and she kissed me gently.

"The batman will be along any moment," I warned her. "There'll be hell to pay if I'm found with a woman in my room." Natalie did the only sensible thing and curled up and went back to sleep.

I panicked, trying desperately to think out the best course of action. I was too late for breakfast but if I hurried, I could make met briefing in time. Normally we assisted the ground crew to manoeuvre the aircraft out of the hangars first but today they'd have to manage without me.

Meanwhile, there was a woman's body to be disposed of. Provided she left immediately via the bedroom window, and assuming nobody else was looking out of a window at the time, she could get away undetected and so avoid trouble.

Unfortunately Natalie still showed no inclination to wake. I gazed at her sleeping form while racking my brains for ideas. The batman would be along any moment now; once he saw a woman in my room, the news would be all over the mess like a rash. I ran to the door to lock it and my gaze fell to the bedside table.

On it were two very cold cups of tea.

I dressed hurriedly, and just made it to met briefing in time.

I was down for a high-level solo cross-country in a Mark Five, landing at Swinderby in Lincolnshire to refuel on the way back. I forgot my immediate problems in the exhilaration of flight again, it was high summer and from an altitude of six miles I could see north to the Wash, with the fishing port of Grimsby in the distance. Away to the south I could discern the white concrete runways of London Airport and beyond it the patchwork quilt effect of crops growing in the Sussex Weald, Hampshire and Dorset. The first turning point came up and I banked onto the new heading.

Only after returning to land at Oakington did I remember the problem awaiting my return.

I once heard of a silence that could be heard a thousand miles away. Such a silence greeted me on my return to the mess as I sneaked through a side door, anticipating cheers and catcalls to greet my return. The batman would have told his colleagues of my escapade and they would have lost no time in relaying the story round the mess.

Surprisingly, nobody commented. Mike Parry, Switches and Blob Bottom were reading magazines in the anteroom as I came in. As I didn't relish the thought of talking to them, I slunk away to my room.

Every trace of her presence had been removed. I sniffed hopefully for a trace of her perfume but everything, black dress, underwear and filmy black stockings were gone.

I turned towards the hand basin and freshened up before lunch. While I did so, I tried to consider the consequences of last night's reckless action. Whittington would lose no time in using the incident to wreak revenge on me, and the wing commander's reaction I didn't even dare try to anticipate. Realizing I would have to face the consequences sooner or later, I headed for the dining room.

To my surprise, nobody commented on my arrival, indeed they seemed more pre-occupied with something else. I studied the menu before listening to general conversation.

The cause of Singer's crash had been found.

Investigation of the wreckage by experts from Farnborough had revealed the CO_2 bottles of the pilot's dinghy pack were empty. Further research revealed the aircraft was apparently fully serviceable, the engine had been delivering power up until the moment of impact and there were no signs of oxygen deficiency or noxious gases in the pilot's blood. They had therefore concluded the dinghy pack, which the pilot sat on, had suddenly inflated during the latter stages of the approach. To find out what effect this would have, they put a fully equipped test pilot into a Vampire on the ground and inflated the dinghy after closing the cockpit canopy hood. The effect was dramatic – the chambers of the dinghy puffed out, crushing the test pilot up against the top of the canopy and forcing his arms away from the controls. He had no control over the aircraft, not even being able to reach the transmit button to advise ground control of his predicament. Singer's aircraft had flown into the ground with the pilot fully conscious but unable to free himself from the enveloping folds of the inflated dinghy.

It would clearly be hazardous for us to continue flying while the possibility of such an occurrence existed, so the Safety Equipment Section issued every pilot with a small sheath knife, to be sewn onto the shoulder of his flying suit so that in the event of an involuntary inflation, the pilot would have time to pull out the knife and puncture the dinghy.

The knives were available immediately from the Safety Equipment Section and by lunch-time the following day, every pilot had one sewn to his flying suit.

It was nearly one thirty by the time we had finished kicking this item of news around. I was delighted and grateful nobody had commented on my companion of the night before. I collected my notebooks from my room and hurried to afternoon ground school.

The following morning I awoke as my batman brought in my early morning cup of tea. I sat up in bed, struggling to become alert and fully awake.

"Good morning, Sir, another lovely day for flying." He had opened the curtains to allow the morning sun into the room. I grunted agreement while marshalling my thoughts. "It's seven thirty, Sir," he continued, making for the door. I beckoned him to wait a moment; there was something I wanted to discuss. He looked at me and waited with one hand on the door handle.

"Er . . . yesterday morning, there was er . . . something I have to say . . . er discuss with you," I tried unsuccessfully to sound clear and concise while the batman waited patiently for me to continue. "Had a friend come to stay, rather unexpectedly you know . . . don't want the whole world to . . . er well you know what I mean, don't you?" I finished the garbled disjointed sentence with a wave of my hand.

"A friend, Sir? I didn't see anybody."

I looked at him disbelievingly. "You didn't see anybody? What about the two cups of tea?"

"I didn't see anybody, Sir."

I looked at the older man gratefully, suddenly recognizing and appreciating the qualities which had enabled him to serve generations of young Royal Air Force officers without becoming irritated by their gaucheness. He had seen young men rise from pilot officers like myself to air marshals, and had waited upon prime ministers, royalty, foreigners and kings. His knowledge of protocol, etiquette, dress, food and wine would be unsurpassed.

"Will that be all, Sir? I'd better wake the other young gentlemen."

I stared him straight in the eyes, expecting a wink or some other conspiratorial gesture but he returned my gaze unflinchingly.

"Yes, thank you very much. That will be all."

I picked up my tea and drank most of it in one gulp.

A few years later, I was given the opportunity to repay the favour this worthy mess servant had bestowed on me. I was flying for a small charter company and had flown two racing cars and their supporting equipment to Nice for the Grand Prix de Monaco. We stayed at the Hotel des Anglais to wait until the race was over and we could fly the cars back to England.

During the course of many hours of idle conversation with other hotel guests and members of the staff, mention was made of a mysterious distinguished elderly Englishman, who stayed in the hotel for the same ten days each year. Everybody was curious to know who he was, for he was well acquainted with good food and wine, ate and drank sparingly but well, choosing wines of inexpensive but quality vintages. The one cigar he smoked after dinner was rolled from the finest Cuban leaf, and his clothes while never flamboyant were faultlessly cut. He never asked for information about others or volunteered information about himself so because of this he had aroused the curiosity of the whole hotel. While this mysterious stranger was being discussed, he entered the dining room punctually at 7 p.m.

I started with surprise when I saw his face. It was my old batman from Oakington! The old fox, for ten days of every year he lived the life of the gentlemen he watched and waited on in the Royal Air Force! Several of my group detected my surprise.

"Do you know him? Is he a duke or something?" a loud-mouthed Skyways pilot demanded. I continued staring directly at the figure. He looked round the room and noticed me; we stared at each other for maybe fifteen seconds before he regained his composure and sat down, a rueful smile on his face. His secret was out, he was about to be exposed.

"Do you know him?" the Skyways pilot persisted. "Come on, tell us who he is? I bet he's a pre-war film producer – am I right, do you know him?"

My gaze fell away from where the old Englishman sat. Memory raced back five years to the Oakington Officers' Mess and two cold cups of tea beside the bed one morning, and the innocent reassurance to my clumsy questioning next day.

"Do you know him?"

I directed my attention back to my circle of new found friends. Some of them were pilots from other charter companies, all good raconteurs. This story would be the sensation of the evening.

"Never seen him in my life," I disappointed them. "Could he be Anna Neagle's first husband, what was his name . . . ?"

Chapter 31

Owed to a Daffodil

Because of the earlier ban on our use of the bar and public rooms in the mess after the Oakington Gold Cup incident, we had become accustomed to whiling away a lot of our free evenings in the George and Dragon local pub.

George Trussler, the landlord, had been a Typhoon pilot during the war and, when things were quiet in the bar, could sometimes be persuaded to talk about his flying days. He had heard about the Oakington Gold Cup and still chuckled at the details.

"I don't imagine that endeared you to your squadron commander?" he commented one evening. I had to agree, it was a fact of life that Whittington hated all national servicemen, probably because they were the exact opposite to him, a career military officer. He never lost an opportunity to run down the 'part time' pilots as he liked to call us.

However, since there were now no more national servicemen coming through on junior courses, this thorn would soon be removed from his side. I only wished I could be the one to pull it out!

While we spent our evenings in beerful contemplation of Whittington and his complex, the subject of our attention was preparing something even more fiendish for us. Survival course!

Part of our training included a ten-day survival, escape and evasion exercise, normally held in the Cairngorms of Scotland. Our first hint that we were about to head north was an announcement from Whittington that he wanted to address us that afternoon. We assembled in the crew room after lunch and waited for him to address us.

"Survival training, a vital part of a military pilot's training," he began. "You are about to be taken to Aviemore, in the Scottish Highlands, for your survival course. It'll start with five days of toughening up, cross-country marches across mountainous terrain, rock climbing, cooking in the open, sleeping under canvas. Then, when the Air Force has toughened you up enough, we'll start the main part of the course, a five-day escape and evasion exercise."

He paused to look round and check everybody was listening. "Now, I've promulgated details in Station Routine Orders (SROs), which you would be well advised to study." He held up a sheaf of mimeographed A4 sheets of paper, SROs, which came out every week with details of forthcoming parades, visiting dignitaries, personnel movements, orderly officer rosters and other events around the station. We made a mental note to study SROs to ensure we had all the details of the next ten days. It all sounded rather complicated.

Whittington rambled on with other details, continually emphasizing that only those in peak physical condition could expect to withstand the rigours of the course. He accompanied these assurances with pointed glances in our direction and made a remark directed to those "who abuse their bodies with excessive alcohol and tobacco", assuring us they would be the first to fall by the wayside. Behind me, a muted voice told him to "go abuse yerself".

I read SROs carefully before dinner. It all seemed perfectly straightforward, we would be taken to Cambridge tomorrow to catch British Railways northbound, arriving at Aviemore in the late afternoon. We would then be taken by trucks to our first campsite for the night. Whittington's recommendation that we diligently study SROs lest we miss some vital item of information was neatly summed up by one person as "A load of shit." Somebody else must have thought so too, because next morning there was toilet paper between each page.

Aviemore in the Cairn Gorms is a beautiful place in summertime; we pitched camp beside Loch Erin and admired the setting rays of the sun reflected on the Grampian Mountains on the far side of the water.

Next morning the course started with early morning physical training (PT) to help straighten out the aches and pains caused by a night in a sleeping bag without a mattress. The ground was still moist from melted snow and most of us had quickly learned to collect twigs and dried bracken, which we placed under the tent's ground sheet to insulate us from the chill and damp while we slept.

PT gave us a healthy appetite for breakfast served in billycans from a field kitchen. After breakfast we packed up tents and equipment before setting off on the first exercise, a comparatively short ten-mile slog across the hills to a specific map reference then back to the campsite. This initial part of the survival course, as well as toughening us up for what lay ahead, also taught us the use of Ordnance Survey maps and the hand-held compass. It also taught us that the best footwear for scrambling over rocks and through streams was a pair of regulation issue RAF drill boots.

Everybody was exhausted by the time we'd completed the first day's short tramp. Whittington's remarks about being in top physical condition kept ringing in my ears, especially when I imagined the pleasure he'd derive if anybody should 'fall by the wayside'.

The next few days brought longer and more arduous marches. By now, most of us had caught severe colds through sleeping in the damp, particularly Blob Bottom who had problems sleeping at night. The problems of coping with the rigours of the course were compounded by our constantly running noses. It was bad enough to be hanging by your fingernails from some impossibly high crag, knowing that to fall would result in being smashed on the rocks below, possibly taking others of your team with you, but when your nose is running constantly . . . well it seems much harder!

Wherever our route crossed a road, Don Whittington was there, comfortably seated in an Air Force Land Rover, exhorting us to greater efforts while peering hopefully for any signs of weakening of morale, or deterioration in physical condition.

Then on the fourth day, a strange metamorphosis occurred. The habitual drinkers, smokers and late night carousers had found the initial part of the course very demanding, in contrast to the more athletic and clean living members of our course, who covered the initial distances effortlessly. For a while it looked like the survival course would provide irrefutable proof of the advantages of clean living – until the third day, when the more athletic began to find the camp food inadequate to replenish the energy they had expended during the day.

Meanwhile the smokers, drinkers and carousers, whose bodies had been abused by excessive amounts of tobacco and alcohol, and rarely given regular wholesome food, had adapted to the new conditions more readily and after a cigarette and a good spew, were usually ready to start the day's rigours. As the survival course entered its fifth day, I noticed several pentathletes, sprinters and hurdlers looking very pale and wan, for like pedigree race horses, they could only deliver maximum performance if they were provided with the correct food as fuel. Several of them had to attend the doctor after breakfast, much to the delight of many others, who took great delight in asking Don Whittington what the matter was with them.

The final five days were the escape and evasion exercise. For this, we would be issued with 'Iron Rations' and handed a sealed envelope.

Whittington explained each envelope contained a map reference, to which we had to navigate. On arrival there, a member of his staff would tell us another map reference to make for. It sounded quite easy until he informed us a regiment of Seaforth and Sutherland Highlanders were acting as 'the enemy', with instructions to capture us and take us back to the start. In case any of our number proved too elusive for them, a team of police dogs and their handlers were also after us.

It all sounded like good clean fun – for the pursuers!

Over the Top

The escape and evasion exercise started after an early breakfast on the sixth day. I was teamed up with Shit'ead, Jack Hennessey, Blob Bottom and Big Dick. The sealed envelope was handed to Blob Bottom after breakfast and after packing up our gear, we opened it and headed off for the first designated position.

We soon learned to keep away from skylines, where the probing Highlanders' eyes could detect us relatively easily and take off in pursuit. Their intimate knowledge of the local countryside was another advantage in their favour, as well as being motorised, so as soon as they saw a line of figures, they knew which roads to take to head them off. Several parties were caught in this way and I was pleasantly surprised when we reached the first rendezvous point without being intercepted and captured.

We paused for a short breather and while we were planning the best route to cross a formidable line of hills ahead, Don Whittington drove up, wearing an Air Force anorak and shiny new boots. "Taking a rest, are you? Not feeling a trifle run down after all this physical exercise, I hope?" he enquired anticipatively.

"No, sir, just planning our next sector," Jack Hennessey explained patiently. Whittington guffawed with amusement.

"The shortest distance between two points is a straight line," he informed us, ignoring a reminder that ships and aircraft usually steer great circle tracks. His delight at our rather debilitated appearance then caused him to make a very stupid error of judgement. In an attack of overconfidence, Don Whittington, who had spent the last five nights in a comfortable bed and eaten regular nourishing cooked meals, decided he would accompany us on the next sector. Blob Bottom caught Jack's eye and winked.

"OK, we'll go in a straight line," Jack pointed towards the range of mountains. "Over the top." The party set off, Whittington taking up the rear of the column, constantly exhorting us to "Speed it up a bit, can't you?" Six days of marching across the Highlands over rocky terrain and through heather had taught us to make haste slowly and conserve our strength, a bit like the old bull in the story, who after a young bull had found the gate to a field of cows open and suggested they gallop down and mate a couple quickly, had suggested walking down slowly and mating the whole field!

Accompanied by a load of bull behind us, we headed for the hills.

When the Going Gets Tough

Whittington didn't keep up his stream of talk very long. By the time we'd traversed two miles of rocky terrain, he was curiously quiet. When Jack called a halt to catch our breath and check our progress on the map, Whittington was showing definite signs of wear.

After establishing our position, we began the steep climb up into the hills. Now the going was getting a lot tougher and we felt grateful we had conserved our energy earlier. At the next rest, Whittington took more than a casual interest in our position on the map.

"What's that mountain directly ahead of us?" he demanded of Jack.

"Mount Ferguson Sir, over 3,800 feet high."

Whittington groaned and sat down on a piece of sharp rock. "Is that the last mountain before the next rendezvous point?" he enquired hopefully. Jack Hennessey shook his head. "Negative Sir, there's Mount Aspiring, which is . . . er let me see, 4,010 and then there's Mount McCormack after that . . . "

"Which is even higher but there's a fabulous view from the top," Big Dick interjected. "It's on our straight line route to the next rendezvous point."

Whittington groaned as somebody gave the order to start. I noticed he was beginning to limp rather painfully now.

"New boots hurting, are they Sir?" I smirked quietly as I strode past him.

It soon became obvious Don wasn't going to make it to the next rendezvous. His limp rapidly worsened and we had to stop more and more frequently for him to rest and regain his breath. Somebody reminded him that only those in top physical condition could expect to withstand the rigours of the survival course and Big Dick enquired whether he'd been abusing his body with excessive alcohol or tobacco recently. Whittington glared back at his accusers with undisguised hatred. Then he tried to stand up and it became painfully obvious he wasn't going to make it any further. We consulted the map and saw a sealed road ran through the valley below.

"The best thing would be for us to carry him to the road," Jack pointed to the map. "And wait for an Army truck to find us."

"But we'll get captured!" Blob Bottom observed.

"Well, he can't go any further," Jack retorted. "And we can't leave him here."

I noticed the clouds above the adjacent hills were darkening and the sun was setting. There are fewer bleaker places than the Scottish Highlands at night.

"Why can't we just leave him here?" Shit'ead suddenly suggested. Like the rest of us, he didn't relish the prospect of being captured by the Pongos (Army) and taken back to base camp to start the arduous course all over again.

"He'd die of exposure," Jack explained, gesturing towards the darkening hills to the east.

"Seems a pity to get captured, though," Shit'ead persisted. Behind me I thought I heard Whittington whimper.

"Surely you wouldn't want to leave him here to die," we demanded indignantly of Shit'ead.

"This is a place of outstanding natural beauty," somebody protested. "We couldn't leave him here." Whittington shook his head in vehement agreement and even Shit'ead seemed to go along with this reasoning.

"Remember Captain Oates, Sir?" Jack asked the whimpering Whittington, who shook his head.

"Oates, which course was he on?" he enquired.

We turned away resignedly; there was little likelihood of Whittington doing a similar decent thing, he wasn't the type. If he was going to perish, he'd close all the hatches and take the whole crew with him. Resignedly, we gathered together to map out the best route to the valley floor below. The best plan would be for two of us to carry the injured man for a couple of hundred yards then hand him over to another two. This sounded very simple in discussion but in practice it proved very hazardous. The ground dropped away steeply to the valley floor below, often at an angle of forty-five degrees or more. The rocks were wet and covered with slippery lichen, which our feet slithered and slipped over. A descent like this would have demanded our utmost skill in optimum conditions but when fading light, an injured man and constantly running noses were added to the task, it became downright dangerous.

Eventually, long after nightfall, we reached the valley floor and waded through freezing marshes and climbed over rocky outcrops to reach the road. The temperature had dropped alarmingly as a katabatic wind roared down the valley, further adding to out discomfort. We pitched our tiny one-man pup tents and tried to light a fire to keep warm but it proved impossible in the damp and windy conditions. We huddled together for mutual warmth and chewed emergency rations – concentrated chocolate and Bovril, while waiting for the dawn.

After a very uncomfortable night, the day dawned wet and blustery. Whittington now looked alarmingly ill; as well as having great difficulty in walking or even standing, he had a severe cold and shivered continually, despite the layers of additional clothing we had discarded to wrap round him. We waited beside the road for a patrolling truck, and hoped.

Just as we were thinking of sending two of our team to off to seek help, a canvas-covered Army truck came into view. Big Dick and I waved it down and a squad of Seaforth and Sutherland Highlanders leaped from the back. We pointed to the shivering Whittington while swiftly explaining the situation to their officer in charge. He issued an order and four Highlanders loaded Don into the truck. He then turned to us and sportingly offered us the choice of either escorting Whittington to hospital or continuing on the exercise. Since nobody could see any point in escorting our incapacitated squadron commander, we chose to continue. The Army officer bade us "goodbye and good luck" and drove off in the truck while we set off through the heather to the next rendezvous.

Two mountains and five hours later, we reached it. The Rock Ape's CO handed us another envelope. "Your squadron commander has been admitted to hospital with a torn thigh muscle and suspected bronchial pneumonia," he informed us. "How the devil did he get all that?"

"Can't have been in top physical condition, can he, Sir?" Blob Bottom enquired ingenuously.

Our next rendezvous point took us closer to habitation. We headed towards a saddle between two hills and quietly discussed how to escape notice as we passed farms and houses.

From a concealed position below the skyline, we surveyed the route below. The town of Boat of Garten lay a couple of miles ahead and below, with a reasonably wide river bisecting it. Apart from the chilling prospect of swimming, the only way to cross the river was via the only bridge right in the centre of town.

The Pongos would have thought of this and placed guards on the bridge. Somebody suggested floating across the river on a home-made raft or stolen boat, but the chances of being caught while building the raft or stealing a boat seemed too high.

While we debated our various alternatives, two Army trucks appeared driving along the road below. We could see the red cockaded berets and khaki battledress of Highlanders seated in the canvas-covered rear of each truck.

I glanced at my watch; the time was 1 p.m.

"Thy must be the afternoon squad coming on duty," Jack Hennessey whispered in my ear. I stole a swift glance round a clump of heather, and counted about twenty-five men in each truck, making fifty in all, enough to patrol every road, street corner, field and farmhouse to catch any members of our course making for the bridge.

Nobody could think of a way to avoid them.

Something must have attracted their attention, because I saw an Army lieutenant in the lead truck point in our general direction. Both vehicles stopped and the lieutenant climbed down from the cab, while we hunched closer together in the heather and bracken. When five minutes had passed and nothing had happened, I stole another glance through the heather and saw a second officer gesticulating while conferring with the first, occasionally pointing up in our direction. He suddenly pointed directly at us and the other ran to the truck, appearing moments later with a funnel shaped object, which he placed to his mouth. His amplified voice echoed off the sides of the valley.

"We've seen you," he announced in a staccato voice. "Come down and surrender."

"Go jump in the loch!" Blob Bottom murmured in reply.

"Come down and surrender, we know you're up there," the voice repeated. We sat where we were, confident that provided we remained concealed, they would take two or three hours to find us. "This is your last chance," the voice announced. I stole another glance down the escarpment and saw the other Army officer talking into a walkie-talkie radio carried on the back of a tall Highlander.

Blob Bottom and Jack crawled to a position beside me. "We'll bluff it out," Jack whispered. "It will take them hours to find us in all this gorse and heather. If we keep out of sight when they start their search, they may go right past us."

"Whaddabout going separate ways?" Shit'ead suggested. "That way at least one or two of us might get away." We squashed the idea, there were too many of them.

Down below, the officer had finished speaking on the radio. He removed the earphones and as he handed them to a soldier an atmosphere of leisure seemed to suddenly take hold of the assembled soldiers. One of the officers produced a pipe, which he began to fill. At a nod from the other officer, soldiers and non-commissioned officers jumped down from the backs of the trucks and stretched their limbs. Several lit cigarettes while others drank from water bottles. Laughter and occasional snatches of conversation reached our ears.

I gesticulated to Jack, hoping he would have some idea of what was happening but he too was baffled. If the Pongos intended to guard the road, they would have placed men along it at regular intervals, every twenty-five yards or so. Why then were they clustered casually round their trucks, smoking, talking and taking little notice of their quarry?

Further speculation was made even more difficult by the arrival of two Army Land Rovers driven by peak-capped figures. The pipe-smoking Pongo seemed especially pleased at their arrival; he tapped out his pipe and hurried over to the nearer vehicle. After a quick exchange of conversation, accompanied by a lot of pointing and staring in our direction, the drivers climbed out and made towards the back of each vehicle while the pipe smoker retrieved his loud hailer from its stowage and prepared to address us again. Behind him, the drivers of the Land Rovers were opening wire doors at the rear of their vehicles while the Highlanders looked on expectantly, some of them laughing excitedly as if in anticipation of something good or exciting about to happen.

"All right then, one last chance to give yourselves up and surrender," the loud hailer echoed across the heather up to our position on the side of the hill.

Blob Bottom quietly repeated his invitation to bathe. Down in the valley, the Pongo officer waited a few seconds before speaking into the loud hailer again. "All right then, you've had your last chance, now we're sending the dogs after you!" he announced, while behind him, four Dobermann Pinscher tracker dogs leaped down from the back of the first Land Rovers. More emerged from the other vehicle.

"These dogs are trained to track and kill, if necessary," he cautioned. I felt the sickly taste of fear in my throat. "If you give yourselves up now, it will save a lot of unnecessary suffering," the voice suggested. "Just stand up in your present position, with your hands above your heads and don't move. The dogs won't come after you unless their handlers release them."

I began to rise to my feet; we had been told about these dogs, they were trained to track down escaping prisoners and escapees. Identical dogs had been used by the prison authorities in the last century. Their baying as they pursued escaping convicts struck terror into every heart; mice threw themselves on the traps when they heard the sound. Armed with a keen sense of smell, acute hearing and good eyesight, these dogs would emit the spine-chilling baying sound while relentlessly tracking down their quarry. When they finally overhauled their prey, they used their immense size to bowl them over effortlessly. Once the prisoner was on the ground, they would stand guard over him.

Well that was the theory – provided you didn't move or attempt to flee, they wouldn't harm you but the slightest movement would excite the dog and provoke him into savaging the prisoner. Tales were repeated of dogs becoming so excited by the thrill of the chase that they forgot their training, attacking and savaging their quarry after capture.

Now I was about to be the object of their pursuit, unless I quickly surrendered before they came after us. I began to rise to my feet but a restraining hand held me back.

"Wait a minute," Jack hissed.

"Why? Those bloody hounds are going to rip us apart and I'm too young to die; I've got my whole life ahead of me . . . "

"We're not alone," Jack insisted.

"Yeah and there's more company on the way," I reminded him.

"Keep down!" Something in his tone of voice persuaded me to stay firmly rooted to the ground, although I could hear the dogs baying as they strained at their leashes. Blob Bottom, Big Dick and Shit'ead pressed themselves closer to the gorse-covered ground beside us. I decided that once the dogs were released, I was going to surrender.

"That's better. Now walk down the hillside slowly, remember the dogs," the loud hailer instructed. I directed a puzzled glance at my companions. "Move over to the left, you'll find a pathway there. Don't worry about the dogs, they're quite secure," the voice continued.

What the hell was happening? Two more minutes passed; I didn't dare steal a glance.

"All right now, form up on the road, you can drop your packs in the trucks later. Now when the sergeant comes up to you, give him your name and identification number, then get into one of the trucks. You're being taken back to base camp to start over again."

Finally I stole a cautious glance and saw twenty or more APOs assembling on the road below, anxious to escape the fangs of the tracker dogs. "The whole blooming course has been hiding out on the hillside!" I exclaimed to Jack, who hushed me quiet.

One by one, those captured had their names recorded before clambering over the tailgates into the trucks. The Highlanders climbed in after them, anxious to block any escape attempts while returning to base camp. I recognised Mike Parry, Don Reid, Kiwi Green and Mlig among the last to climb in. Behind them, the tracker dogs were returned to their cages.

The truck engines roared into life and the drivers headed the heavy vehicles back towards Aviemore, with the peak-capped soldiers following in the Land Rovers. Soon only the faint memory of those terrible dogs remained.

We lay hidden for another ten or fifteen minutes before Jack looked up; not a soul remained; it was our lucky day, the Pongos would be chortling in jubilation as they escorted their prisoners back to the start, leaving us a clear half hour in which to cross the bridge in the centre of town en route to the next rendezvous.

We were given our final instructions after arrival at the next rendezvous point. We were to head back to Aviemore, a distance of only twenty miles in a straight line but the equivalent of thirty over mountainous terrain. It was late afternoon as we headed into the hills, with Big Dick navigating and Blob Bottom picking the best path between rocky outcrops and clumps of gorse. We had decided to continue until dusk then find a suitable place to camp before dark, settle down for the night and complete the remaining distance tomorrow. Don Whittington's experience had taught us that scrambling over rocks at night was a good way to tear a muscle or break an ankle. It would be far better to start the final day well rested and fit.

We pitched camp beside a small loch and gathered up dry gorse and bracken for a fire. Our sole topic of conversation was the strange quirk of fate that had removed the guards from our path, enabling us to reach the rendezvous while those less lucky were taken back to base camp to start all over again. From what we had gathered at the last turning point, nobody else had made it this far yet. A crescent moon rose into a clear night sky and added faint illumination to the scene.

Next day our plan of campaign went as intended. After breakfast, cooked to gourmet standard by Jack Hennessey and tasting better than anything the Cordon Bleu cookery school could have prepared, we broke camp and set out for the finish.

We marched until noon, pausing only occasionally to check our position on the Ordnance Survey map, and taking a half-hour break for lunch when we reckoned we could afford the time. The remaining distance was over comparatively flat pasture land, so an average speed of three miles an hour shouldn't be difficult to maintain. By three o'clock we were hidden in a farmer's barn looking down a gently sloping meadow to the main A9 running into Aviemore.

"That's the finishing line," Big Dick finished consulting the map and pointed to the tarmacadamed ribbon of road below. "We have to cross it between 4.30 and 6 p.m."

"Looks simple enough,"Shit'ead stated. The rest of us agreed; we'd wait until just before half past four then head off down the gently sloping meadow. Meanwhile, there was an hour and a half to while away before the deadline, so we took turns at maintaining a look out for Pongos while the rest dozed off in the comfortable straw in the barn. Things were beginning to look good.

Unfortunately, just before the appointed time, several squads of Pongos arrived in the local area, necessitating a last minute change of plan. Now rather than walking down the meadow to the road below, our best route would be via a heavily overgrown hedgerow to our left.

We began cautiously making our way to the finishing line. We had less than two hundred yards to go when two Highlanders appeared, walking uphill along our side of the hedge. They hadn't seen us yet but as they were directly in our desired line of travel, we decided the best course of action would be to drop our back packs and sprint for the finish, relying on surprise and speed to reach the finish before the patrolling soldiers became aware of our presence.

It almost worked! By the time they had recovered from their surprise and set off after us, we were already halfway there, but the meadow sloped away at a steeper angle than we had appreciated and my feet began to run away from underneath me. I hurtled over a small ridge, almost out of control and was flying down the other side when two more khaki-clad figures appeared before me, carrying rifles with fixed bayonets!

"Halt!" a Highland burr instructed.

"I can't!" I thought, now totally out of control. They adopted a kneeling position as I rocketed towards them.

"Halt or we'll bayonet ye, yer Sassenach bastaarrd!" They meant it too! I couldn't halt my headlong rush; I was going to end my flying career impaled on the end of a Scottish bayonet! Suddenly I stumbled and fell into soft mud, slithering another ten yards further downhill before stopping inches away from the tip of one of the bayonets.

For me the war was over but behind my captors I saw Big Dick and the others make it to the finishing line.

The exercise was now officially over. That evening we celebrated in the local tavern by abusing our bodies with excesses of food, alcohol and tobacco. Tomorrow a few of us were paying Don Whittington a courtesy visit in hospital before heading south back to Oakington.

The Tough Get Going

A severely starched matron made each of us cover our grimy denims with white hospital gowns before she would take us to see Don Whittington. We trailed her along endless corridors to our squadron commander's room.

"He's still in quite critical condition," she informed us. "There's several things wrong with him still."

"Nothing trivial, we hope?" somebody enquired. She giggled unexpectedly.

"He has been rather a difficult patient," she confided. "He won't take his medication and orders my nurses around as if they were under his command; why only this morning he threw the most dreadful tantrum when one of the young nurses came to take his temperature."

We entered a private room and found Don lying in a hospital bed, dozing. A quantity of reading matter lay nearby, which he appeared to have made no effort to read. A vase of late flowering daffodils had been thoughtfully provided by the hospital to brighten the otherwise rather drab room. Don turned his head sideways, recognised us and closed his eyes disinterestedly. The matron tried to arouse some interest from him.

"These nice officers have come to see how you are, squadron leader," she began. "I expect you'll be anxious to hear all their news."

Whittington groaned once and turned his face to the wall. The matron eyed him up and down for a second then prepared to leave for more important tasks. "Don't stay for too long," she instructed us. "He's still very feverish and his lungs are badly congested. Another officer's coming to see him in a quarter of an hour, so don't tire him too much, he's very weak and the fever's making him more unpleasant than he'd normally be . . . "

Several remarked they hadn't noticed any personality change as the matron hurried off on her endless chores, leaving us to attempt conversation with Don.

To be fair to him, he did look extremely ill. A plastic tube disappeared up one nostril, his eyes had a disinterested glaze and his complexion was best described as deathly white.

After several unsuccessful attempts to initiate a conversation, we decided the best course of action was to leave him to his own self pity, so began filing out the room, Shit'ead and Big Dick first, with Jack and others close behind. Mike Parry and I were about to make our farewells when a burly hospital orderly muscled into the room.

"Time to turrun ye over, squadron lidder," he announced in a thick Glaswegian burr. Don moaned and muttered something almost unintelligible, which the orderly heard. "Shame on ye, surr. It's for ye own good that we take such trouble." He attempted to manhandle Whittington over onto his stomach but the patient had other ideas and held on to the metal bed frame with both hands while we looked on helplessly.

"Cou'd yew two gen'lemen pawssibly help me here?" the orderly asked after three unsuccessful attempts to turn Don over. Mike and I stationed ourselves on opposite sides of the bed to constrain Don's hands while the orderly turned him onto his chest. He explained it was necessary to move the patient in this manner to prevent the congestion in his lungs causing further damage to his respiratory system. His explanation was frequently interrupted by indistinct expletives from the patient.

Anxious to get away from Whittington's bad temper, we bade farewell and backed out the door, which was probably the reason we didn't see the young probationer nurse wheeling a trolley through the doorway. The metal trolley banged against the wall and a tray containing thermometers, saucers of pills and other medication tumbled to the floor.

"Here, let me help you pick all this up," I volunteered, kneeling down to where the nurse was already retrieving things from the floor. She smiled and I noticed she was very young.

"This will all have to be thrown away," she pointed to the pills and medications on the floor. "I'll go back to the dispensary for a fresh lot." Mike and I accompanied her as she returned to the dispensary for a second batch. We exchanged idle conversation while she waited for the pharmacist to replenish her tray.

Her face took on a sympathetic expression when she learned we were in the Air Force under Whittington's command.

"He's a difficult man at times," she observed. "He refused to have his temperature taken this morning and kept ordering me from the room. Mind you, he's probably a little dopey from all the pills he's been getting." We nodded sympathetically; Don was a right bastard normally so under the effects of a few drugs he'd be a demon. "I've got to take his temperature now," she continued. "Just the thought of it has been worrying me all morning."

When we offered to accompany her for moral support; she gazed at us gratefully and accepted.

We returned to Don's room and, acting on our advice, she pushed the trolley through the door while announcing in a firm 'no nonsense' voice that it was "Time for temperatures, squadron leader." A muffled grunt from the face in the pillow was fortunately unintelligible to her as she rummaged around in the tray and produced a rectal thermometer. I chuckled to myself, feeling some slight sympathy for Don Whittington, who because of his face down posture, was going to have to have his temperature taken in this rather ignominious manner.

His young nurse peeled back the sheets and blankets and slid the regulation hospital pyjama pants down past Don's pink buttocks. It was obvious from the scarlet flush rising up from her neck that she found the next part of the operation acutely embarrassing. She picked up the rectal thermometer and hesitated, horribly uncomfortable. Mike Parry hurried over, took the thermometer from her hand and pointed to the door. Gratefully she slipped out as Mike advanced on the cheeky figure on the bed. Then a devilish thought suddenly occurred to him and he pocketed the thermometer, removed a daffodil from the vase of flowers and placed it between Don's buttocks. The patient twitched a little when the cold stem chilled his flesh but otherwise said nothing.

Mike and I joined the grateful young nurse outside. "I can't tell you how grateful I am to you . . . " she assured us.

Mike looked at her pretty young face. "It was a pleasure," he assured her.

We hurried down the seemingly endless corridors to rejoin the others. They had just finished removing the white hospital gowns when a large Air Force staff car pulled up at the hospital entrance and the bulky figure of Air Marshal Sir Richard Atcherley emerged from the rear compartment and hurried through the entrance.

Mike and the rest of us snapped to attention as the air marshal paused in the reception area. "Good morning, Sir."

"Good morning, I've come to see your commanding officer," Batchy eyed us up and down critically. "I understand you fellows had a pretty tough time of it out there in the Highlands; if it hadn't been for him, some of you would still be lost out there, probably dying from of exposure."

We gasped in astonishment but Batchy had resumed speaking before we could reply.

"Where is he? I want to congratulate him."

"Down the end of the long corridor to your right, last room on the left," Mike directed.

"How is he? Not in any pain, is he?" the air marshal enquired.

Mike shook his head. "He's in peak physical condition," he assured the older man. "You'll be quite surprised when you see him, Sir!"

Batchy harrumphed something unintelligible and hurried off down the corridor.

Chapter 32

The Last of Wisdom

After ten days in an open-necked shirt it was wonderful to return to civilisation. Cushioned seats seemed the very height of luxury after sitting on cold rocks and damp ground for ten days, and a cup of hot tea in clean china tasted like nectar.

While British Rail rattled us south-west to Glasgow, our thoughts turned to the epicurean delights of that city. We were unanimous in our desire to devour the biggest and best meal available but unfortunately our immediate financial status was rather lean. Nobody had brought much money with them, lest we lose it on the escape and evasion exercise, credit cards were virtually unknown and it was highly unlikely any restaurant would accept cheques from our scruffy denimed mob.

Mlig volunteered the information that he knew of a new type of Scandinavian restaurant that had opened recently, called a *smorgasbord* where you could eat as much as you wanted for a fixed amount. He described an earlier sortie to the restaurant, when for only a guinea[1], he had feasted on platefuls of roast beef with Brussels sprouts, roast potatoes and gravy followed by a dessert of generous helpings of fruit salad topped with cream. Our mouths salivated as he described each course in detail.

The smorgasbord was called, rather appropriately, the Pig and Guinea, and by the time our train pulled in to Glasgow, we were united in our firm resolve to eat there. After pooling our cash, we found we had enough to pay for the meal and a cab to take everybody back to the station.

---

1. A guinea is £1.05 or $1.55.

Ten minutes later, two taxis deposited our scruffy-looking party outside the restaurant. I feared it was closed at first, for the doors were firmly locked and only a few lights shone inside. "I'm bloody starving!" Shit'ead announced unnecessarily, banging on the window.

I gazed at the others in hungry dismay. "It's Sunday!" I realized. "They must be shut." At that instant a face appeared at the window, gestured at a sign then pointed at his watch. "They don't open until half past twelve," I read from the sign. It was now quarter past, so we paced the pavement outside for what seemed like the longest fifteen minutes of our lives.

By the time the doors opened for business, each of us could have eaten a horse apiece then called for the menu. Big Dick handed our funds over to the girl behind the cash register and we trooped into the restaurant.

"Take a plate and help yourself to whatever you want," Mlig gestured towards the buffet-style lay out. "And if you want a second helping, keep your knife and fork and go up again. It's a Scandinavian idea, pay first and eat all you can."

"The Scandinavians do have some great ideas," Big Dick declared as he helped himself to copious pieces of cold roast chicken. I agreed with him while concentrating on the seafood. Either side of me, the others tucked in.

The food lived up to our highest expectations. For the princely sum of twenty-one shillings, we ate like kings. Prawn cocktails were followed by plates of roast beef with vegetables, cold cuts of assorted meats were followed by fruit salad, cheese and afterwards we sat around, contentedly reminiscing about the events of the last ten days.

"It's certainly made me appreciate home cooking," Lord Jim remarked.

"You can say that again. I'll never look another Oxo cube in the face again."

"Nor could I, but you know what? Talking of food has made me hungry again. I think I could manage another plate of chicken. Do we just go up and help ourselves?"

"Most definitely," Mlig assured him. "Take all you can eat for a guinea." In ones and twos, we returned to the centre table for second helpings, which after a twenty-minute rest, were followed by third helpings. Other diners in the restaurant began to notice the amount of food we'd consumed. By three o'clock we'd eaten without interruption for two and a half hours.

I was taking a last mouthful of Crayfish Mornay and thinking what a pity it was that our finances couldn't stretch to a glass of dry white wine each to accompany the meal, when I detected activity in the direction of the cash register.

A bald-headed Scotsman, clad in form-fitting chalk stripe suit and floral tie, was conversing anxiously with the cashier and two waitresses. As they conferred together, they stole furtive glances in our direction; I saw one of the waitresses mouth the word 'five' and point at Blob Bottom. I sat back in the comfortable seat and ruminated whether to go onto the fruit salad or try the roast chicken. Mike and Blob Bottom arrived back with heaped plates and in the distance I saw the waitress mouth the word 'six' to the man, while I concentrated on making the difficult decision between chicken and fruit.

It was now quarter past three and the lunchtime clientele had thinned out to half a dozen diners apart from us.

"Certainly is good value for money," we all agreed.

"I dunno how they do it for the price."

I decided to stay with the chicken. Ten days in Scotland's Cairngorms can give a man a formidable appetite. I tried to rise from my seat, plate in hand, but a pair of strong hands pushed me back into the padded upholstery.

"You boys enjoying yourselves?" the worried proprietor enquired conversationally. We nodded our unanimous approval. "Wonderful food," Blob Bottom assured him. "Best in Glasgow I'd say." The proprietor smiled a thin smile at the compliment to his cuisine. "Dunno how you do it for the price, why, I've had er, let me see, four or was it five helpings so far . . . "

"Six," the man corrected.

"Was it really six?" Blob Bottom exclaimed surprisedly. "Doesn't time fly when you're having fun?" The stern-faced proprietor ignored the question.

"Where are you boys from?" he next enquired, his hand still on my shoulder. I looked at him in a new light; I thought I knew what was about to happen. He probably had a son about our age, maybe doing his National Service in the Army in Malaya, or perhaps his son was a pilot too. Now the kind-hearted father was about to invite us to have a drink with our meal; he might even invite us back this evening for a repeat performance. I looked at him with affection and respect as I answered. "We're from Royal Air Force Oakington and we've just spent ten days in the Highlands on an exercise."

The proprietor digested this information carefully while I waited for him to call for wine and glasses. He didn't.

"Where did you say you were from?"

"Oakington, that's near Cambridge, 600 miles from here . . . "

The eyes narrowed as they regarded me for several seconds. "Cambridge eh?" he mused aloud. "Across the border, way down in southern England."

"Er well . . . yes, that's right." I wondered whether he'd offer us a choice of wine; I'd prefer a dry white, maybe a Riesling. There was a long pause.

"Cambridge eh? Well why don't you all fuck off back there? You've eaten the week's profits here!" he suddenly shouted. A door at the far end of the restaurant slammed behind him as he stormed from the room.

We gazed at other each dumbstruck; and to think I had thought he was about to order wine on the house!

Lord Jim was the first to recover. "More chicken anybody?"

On arrival back at Oakington, we were forcibly reminded the flying course wasn't satisfactorily concluded yet. Tony Mlig performed rather poorly on a progress flight check so was put up for a Flight Commander's check. He failed to impress on the second occasion and was passed on to the squadron commander.

As Don Whittington was still sprouting daffodils in Scotland, another squadron commander was called in. By this time, Mlig was a nervous gibbering wreck. On take-off he retracted the landing gear 'Up' too early and the aircraft sank back towards the runway. The check pilot hauled back on the control column but was too late to prevent the 'D' doors, which covered the main wheels in flight, striking the concrete surface of the runway. This completely destroyed the small amount of Mlig's remaining confidence and a further check flight was just as bad. We commiserated with him over his run of bad luck but he was almost inconsolable. I realized with surprise that he had psyched himself into failing the forthcoming wing commander's check.

When the time came for Mlig's final scrub check, the whole course and several instructors were on hand to advise and encourage him. The wing commander was also more than helpful and jokingly chided Mlig for unnecessarily getting him out of a nice comfortable office to go flying in a noisy aeroplane.

Despite every possible bit of assistance, Mlig's facial expression after landing told us he was chopped. The wing commander took him to his office and debriefed him on the whole flight, praising the good points and offering helpful criticism on any errors or inaccuracies in his flying. At the end of the debrief, Mlig walked out of the office and gave us the thumbs down sign, indicating he'd got the chop.

The next morning he made the lonely journey through the guard room gates to civilian life. Because his commissioned rank was now confirmed, there was no question of him reverting back to airman rank and having to serve the remainder of his National Service in a ground trade. Instead, he was released from the service prematurely.

Subsequently we learned Mlig had suffered a family bereavement at this time, which may have contributed to his sudden loss of confidence.

Flying training continued through July; flying conditions were perfect for two months and the whole course maintained its programmed schedule of flying hours until a spate of bad weather caused us to slip behind the monthly target quota.

The arrival of the miserable weather coincided with the return of Whittington, now fully recovered form his ordeal in Scotland. His appearance in the bar that night evoked faked concern from other squadron commanders that he might be abusing his health with excesses of alcohol. This, like an enquiry from Mike Parry whether Don was now in top physical condition, was rudely ignored. Such subtlety was wasted on him anyway.

The lull in flying gave me an opportunity to sort out a personal problem of my own – Natalie. I decided to tackle the fence head on and arranged to meet her at the tennis club on Saturday morning.

I spent an anxious evening in my room, composing what I would say to her. I decided I'd be politely correct towards her and would take the first opportunity to point out the foolhardiness of our relationship. I would then tell her, very firmly, that it had to stop.

That was the theory side; I now had to put theory into practice.

Saturday morning was dull and overcast like the rest of the week had been. I drove down to the tennis courts shortly after breakfast and found Natalie and several other players in the clubhouse. She spotted me immediately and came towards me, smiling.

"Why hello, stranger, how were the Scottish Highlands?" she tucked her arm into mine and steered me towards the others. I made some sort of reply as I tried to ignore the exciting effect of the tingle of her bare skin against mine. She was wearing that perfume again . . .

We sat down and exchanged tennis talk for half an hour. A squadron leader accounts wife made coffee and we sat there, waiting for the weather to improve. I tried to pick an opportunity to get Natalie on her own for a few minutes but she misconstrued my intentions and told me to "wait, you naughty boy". This instruction was delivered with a playful slap on the knee and a suggestive glance that set my pulse racing.

So far the morning hadn't gone quite as planned.

The weather improved and we joined another couple for mixed doubles. At midday we sat down alone for the first time. Here was my opportunity; I cleared my throat. "I've been doing some thinking." I began.

Natalie appeared not to have heard, for she shivered and turned towards me. "Brr, it's turned cold all of a sudden," she remarked.

"Can I get you a jersey or something?" I offered. She smiled sweetly.

"I've left mine at home, I didn't realize it was going to be so cold and this dress is so thin." She gave me a sweet smile of appreciation when I draped my jacket across her shoulders.

"There's something I want to talk to you about," I tried again. She gave me another sweet smile.

"And I want to hear all about Scotland," she assured me. "Let's go home; I've made us a cold lunch. We can sit outside and talk all afternoon."

"No! We can't do that, people will talk . . . "

"Nonsense, who would see us? Anyway, I'm only suggesting lunch together . . . " she finished the sentence with a naughty glint in her eye.

"I've got to go out this afternoon," I floundered.

"Nonsense, come and have lunch."

I mentally consulted my prepared speech. Now was not the best time or place to say what I had to say. I stood up and Natalie also rose and we walked towards our vehicles.

"We've got to behave sensibly," I insisted, once we were out of earshot.

"Why? Come and have some lunch."

"You haven't been listening to a word I've said."

"I've heard every word. Now come and have lunch and tell me what you have to." I weakened momentarily, thinking of the pleasant prospect of a cool drink in the garden with this delectable creature.

"I've got to go out," I lied.

"Goodbye then!" she climbed into her car with an air of finality, pressed the starter and waved once as she reversed out of the parking space. I waved back as I began walking towards the Pheasant Plucker.

Damn and blast! The keys were in my jacket pocket with Natalie! I pounded my fist in angry frustration at this turn of fate. I raced after her but she was soon disappearing down the road to the station married patch, leaving me no alternative but to hurry the short distance to the wing commander's house.

She'd parked the car in the garage and was inside the house when I knocked on the door. Through the frosted glass panel of the door I spied her indistinct form pause in front of a mirror before unlatching the lock.

"Surprise, surprise, you've changed your mind. I'm so glad."

"No, actually you see, you've got my car keys . . . " I stopped quarter way in my faltering explanation, Natalie had sauntered back inside the house after issuing a casual "come in" over her shoulder. I shuffled into her airy kitchen.

"Sherry? You like it dry, don't you?" she'd remembered. I raised my glass.

"Cheers!"

"Cheers!" We clinked glasses and she led me into the lounge. "Make yourself comfortable." I noticed she already had. I took a gulp of the sherry and tried to deliver my set speech again.

"Look, there's something I want to say . . . "

"Hungry?"

"Starving . . . er . . . no, I mean no. Look, sit down and listen for a minute, can't you?" She ignored my command and stood up, making me suddenly aware of her long legs and beautiful bare arms contrasting with the white of her tennis outfit.

"Keep talking while I get us some lunch. I can hear you from the kitchen."

I floundered on for a while, making no sense at all. I could see her reflected in the open glass connecting door between the kitchen and lounge.

"Camembert or Cheddar?"

"Camembert."

"Onions?"

"Yes please."

"Hmm, I'd better have some too then."

She busied herself at the sink bench, placing cheeses and biscuits on a wooden platter before reaching into the fridge to remove a bottle of my favourite wine, a German Riesling! I watched her reflection in the door, musing to myself that any woman who serves Hock at lunchtime can't be all bad. She was about to carry the platter into the lounge when I saw her put it down again. She reached under the back of her tennis blouse and as I watched fascinated, removed her bra.

"Here we are, and a little surprise to go with it!" she hinted coquettishly, leaning across me.

I looked at her in feigned surprise and complimented her on the choice of wine. She sat close beside me and once again I noticed her beautiful long legs, the sunburned neck and arms, and beneath the thin cotton of her tennis blouse I could discern the shape of her firm smooth breasts. I caught a whiff of her perfume and the last of my resolve flew out of the window, to hell with theory! I groaned in delicious ecstasy as she sidled towards me.

"I'm putty in your hands," I admitted before succumbing. She snuggled up to me and my right hand found her right breast and caressed the nipple as our lips met. She pulled away briefly.

"Putty hardens," she reminded me.

"Squadron leader Whittington wants to see you in his office." The message was delivered by an instructor on Monday morning. My palms moistened in fear; this was how it was going to end, no farewells, no parade, no handshake, just a curt dismissal from the service.

And I had only myself to blame! I trudged the short distance to the squadron commander's office and knocked timidly on the door.

"He's not here yet, Sir," the airman typist informed me. "Instructors' meeting every second Monday of the month. He's in with wing commander Lyon." I fought back a rising taste of nausea in my throat. Whittington was probably now walking slowly back to his office, savouring what the wing commander had told him of the events of last Saturday lunchtime.

"Would you like to wait in his office, Sir? He'll only be a few minutes." I entered Whittington's inner office and waited.

My right hand had been cupped round Natalie's firm right breast and I felt her nipple harden as I kissed her.

Suddenly she froze rigid, her frightened gaze directed towards the door behind me.

"When did you get back?" she hissed, pushing my hand away and pulling down her blouse. It was too late, her husband, the Wing Commander Flying, had appeared in the doorway. I stood respectfully to attention like a three legged stool, while Natalie continued to stare at her husband confusedly. "You're home early!" she stated accusingly. He nodded in agreement and helped himself to cheese and biscuits.

"Yes, there was nothing further that concerned me, so I left." He poured himself a glass of wine as he spoke. I remembered he'd been to Central Flying School at Little Rissington for re-categorisation of his instructor's rating.

Husband and wife exchanged banalities for several moments while I tried to decide what to do.

"The man came about the refrigerator and said it's still under guarantee."

"Good, I was hoping that would happen. Any news about the leak in the roof?"

"The plumber phoned back yesterday, it's probably the guttering. He's booked up until Tuesday."

"Well, if you've finished with my jacket, I'll be off . . . " I volunteered. Natalie handed me my coat and silently escorted me to the door.

Now, early on Monday morning, I was waiting for Whittington to throw me in to Wing Commander Lyon's den. The phone rang and I automatically picked it up. "No. 1 Squadron," I answered dully.

"Don, it's Wing Commander Abbott from Engineering here. Look, I've just checked the mod' states of your aircraft and they're way behind, so I spoke to the Wing Co Flying about your suggestion to stop the National Service pilots' training to allow the regulars to complete theirs. He thinks it's a good idea, after all, it doesn't really matter whether they complete their training or not. We'll never see them again."

I listened to this in a semi-bemused state, trying to think of a way to explain I wasn't Don Whittington while also wanting to debate this decision with the Wing Commander from Engineering.

Too late! The Wing Co Eng, always a busy man, had rung off. My thoughts returned to my own unhappy predicament as Whittington breezed into the office, and I stood to attention.

"Er good morning, Clapshaw. I've just come from an instructors' meeting." He didn't invite me to sit down. "The Wing Commander Flying would like to see you this afternoon at four-thirty, after ground school," he announced. "What's it about, do you know?"

I looked at him incredulously, thinking what a prize prick he was to keep me in limbo in this manner. Who did he think he was fooling when he asked me what it was all about? He'd just spent an hour with the Wing Commander. Yet a genuine expression of curiosity was on his face.

"I think it's about tennis last weekend," I answered lamely. "Some confusion over mixed doubles."

He nodded disinterestedly and indicated the interview was over.

"Where the hell have you been dawdling?" the angry voice of Bert Giles my instructor greeted me as I entered the flight hut.

"Seeing the squadron commander . . . " I began. What was there to hurry up for, I only had a few hours remaining in the service?

"Well get your flying kit on then, we're doing general handling and practice emergency procedures," he urged. "We might have time for some practice aeros at the end."

"But surely I'm not down for flying today . . . am I?" I asked incredulously. Bert pushed me roughly towards the day's flying programme chalked up on the board.

"Well if you're not, somebody else with your name is," he urged. "So get a move on fer Chrissake . . . I'll be out at the aircraft."

I raced into the locker room and pulled on my flying overalls, boots and Mae West, then grabbing the rest of my equipment, I ran to the aircraft. The great clobbering system hadn't caught up with me yet, I still had one last flight and I was going to enjoy it.

Bert commented favourably on the flight afterwards.

"Why don't you fly like that all the time?" he enquired. "We might even be able to find a job for you!" I laughed for I had temporarily forgotten what lay in store for me later that afternoon.

During lunch, I confided to Mike Parry that I thought I was about to be chopped. He listened to the details and whistled sympathetically. "Bloody women ruin our lives," he announced. "Trouble is, her husband's a lot older then her, so they probably don't have much of a physical relationship, which is hard for a woman so young and attractive." He asked if there was anything he could do to help and I regretfully told him I didn't think so; the Wing Commander could either go the whole hog and cite me as co-respondent in a divorce action, or chop me instantly for lack of OQs. The second choice would be quicker and cheaper; I preferred that!

I didn't assimilate a thing in afternoon ground school. I didn't need to anyway, I reflected. When the last lecture finished at 4 o'clock, I headed down the end of the flight line to the Wing Commander's office.

"Good luck!" somebody called out.

"Thanks, I'll need it!"

A WRAF corporal greeted me with the kind of pitying expression usually reserved for dogs with three legs when I entered the Wing Commander Flying's headquarters.

"I was told to report at 4.30," I began. "I'm a little early; I don't mind waiting . . . "

"He's in his office, Sir, he's been expecting you. I've just made him a cup of tea, would you like one too?" What a terribly British thought for a condemned man! A nice cup of tea! I shook my head, I couldn't swallow anything in my present nervous condition and if he began throwing things at me, something might get broken.

"Wentworth!" a voice of authority bellowed from the inner office. "Is that Clapshaw I hear out there? Send him in!" I took three paces into his office, halted and saluted smartly. The Wing Commander Flying was leaned back in a comfortable chair with his feet resting in an open drawer of his desk. His uniform jacket was unbuttoned and he held a cup of tea in one hand and a biscuit in the other. He returned my salute with a casual wave, gestured for me to sit down and told the WRAF corporal to close the door and remain outside.

Once his office door was closed, the Wing Commander sat up straight and stared at me. He paused in this manner for several seconds before speaking.

"I'm worried about Natalie," he began. "She's much younger than I am, twenty-five years younger. I'd like to ask your advice on a man-to-man basis".

The situation had resolved itself, although I could take no credit for its resolution. We talked for more than an hour and from that moment on, I could do nothing wrong in the Wing Commander's eyes.

In the stress of the previous hours, I had forgotten about the phone call in Whittington's office that morning. Later, when I remembered, I decided not to pass it on to Don.

By the time the last National Service pilot had gained his wings, I had long ceased worrying about my deception.

Chapter 33

Bandits at
Twelve O'Clock

Now we began night flying.

There is something rather special about walking out to a darkened aircraft and taking off into the blackness of night. Once aloft, a feeling of remoteness envelopes the pilot to make him feel strangely isolated from the earth below. Lights of towns and villages testify to the existence of other beings but the pilot's only tangible link with Mother Earth is the electronic one of the controller's voice and other aircraft in his earphones.

"Juliet Delta finals three greens."

"Juliet Delta cleared to land."

"Oscar Golf ready."

"Oscar Golf, hold clear, one landing."

"Juliet Delta clear of the active."

"Roger Juliet Delta, is that your lot?"

"Affirmative, returning to dispersal."

"Roger. Break. Oscar Golf, cleared to line up."

"Juliet Bravo downwind . . . "

The constant patter of R/T bound us electronically to the controllers in the darkened tower.

Bert Giles took me for a dual sortie in a Vampire T-11. Because it was midsummer, darkness didn't commence until after 10 p.m. We reported for met briefing at nine then headed towards 'Flights' to be briefed by our instructors before getting kitted up for the first take off at ten-fifteen.

Because we took off soon after sunset, the sky lightened as we climbed to altitude. Bert did a few aerobatics in the fading daylight then, once it was truly night, pointed out a few landmarks.

Darkness tends to telescope distance; I remembered how surprised I had been during our elementary flight training at Ternhill to learn that a cluster of lights almost immediately below was in fact fifteen miles away. Now at three or four times the altitudes we flew those piston-engined trainers, the telescoping effect was even more pronounced. London lay to the south-west, resembling an enormous horde of jewels carelessly flung onto black velvet. Further south, a dark void was the Sussex Weald, interspersed with occasional lights of towns – Horsham, Lewes, Hayward's Heath, and a jewelled border along the south coast would be Brighton, Hove and Worthing. Below us, the lights of various airfields in East Anglia and Lincolnshire showed up clearly – Waterbeach, Oakington our own base, Stansted and others. The outline of the Thames Estuary was clearly defined before the coastline bulged northward round East Anglia – Clacton, Lowestoft, Great Yarmouth, Cromer and the indent of the Wash.

I was fortunate that the first night was so clear, for it left an indelible memory of the lights of southern and central England on my mind. Seated aloft in the warm cramped confines of the T-11 cockpit, I could imagine how it must have felt fifteen years previously in the cockpit of a Mosquito night fighter, hunting down German night intruders as they came across the Channel to bomb London.

"Target ten o'clock skipper, range seven miles moving left to right."

"No contact."

"OK, turn left onto zero four zero, target now at twelve o'clock, range seven miles, closing rapidly. Gottim?"

"Negative contact."

"Hold zero four zero, target now five miles, closing rapidly, now dead ahead at two miles, closing rapid . . . "

"OK, I've got him, eleven o'clock low, looks like a Ju 88. Good show nav, tally ho!"

"OK let's head back to base for a couple of circuits," Something banged hard on my bone dome. I snapped out of my reverie as Bert's voice came over the intercom. "Hey Cat's Eyes, are you still with us? I said let's head back to base for a few circuits!" I blinked twice and returned rapidly to the jet age and 1957. Below me the shape of the mythical Ju 88 bomber dissolved into a thin layer of cloud over Luton. We returned to Oakington and spent our remaining time and fuel in the circuit.

On returning to the Flight hut, a wartime scene greeted my eyes. Kiwi Green, Switches and Big Dick were huddled in armchairs with bone domes and inner helmets on the floor beside them. A thin stratus layer of cigarette smoke hung undisturbed above their heads.

"How did it go?" Trev Green demanded.

"Fine, you can see a helluva lot further at night."

"Do any circuits?"

"Yeah, a couple. I'm down for a circuits detail tomorrow night."

We conversed on the wonders of night flying as each student was called by his instructor.

"You have to watch your instruments more . . . "

"Why's that?"

"You can't judge your speed or position by anything outside . . . "

"Green!" a voice roared.

"Coming, Sir. See you later," Trev scrambled out of his armchair and grabbed his helmet as he sprinted for the door.

"What's it like trying to land a jet at night?" Big Dick enquired.

"Howard!" another voice called from the instructors' room.

"Coming, Sir. You can tell me later, OK?"

"Parry!"

"Hennessey!"

"Coming, Sir. See you later."

The next night was similar. I flew a dual sortie with Bert, solely circuits and landings after which he authorised me for a solo detail.

When I landed back from this, mine was the last aircraft to taxi into dispersal. I felt the complete night fighter pilot as an airman marshalled me in with two illuminated wands, finally crossing them over his head as the signal to cut the engine. The de Havilland Goblin engine whined down to a low whistle as I opened the canopy and began to disengage myself from the enveloping tentacles of ejector seat harness, parachute webbing, oxygen mask, R/T lead and chamois leather flying gloves.

"How did it go, Sir?" The airman helped me find my foothold as I climbed down from the cockpit. I looked aloft into the night sky, expecting to see thin pencil beams of searchlights probing for enemy intruders. The dull crump-crump sound of anti-aircraft fire must have been my ears clearing after the descent.

"Fine thanks!" I replied. "Got a brace of Heinkels over Sevenoaks and damaged a Junkers 88 over Luton but his rear gunner got me in the left arm . . . "

"Pardon, Sir?"

"Oh nothing," I replied embarrassedly. "Better go in and make out my report." I hurried into the Flight hut and found it almost empty. Kiwi Green nearly knocked me over as he rushed out as I entered.

"Where is everybody?" I picked myself up dazedly.

"Sorry 'bout that. Mushrooming."

"What?"

"Collecting mushrooms for breakfast. They get some good ones on the airfield at this time of year, better hurry . . . "

I strode out onto the grass airfield and filled my briefcase with mushrooms for breakfast. The most satisfying meal in the world is egg and mushrooms at 3a.m. after a first night solo in a Vampire.

We flew for three more nights, practising night navigation and more circuits, then left darkness to the bats and owls.

Life in the mess continued normally throughout our training. Our banishment from the use of the bar had long been lifted but we had found we preferred the atmosphere of the George and Dragon for after-dinner drinking. A typical evening would start with a couple of half pints in the mess before dinner, then afterwards we would cram into one or more of the course chariots and head for the George and Dragon. It had the advantage of being not only a pleasant place to while away the evening but also a place where we could talk 'shop' to our hearts' content, for in the mess, it was considered bad form to carry on shop talk in off-duty hours.

Additionally, the George was a good place to go when you wanted to get away from the prying eyes of the Air Force for a few hours. The landlord, George Trussler, was rather exceptional; having been a wartime pilot himself, he could understand the motives of pilots who frequented his pub, although he could just as easily lend a sympathetic ear to a local farmer wanting to get away from the land or a nagging wife.

Although George's ear and dry shoulder were always available, the information that went in that ear never leaked out through the mouth; some publican's Hippocratic oath forbade him divulging confidences.

It was about this time that I noticed a dropping off in numbers of our course members propping up the bars of the various watering holes we frequented. At first vague excuses were made for these non-appearances. "Sorry I didn't join you last night, had something to do . . . "

Soon it became obvious almost everybody on the course was spending most of their time alone in their rooms. I wandered along to Mike Parry's room early one evening to discuss the matter with him and was startled to find him seated behind a large pile of books on various subjects like aerodynamics, meteorology and navigation. He waved me into a chair.

"Hi, I was wondering where everybody was," I began.

"Working for the final tests, I expect. Big Dick and Jack Hennessey are coming along soon to run through a few points on met."

I became thoughtful. We had already learned most of what we needed to know about flying but the final tests had a nasty habit of asking obscure theoretical questions on subjects long forgotten about.

"Name the five phenomena you would associate with the passage of a warm front?" Big Dick had joined us brandishing a previous met paper.

"Well er, change in wind direction after frontal passage, increase in temperature, stratified rather than cumulo-form cloud, how many's that?"

"Three."

"Well, probably some precipitation."

"That's four."

"Turbulence?"

More questions from previous test papers followed, many of which I could only answer partially. Now I began to understand the reasons for the absenteeism from the pub.

Our daytime hours still alternated with ground school and flying, although the time in ground school was mainly confined to brushing up what we had learned and were expected to have remembered. The flying part progressed on to advanced navigational exercises and formation flying.

If night flying was satisfying, formation flying was exhilarating! Even the call signs chosen for the formations evoked dreams of wartime flying. 'Skyline' formation, 'Mainstream' or 'Timberwolf' somehow captured the purposeful atmosphere of military flying . . .

Vampire formation.

"Timberwolf leader, this is Timberwolf three, I have a warning light."

"Roger this is Timberwolf leader, what's your problem?"

"Engine's on fire and the whole port wing's a sheet of flame."

"Anything serious, Timberwolf Three?"

"Negative, leader."

We might then engage the enemy, bag a couple of Huns apiece and return to the mess for lunch.

"Coming into London tonight, Cholmondeley? Flanagan and Allan are on at the Victoria Palace."

"Better not, gotta get these burns dressed if I hope to fly tomorrow."

The most satisfying part of formation flying was the spectacular finish, when the formation leader would lead his flock down the duty runway and carry out a 'run and break'. The reason for such a manoeuvre was a leftover from the early days of jet flying, when the faster and more streamlined early jet aircraft took considerably longer to slow down to approach speed than their piston-engined predecessors. The early jet pilots soon discovered that pulling up into a climbing steep turn washed off the speed quicker and deployed the formation into the correct spacing downwind for a stream landing.

Although the main reason for the run and break manoeuvre was to achieve the required separation for the final approach and landing, it provided a spectacular sight for those on the ground and did wonders for the pilot's egos.

A typical run and break would begin with the formation leader leading his aircraft down the runway in an echelon formation to starboard if the circuit was left handed and announcing "Timberwolf formation, breaking left, breaking left. Go!"

He would then bank left almost vertically, pulling up at the same time, followed two seconds later by his number two, followed by the rest of the formation at similar time intervals. Airbrakes were extended to reduce airspeed, downwind checks were carried out, the undercarriage re-emerged from the underside of the aircraft, the flaps went down and the turn was continued onto finals, while all the time you were keeping a close eye on your airspeed and the aircraft in front to ensure you weren't overtaking him. Aircraft landed on the left and right sides of the runway to avoid collision and the preceding aircraft were careful not to use excessive braking in order to prevent a following aircraft running into them. After landing, we would taxi in together, park in a straight line and cut our engines simultaneously. It was a very satisfying type of flying for extroverts.

Formation flying concluded the end of the learning phase of the wings course. Now only a few navigational exercises remained.

For my next trip, I was down for a dual sortie with Bert for 'brushing up' before taking the final handling check. Although we had got this far in the course, success was not assured, indeed students had sometimes been chopped on their final handling check.

An aura of intense concentration now enveloped everybody. Daytime was spent brushing up manoeuvres and procedures in the air, or revision in ground school. Evenings were spent clustered in twos and threes in somebody's room, swotting up what we had forgotten.

"What was Bernoulli's theorem again?"

"Shit! Now who was he again?"

"Wasn't he the fellow always standing with his back to the wind?"

"No, I'm sure that was Buys Ballot."

"I thought it was Bernoulli; are you sure?"

"Must have been uncomfortable and cold whoever it was."

The harder we studied, the more we realized how much we had forgotten. Everybody's mood became desperate and we even worked Saturday mornings. The Pheasant Plucker and Lady Chatterley's Lover waited woefully neglected in the car park. Only Saturday nights were still sacrosanct; we still devoted them to the earnest pursuit of pleasure.

After a couple of airborne brushing up details with Bert, I was suddenly put up for a final handling check on the first Monday morning detail. Lord Jim, Kiwi Green and Blob Bottom were also down for the same thing. Switches Phipps, Big Dick and Mike Parry had to wait for the second detail.

Lord Jim flew with a squadron leader from Standards Flight, Kiwi Green drew another squadron commander and Blob Bottom was teamed up with the Number Two squadron CO.

It came as an unpleasant surprise to me to find Whittington had chosen me as his examinee.

My briefing was conducted in an icily correct manner. He drew diagrams on the blackboard showing exactly what he wanted me to do.

Final handling checks mainly consisted of emergency procedures, aerobatics and various types of circuits and landings, and usually lasted an hour. I felt physically sick with fear as I felt Whittington watching closely as I carried out the pre-flight check of the aircraft, examining vents, drains, linkages, control surfaces, undercarriage and wheel wells. He had the perfect opportunity to wreak vengeance.

We then climbed into our aircraft prior to starting the engine and taxiing out. Throughout the exercise his eyes watched everything and he said nothing.

Tower cleared us for take-off ten minutes later, after I had started the Goblin engine and taxied 200 yards to the holding point. I applied the power while lining up and felt the usual exhilaration as the aircraft gathered pace down the runway. As the speed built up I raised the nose wheel fractionally from the runway so that the aircraft ran only on the main undercarriage wheels. Gentle back pressure on the control column got us airborne and the airspeed began increasing rapidly. I squeezed the wheel brakes and moved the undercarriage lever up. The wheels retracted into the wings and fuselage with a satisfying series of bumps, and the aircraft accelerated even faster with the decreased drag.

Just as I was settling down to enjoy the sensation of being airborne, the engine abruptly lost power, the rpm indicator winding down rapidly. A moment of panic ensued while I tried to make out what was happening then memory returned and I recalled the many practice 'turn backs' Bert and I had practised. Turning into whatever crosswind there was that morning, I quickly advised the tower I had suffered a flameout and was turning back, prefixing the word 'flame out' with 'practice', for out of the corner of my eye I could see that Don had closed the throttle to simulate engine failure. Converting speed to height and keeping the turn going, I selected undercarriage down just before the airfield came back into view. I judged the distance past the threshold, turning in a descending oval until we were lined up on the correct final approach path. Just as I was about to apply full flap, Don's hand pushed the throttle forward and his voice in my earphones told me to overshoot for another circuit.

So far so good and I noticed the sickly sensation of fear had left me once things got a bit busy.

I carried out a flapless circuit, again without any apparent problems and Don then told me to climb to altitude for aerobatics and steep turns. After this, I was asked to take the aircraft close to its limiting Mach number to demonstrate compressibility. As the needle of the Mach meter crept closer and closer to Mach One, supersonic speed, the aircraft began vibrating slightly. The Mach number increased to Mach point seven five (75% of the speed of sound) and the vibration became a definite juddering, becoming worse as the Mach number crept higher. Finally, when the aircraft was close to its limiting Mach number and about to start porpoising unless something was done to immediately rectify the situation, Don gave the order to recover – so muttering the drills, I closed the throttle, deployed airbrakes, raise the nose to reduce speed, the vibration lessened and finally stopped altogether. I re-applied the power, retracted the air brakes and recovered our slight height loss.

The final handling check continued with a practice flameout. It had been repeatedly drilled into our skulls that a Vampire cockpit wasn't a healthy place for a young fellow to be when an engine caught fire for one of the first things to burn through would be one or both tail booms connecting the tail surfaces to the rest of the airframe. Estimates varied on how long it would take the booms to let go after an engine fire; some were as low as ten seconds. For this reason, in the event of a flameout at altitude, the first action was to pull up into a climbing left turn, looking back over your left shoulder for evidence of smoke or fire behind. If you saw smoke, the safest course of action was a Martin Baker let down (eject!), for once the booms gave way, the aircraft would become uncontrollable and somersault like a demented thing, making it impossible for the pilot to reach the ejector seat handle above his head.

Today was a practice manoeuvre however, and Don watched to see whether I handled it in the approved manner.

All over England there are RAF ground controllers manning the emergency fixer service. An aircraft suffering a flameout or other emergency only has to call them up and they will talk him down to a safe landing at a suitable airfield. On this morning, I changed to the emergency channel and called the fixer service.

"Practice Pan, practice Pan, practice Pan, this is Oakington Delta Kilo," I spoke into my oxygen mask microphone slowly and distinctly, emphasising the word 'practice' slightly more than the rest of the message. The word 'Pan' was a form of emergency call, less urgent than the better known 'Mayday' which is only used when an aircraft is threatened by serious and imminent danger and requires immediate assistance. 'Pan' indicates that the situation is precarious but recoverable, which I felt described our practice manoeuvre today.

A soothing competent sounding ground controller bade me go ahead with my message. I did so and under his direction I was vectored down to a suitable airfield, which happened to be Oakington. Whittington was apparently satisfied with my performance, for removing his hand from the closed throttle he told me to carry out a bad weather circuit.

We eventually landed and taxied back along the taxiway to our dispersal area. I stole several sideways glances at Whittington in an effort to gauge his assessment of my performance but could see nothing beneath his oxygen mask, helmet and visor.

We returned to Flights and he debriefed me in front of the blackboard, criticising one or two things, praising others and offering helpful advice on some manoeuvres. To be completely fair to him, I had to admit he had conducted my check without prejudice or bias; he had been the perfect examiner. He retired to his office to write his report on my Final Handling Check; I had passed with an average assessment.

Big Dick was leaving the crew room as I entered.

"How did it go? I saw you had Whittington!"

"OK. He just sat there and told me what he wanted me to do, same as we've all practised."

"Yeah, I hope so, I'm doing mine next."

"Good luck!"

"Eh?"

"I said good luck!"

"Oh yeah, thanks."

I flopped into an armchair and waited for the others to return.

Strangely, work still continued, despite the fact we had now all passed the flying part of the course. Final exams were now only days away and we spent every spare moment cramming examination subjects.

Even more strangely, flying continued. The advanced (jet) flying training syllabus required us to do 120 hours' flying, a figure which most of us were a few hours short of, so every day, either in the morning or after ground school in the afternoon, we completed the final few exercises. Having passed the Final Handling Check, we could now settle down and enjoy the flying for a change.

Like an execution date or the end of a perfect holiday, the morning of the final exams finally arrived. Each candidate was seated at a frail wooden table and allowed only a ruler, a Dalton navigation computer and writing instruments. The Ground Instructors regarded us with pitying expressions as we took our seats.

Exam papers were placed on each table face down, with stern instructions not to turn them over and read until told to do so. We waited silently for the hands of the clock behind the invigilator's desk to reach nine o'clock.

The first exam subject was meteorology; time allowed: two hours.

Examinations continued until lunchtime on the third day. After each paper, we gathered together in anxious knots outside the classroom and discussed each question. By the third day, most of us were reasonably confident we might just scrape through. The pass mark was seventy per cent overall average, so a low mark in one subject could be boosted by a higher mark in another.

After the final exam paper, the CGI dismissed us with an assurance the results would be available on Monday morning. Together with Jack Hennessy and Kiwi Green, I headed towards flights.

Bert was waiting for me. "You need another forty minutes to make up your 120 hours," he informed me. "So you can do it this afternoon. How did the exams go, by the way?"

We discussed the various examination subjects while he filled out the authorisation sheet. I signed in the appropriate space and waited for him to lead the way into the briefing room.

"General handling," he declared vaguely. "Do whatever you want, but make sure you log forty minutes' flying time."

I changed into flying kit and contemplated the delights of the forthcoming flight. The Air Force had laid on a beautiful August summer afternoon for my last trip; the air was as smooth as a cat pissing on silk, there wasn't a cloud in the sky, visibility was unlimited and the aircraft was a single-seat Mark Five, the machine we had all coveted so devoutly on first arriving at Oakington.

Climbing to high level (35,000 feet) where a jet engine is most fuel efficient, I gazed down at the scene five miles below. The city of Cambridge lay beneath a thin haze, its student population now away on summer holidays. Thirty years later I would look down on the same scene from the cockpit of a very different aircraft and try to picture my eldest son walking to lectures.

The Thames Estuary with its horde of model ships lay further south; to the north, the beaches of various holiday resorts could be discerned, cluttered with picnicking holiday makers. The sun glinted on the metal panels of a Viscount airliner several thousand feet below me.

I suddenly realized I didn't know what to do!

Here I was, at the end of two years expensive government-provided training, having been lent an aeroplane to amuse myself in for three quarters of an hour, and I didn't know what I wanted to do. Until now, every flight, whether dual or solo, had been for a particular reason – navigation, practice circuits, aerobatics, flameouts, upper air work etc. Now all these exercises were completed and I was merely filling in time.

I decided to do some aerobatics – checking carefully around, I accelerated to 350 knots before pulling up to just under 5G for a vertical figure eight. Approaching the vertical, I kept the aircraft on the verge of the buffet until we were at the top of the loop. Indicated air speed was 170 knots, I allowed the nose to drop below the horizon before rolling upright and pulling up into a second loop. Bert wouldn't have been impressed at its shape or direction but I got round OK. Airspeed began to increase rapidly, even with airbrakes out and throttle closed. At the bottom of the loop I rolled inverted and pulled as much 'G' as I could handle until the horizon came into view again.

Other aerobatics seemed tame after that, I turned left and did a roll. Soon all this seemed rather pointless; I glanced at my watch and found I had been airborne for less than twenty five minutes. More aerobatics then back to Oakington. I called up the tower and requested clearance for a 'run and break in four minutes', a manoeuvre usually reserved for formations.

"Roger Delta Kilo, runway is two three, cleared run and break." I recognised the voice of a friend; he probably realized this was my last sortie and he co-operated accordingly. I dived to three hundred miles per hour then abeam the tower I pulled up into a steep climbing turn, closing the throttles and extending the airbrake to slow to 174 knots before extending the undercarriage.

"Delta Kilo cleared to finals."

"Roger, Delta Kilo three greens."

"Cleared to land, Delta Kilo."

"Roger."

Vampire FB5 single seater on approach.

Speed was decaying nicely with full flap providing plenty of drag to slow me down. Over the runway threshold, the white runway numbers flew by underneath then the main wheels touched. Hold the nose-wheel off for a few seconds, release the back pressure on the control column to allow it to meet the runway, commence squeezing the bicycle grip hand brake on the control column to slow down, turn off the runway, retract the flaps, taking care not to pull up the gear, and call the tower.

"Delta Kilo clear of the active."

"Roger Delta Kilo, is that all?" the tower operator wanted to know if I was taking off again.

"Yep, that's my lot," I taxied back for the last time and parked. Back in Flights I took off my oil-stained flying gear and hung everything in my tin locker. I suddenly realized how 'operational' it looked, compared to the first time I had put it all on, only eighteen months ago.

By the end of the week, everybody had taken and passed their final handling checks. We now had to wait until Monday for the results of the written tests. Passing the Final Handling Check was an excuse for a party in the George and Dragon on Saturday night. Landlord George laid out some tables in the garden with all sorts of goodies that the Dragon had cooked up especially for us. We helped ourselves to draught beer from a large keg provided for the occasion.

George and his wife came out from behind the bar that night and joined us, leaving two barmaids to attend to the other customers.

"What are you fellows going to do now?" the Dragon asked me.

"Dunno really," I shrugged my shoulders vaguely. "I thought I might go civil flying." Big Dick admitted to similar ambitions. British Overseas Airways needed pilots and had sent a recruiting team to Oakington to interview any suitable applicants but I hadn't troubled to apply yet.

Vampire FB5 final landing.

Shit'ead was going back to the second-hand car business and thought he might open an aviation division. Blob Bottom admitted he was going back to his old job in the bank. We looked at him incredulously.

"How can you go back to a nine to five job after all this?" we demanded.

"Security," Blob Bottom stated firmly. "I'll always have job security in the bank."

"That's about all you will have! They pay a manager about a tenner a week so goodness knows what you'd get. Why not try civil aviation, join British European Airways (BEA)? They pay four times as much as your miserable bank job."

Blob Bottom wavered momentarily but stuck to his guns. "Security, that's what's important today, financial security. If I worked for an airline, I might get laid off and be without a job."

We considered his choice of occupation quietly.

"What about you, Henessey?" the Dragon enquired.

"I'm going into aerial crop spraying," Jack answered. He and Lord Jim planned to start a small aerial application business in East Anglia, with capital provided by Lord Jim's banking connections. This combination sounded formidable!

"What's going to happen to the regulars?" George enquired, referring to those of our course who had signed up for eight or twelve years in an Air Force where pilots' jobs were scarcer than hens' teeth.

"Most will be posted to the aircrew holding unit at Valley and wait for postings," Mike Parry explained. "One or two might be fortunate to get posted to operational squadrons but the remainder will probably end up as second pilots on transport aircraft or go straight into a ground tour, which could be station married families officer at Back of Beyond or worse."

We silently contemplated the dismal prospects of the next few years in the peacetime Air Force. The Duncan Sandys 1957 white paper had decimated the number of operational squadrons in the belief that the Blue Streak missile would replace manned fighter aircraft, so jobs for pilots were becoming scarce.

"Bit different from your time, eh George?" Mike suggested, breaking the short gloom.

George Trussler, landlord of the George and Dragon and previously of 486 Tempest Squadron, drew reflectively on his pint of beer. "'fraid so. I was in the Volunteer Reserve before the war so when the balloon went up, I was operational within eight weeks. Meanwhile of course, other lads were being trained direct from school on Tiger Moths, Miles Masters then on to an operational type."

"What were you on?"

"Fighters, Hurricanes initially, then we got Spits and I finished up on

Tempests plus two and a half years, instructing halfway through the war." We listened interestedly for this was the most we'd ever heard George tell of his wartime exploits.

"Why didn't you go into civil flying afterwards?"

"I tried to but had the same problem you chaps will encounter. During the war we had too few pilots; after the war the few became too many and every single one of 'em wanted a job flying commercially. In the end, only the transport fellows got the jobs. There wasn't much demand for fighter pilots in 1945."

I mused that things hadn't changed much in twelve years.

"Hey, why is everybody's glass empty? Fill 'em up and the Dragon will play the piano for us."

We trooped inside, it was getting quite cold in the garden, and positioned ourselves round the pub's battered piano.

Monday morning brought the promised exam results.

Top scorer was Mike Parry with an average of eighty-five per cent. Lord Jim scored eighty per cent for second place and Switches was two per cent behind him in third.

The rest of us had scored in the mid to low seventies except for two of the regulars, who hadn't achieved the seventy per cent average to pass. They would resit the necessary subjects to bring them up to the required mark.

The news of our success was another excuse for celebration, this time in the mess at tea time. The party continued after dinner and once again I staggered to bed somewhat the worse for wear, having drunk so many toasts to people's health that I was in danger of ruining my own! Big Dick summed up the situation rather nicely next morning when he announced he was going to cut down on his drinking 'cos he was "sick and tired of waking up sick and tired".

The 'Wings' parade, when the Air Force finally surrenders its aeronautical maidenhood and accepts its new suitors, was held on the Tuesday afternoon in front of an admiring coterie of parents, girlfriends, brothers and sisters and assorted relatives. A venerable old air marshal was brought out of retirement to present the flying badges and deliver the stock speech about 'Old pilots and bold pilots but no old bold pilots', adding that the days of manned combat aircraft were numbered, pushbutton warfare was just around the corner.

"Yeah, we already have the pushbuttons," Kiwi Green muttered under his breath.

Everybody applauded politely, the parade marched off and we spent the afternoon showing friends and relatives round the station while other courses continued their training.

That night we were dined-out by the other members of the officers' mess. George Trussler had been invited and arrived looking very smart in dinner dress. His appearance at the dinner was a moral victory for us, since Don Whittington had gone through the list of guests' names with the mess manager to ensure all were 'suitable'. When he saw George's occupation listed as publican, he had put a line through the name, expressing surprise at our gaucheness. "A publican in an officer's mess? I don't think that's at all a good idea," he told the mess manager. "I'm afraid he'd be quite out of place. They'll have to explain to him that the mess isn't open to any Tom, Dick or Harry . . . "

Mike Parry quietly pointed out to Whittington that Flight Lieutenant Trussler DFC hadn't felt too out of place in an officers' mess in 1945 when he was a Tempest squadron flight commander, which persuaded him to quickly agree to the invitation.

After the dinner and a deadly boring speech from the wing commander, during which the station commander dozed off and was only prevented from falling sideways out of his chair by the padré, we made for the bar for our final fling.

My recollection of that evening is blurred by an indistinct alcoholic haze. An awkward moment occurred when one of the instructors' wives became tearful on learning she had won the 'Grimmy' competition. Her irate husband threatened to take the organizers outside and thrash them one by one.

The evening ended with the usual bicycle race through the mess.

Just before midnight, as we approached the bar for another round of drinks, one of those sudden lulls occurred in the conversation. Lord Jim heard something and hushed everybody to silence. Soon we heard it too, the plaintive sound of a kitten meowing in the ceiling above.

The gentil parfit knight decided to rescue the rescue the animal in distress. Standing on the bar, he reached a trapdoor in the ceiling and pulled himself up through the hatch.

We waited below for something to happen, which didn't take long!

Lord Jim quickly located the kitten and passed it down to several waiting hands below. He was about to follow it through the hatch when it occurred to him to check for others in the attic. Fumbling drunkenly around in the dark, he missed his foothold on the beams, and one leg went through the lath and plaster surface of the ceiling. This was the signal for much merriment and applause from the audience below, while the luckless prisoner endeavoured to retract his leg from the hole in the ceiling. Unfortunately the wooden lath strips acted as barbs and prevented him withdrawing his leg. We cheered as we watched him turning and twisting for a few minutes then interest waned and we turned our attention back to more immediate matters, leaving Lord Jim up in the air until the Orderly Officer came and rescued him a quarter of an hour later.

It must have been incredibly uncomfortable balancing on one leg on a wooden beam in the dark, with the other leg ensnared in a wood and plaster trap.

Chapter 34

Après Nous le Deluge

Nothing rolls up faster than a red carpet and next morning the station was back to normal, with instructors and their students taking off and landing continuously, but for us it was all over. The exams, the final handling checks, the wings parade and our final dining-out night were now in the past.

It was now late summer 1957 and seventeen years previously our instructors had defended the British Isles against German invasion, finally stemming the tide in the second week of September, 1940. The Air Force was determined nobody would ever forget their finest hour and reminded the peacetime world of it every year by celebrating 'Battle of Britain' week.

Oakington prepared to throw its gates open to the public with a thrilling weekend air display. Neville Duke, Hawker's chief test pilot, was coming over to demonstrate their Hunter jet fighter, Vickers Supermarine were sending their last Spitfire to recapture the sight and sound of flying in the 1940s, the station aerobatic team would put on an exciting display of aerobatics in their single seat Mark Five Vampires and there would also be light aircraft, parachute dropping, gliders, joy rides, model aircraft demonstrations, candy floss, fortune telling, merry-go-rounds and something for everybody, regardless of age.

I was discussing our future with Mike Parry and Switches down at Flights as we cleared our lockers out for the next course to use. I made a large parcel of my flying overalls, bone dome, inner helmet, oxygen mask, flying boots and other assorted flying equipment and threw it all into the back of the Pheasant Plucker to take to 'Stores'.

"I presume you'll practise law?" I asked Mike, who nodded.

"Yep, I start with Netherby, Driscoll and Toombes as soon as the Air Force releases me, which should be next week." I glanced at him quickly. What a strange existence he led; this week he was a fighter pilot, next week he would be a very junior bewigged barrister playing second fiddle to some old Queen's Counsel. I hoped I would one day see him in action in court, for his rapport and wit would be devastating.

"Sounds like a good firm to work for?" I suggested.

"Yes, I thought so too. Frightfully, Boring and Dull, barristers at law. Netherby, Driscoll and Toombes, ditto," he hefted his flying gear into the car.

"Whaddabout you, Switches?" I enquired of Phipps. "Not going into the electrical business, are you?" We chuckled at the recollection of the 'switches' incident at Ternhill, now more than a year away in the past. Switches slammed his locker shut for the last time.

"No fear of that . . . I'm joining my old man in his accountancy practice in Doncaster. Things are relatively quiet at this time of year so I'm taking a few weeks' holiday before settling down."

Further conversation was interrupted by the arrival of squadron leader Whittington, who gazed at us malevolently. "Getting ready to walk out on us, are you?" he enquired unpleasantly. When I explained we were about to hand in our flying kit, he gazed at us distastefully.

"All right then, but don't make any arrangements to depart early, because I've got a job for you next week." We groaned inwardly, this was just like Whittington to keep us as long as he could. "Battle of Britain Day publicity, I'm putting you in charge of it," he informed us.

"Fine, Sir. We'll enjoy that, we should be able to get a good crowd from the surrounding towns," I forced a smile on my face.

"Try to do the job properly this time," Whittington glared at me. "Show the service whether or not you're capable of taking responsibility." I glared at him; he had never forgiven me for the scare I'd given him at Singer's funeral. I resolved to make my last task in the Air Force an outstanding success. Even though our final personal reports were now written, I wouldn't give him the satisfaction of being able to condemn me for the Battle of Britain publicity arrangements.

I thought Whittington must have read my thoughts when he spoke again. "By the way, I'd like the three of you to go to my office to read and sign your personal fitness reports which I've prepared." He was referring to the assessment every commanding officer writes on an officer on being posted away. Normally a number of stereotyped phrases are used, unless the individual was particularly good or bad. Phrases like 'satisfactory conduct throughout' or 'a conscientious officer' would go on record to indicate the subject of the report was OK. Time dulls the memory and most squadron commanders tended to forget the occasional errors in the past. Whittington was no such officer; he forgot and forgave nothing!

I started with surprise when I read my personal fitness report. "An officer who is very diligent in pursuit of his own pleasure," it read. Mike's and Switches' reports were similar, which made us even more determined to perform this final task perfectly. Whittington would never have the satisfaction of knowing how badly this final report irritated us.

Once we got down to the business of arranging Battle of Britain Week End, our original initiative and enthusiasm rose to the surface. Mike arranged for his instructor to take a local radio announcer for a flight in a two-seater Vampire, after which the radio waves were alive with reminders to the public to be sure to go to the air display at Oakington. Switches fed screeds of publicity to the local newspapers, so by the end of the week, only a deaf and blind halfwit could have been unaware of the forthcoming air display.

Our final burst of inspiration came from Don Reid, who offered us his dilapidated tape recorder to tour the surrounding towns and villages in a loudspeaker van, exhorting everybody to 'come to the show'. While Switches and Don Reid negotiated the loan of a suitable vehicle from the Motor Transport section, Mike and I set about composing something suitable to broadcast. It needed to be short and to the point, for we would be moving as we broadcast.

By Wednesday lunchtime, two radio technicians from the electronics section had wired the tape recorder and a record player into the van's loud speaker system and Mike Parry had recorded our message. During lunch, Whittington took the opportunity to enquire whether we'd done anything about Battle of Britain Weekend yet, to which I replied cautiously that most of the arrangements were complete, we just had a few test runs to carry out that afternoon.

After we had finished the tests satisfactorily, I had another rather sad task to perform; the various shareholders in the Pheasant Plucker now wished to convert their shares into cash, so it was now time to dispose of the gallant old vehicle that had served us so well for these two wonderful years. As chairman of the board and a fully paid up shareholder, it was my duty to sell her. I pinned an advertisement on the mess notice board, offering the stately old girl for only twenty-five pounds. She was still running well and I hated to dispose of her after the many escapades and adventures she had taken us to but we had no further use for her.

I was able to salve my conscience with the thought that her days were far from over, for she had many a mile left in her yet and provided she was driven and treated with tender loving care she would continue to serve future generations of APOs in the same way she'd served us. She deserved to be left with friends who would appreciate her rather than being carted away as scrap metal. Only her formidable thirst for petrol and oil deterred any of us from keeping her.

Among the many applicants for the hand of the Pheasant Plucker was a fresh faced young pilot officer who'd recently arrived from Ternhill. As he had the required money readily available, we agreed he could take delivery of her next Monday, the day I officially left the Royal Air Force.

Meanwhile, we had the Battle of Britain to arrange!

After lunch, we gave the loudspeaker van a test run. With Mike driving and two of us at the audio control panel in the back, we drove round the station with various people stationed at strategic positions to listen and comment on the quality of the broadcast. All were unanimous in their praise of our work – the tape was clear and loud enough to be heard quite a distance away. Furthermore, the message was short and to the point. The effect would be quite dramatic when we toured the surrounding towns and villages.

By afternoon teatime, we had completed a few final adjustments to the loudspeaker system and were enjoying a well earned cuppa when Whittington came into the mess. I secretly hoped he would ask whether we had begun the arrangements yet, for such an asinine question would have provoked hoots of derision from everybody, but he didn't. If anything, he looked almost friendly as he approached us. We were flabbergasted when he began by praising our initiative in thinking up the idea of the loudspeaker van, even more so when he asked for a demonstration.

I signalled to Switches to collect the vehicle from the MT section, and while we waited, Whittington waxed enthusiastically over our idea. "Publicity, that's what we need and that's what this idea will give me," he finished gloating as Switches pulled up outside the Mess. I opened the back doors of the van and ushered him inside. After explaining the various controls, I offered to give him a run through of the tape.

He had a better idea. "Let me see if I can operate it," he suggested, so under my instruction, he turned on the power and set the tape playing.

We were rather proud of what we had recorded. It started with the sound of a jet fighter roaring past at low level, then as the noise subsided, Mike's voice began: "That was the sound of a Vampire, one of the many exciting aircraft that can be seen at RAF Oakington next Saturday and Sunday, the 9th and 10th of September. Gates open at 10a.m. so bring along Mum and the family for an afternoon she'll never forget at RAF Oakington." I then stopped the tape and turned on the record player so that the stirring sounds of 'The Dam Busters' March' poured from the loudspeakers. I clicked the record player to 'Stop' and rewound the tape. Whittington was in raptures about it; I began to hope we'd finally found favour in his eyes. When the tape was rewound, he turned it on again and asked to be shown how to rewind it, and how to start the record player at the end.

While the tape was running through, we pointed out one or two hazards in the system. "Don't for heaven's sake press this," I told him, gingerly tapping the 'Record' button of Don Reid's dilapidated machine with one finger. "Otherwise you'll get a complete balls' up which can only be corrected by erasing the whole tape and re-recording".

Whittington nodded eagerly, anxious to learn more about it.

"Don't for Christ's sake touch this button here while the tape's playing," I again emphasised, "or you'll delete what's on it and record what's being said." He nodded his understanding. "Otherwise, there's nothing to it," I assured him.

The tape came to the end and I quickly turned the tape recorder off and showed Whittington how to turn on the 'Dam Busters' March' on the record player.

I cautioned him on one further point. "Make sure you stop the tape once the speaking stops," I cautioned him. "Otherwise anything else on it will be broadcast." He paid scant attention to what I said, he was too ecstatic over the whole set-up.

"Just what we need," he enthused. "Batchey Atcherley, the AOC's coming up for the display; he can't fail to be impressed. This'll do wonders for my career. You've done very well, you three."

We glowed with satisfaction, for praise from Whittington was rare indeed.

"Yes, you've all done very well," he continued. "So well in fact that I'm going to reward you. Want to know what I'm going to do?"

For one glorious moment I thought he was going to rewrite our Personal Fitness Reports.

"I'm going to let you all leave on Friday," he announced. "From now on, I'll take over responsibility for the air show publicity." We offered to stay, explaining we were very proud of our brainchild and would like to see it through to fruition, but he insisted we leave on Friday. "Lots of guests arriving," he lied. "We need the extra rooms for them."

"The little shit," Switches muttered. "Feathering his own nest at our expense, pinching our idea and using it to impress the AOC."

We were rather disappointed: Whittington had everything going his way. Batchy Atcherley the AOC couldn't fail to be impressed at the loudspeaker van idea, and the size of the crowd turning up for the display would impress him even further. Whittington's career was about to receive a boost and he would probably end up wearing the coveted wing commander's three bars he so desperately craved. And we would be responsible for his promotion!

What really irritated us was the fact he hadn't even considered rewriting or modifying our bad personal fitness reports. Although it didn't matter very much whether we left the service with a good, bad or indifferent report, it would have been satisfying to have left the service with some small accolade. I began to feel resentful and wished there was some way of appealing against the harsh report.

I soon forgot my anger and disappointment over the matter. I contacted the Pheasant Plucker's new owner and told him he could have her on Friday instead of Monday. He was delighted and explained his father was coming up to Oakington by air for the weekend and now he'd have something to drive him around in.

Next we began making some hasty farewells. I managed to catch my batman before he left at five o'clock to thank him for everything he'd done for me over the previous months. I pressed a five pound note into his hand as we shook hands for the last time. Our last call was to George and the Dragon to say farewell and explain we were leaving tomorrow. George was out walking the Dragon when we arrived, so we waited behind pints of his best bitter for them to return.

We exchanged hilarious reminiscences and the Dragon mentioned they were both going to the forthcoming air show and hoped to catch up with some of the fellows there. George had heard of our recurring problems with Whittington and sensed fate had dealt us a hard last blow because when we shook hands for the last time, he gave me a sympathetic wink. "You can't win 'em all," he encouraged.

"I suppose not, George, but it seems a shame to leave on such a sour note."

"There's still the AOC's report," George suggested encouragingly. "A good one from him could cancel out Whittington's."

"Unlikely," I muttered. "It would take a bloody miracle for him to do that when he doesn't even know us. I'm not asking for the Central Band of the Royal Air Force to play 'The Dam Buster's March' as we end our service careers, but to leave like this . . . I dunno, it's disappointing."

As we headed the Pheasant Plucker back to the mess, I thought of Uncle Horace and how gloriously his wartime career in the Dam Busters had ended.

I'd promised him I'd do the same.

On my last day in Her Majesty's Royal Air Force, I breakfasted with the rest of the fellows, kept the farewells brief then packed my bag before proceeding to where the Pheasant Plucker waited outside. Her new owner was already up, excitedly pointing out some of her finer points to an older gentleman as I approached.

"New front tyres, new rear floor, original paintwork, I'm lucky to have found such a bargain, Dad," he enthused. He noticed me and waved a duster he'd been using to polish the brass work. "Good morning," he called then turned to his father. "Dad, have you met Guy Clapshaw?"

I started with surprise when I recognised his father for it was Air Marshall Batchy Atcherley the AOC! He was most cordial in his greeting, asked my name and congratulated me on getting my wings. We talked about generalities for a few minutes until I remembered time was marching on. I caught the attention of his son. "I was going to ask you to run me into Cambridge," I began hesitantly. "I was hoping to catch the ten eighteen to London, but as your father's here, I can get a cab."

"Wouldn't hear of it, Guy dear boy," the AOC insisted. "We can all go in together and you can give us a spot of dual instruction on this splendid vehicle you've sold my son."

I murmured my thanks and collected my suitcase from my room. As I emerged with my luggage, young Atcherley climbed into the pilot's seat and Batchy and I sat in style in the back. As we exited through the guard room gates, I noticed Don Whittington heading out ahead of us in the loudspeaker van.

There were three things the old air marshal adored, and they were Air Force, Air Force and Air Force. We conversed animatedly about its role in peacetime and both agreed the service was shrinking too fast. "We need another Korea or a Berlin Air Lift, Guy, something like that to get the Air Force back to its proper size," he assured me. "I wouldn't be surprised if

French Indo-China doesn't blow up into something big one of these days." I listened intently. "In the meantime, we need to keep in the public eye," he continued. "Grab all the publicity we can get. My son told me about your scheme for getting publicity for the Battle of Britain weekend. Capital idea, absolutely capital, we need a hundred more like it."

"I think Squadron leader Whittington will take most of the credit for that one, Sir," I hinted obliquely. We were almost at the station now. We pulled up outside the ticket office and as a porter opened the door, Batchy suddenly grabbed my arm.

"What's that noise?" he exclaimed alarmedly. We could hear the sound of a low flying jet aircraft flying low through the station. Passengers and porters looked expectantly skyward, expecting to glimpse a low flying jet. As the engine's roar subsided away into the distance, a voice came over a loudspeaker. It was Mike Parry's! Don Whittington had followed us into town with the loudspeaker van, hoping to impress the AOC.

"That was the sound of . . . " Mike's voice was interrupted by scratching noises as it began. " . . . a complete balls up . . . " another voice interrupted.

I turned towards the AOC. "Goodbye, Sir Richard, thank you for the lift and good luck!" I tried to shake hands with the old aviator but he was oblivious of my presence. An angry expression had begun to erupt on his face as he listened to the broadcast.

"What's the name of that officer?" he demanded, pointing at Whittington in the back of the van.

"Squadron leader Whittington, Sir. He's descended from a past Lord Mayor of London . . . "

The AOC growled something uncomplimentary about Whittington's lineage. His face had turned an angry choleric red and his blood pressure approached danger level as the broadcast continued.

"Which can only be . . . seen at RAF Oakington, next Saturday and

Sunday the 9th and 10th September . . . don't fer Christ's sake touch . . . Mum and the family for an afternoon she'll never forget . . . and record what's being said . . . otherwise there's nothing . . . on at RAF Oakington."

The Air Marshal was out of the car and striding angrily towards the loudspeaker van. Clicking and scratching sounds indicated Whittington was having problems doing two things at once. A woman's breathless voice came on the air. "Promise me, promise me, Ted."

Batchy Atcherley had reached the van as her voice rose louder. "Stop Ted! We mustn't. Stop, stop, Ted!"

The flustered face of Whittington appeared at the rear window when the air marshal beat his fists on the back of the van. "Squadron leader Whittington, stop that at once!" Batchy screamed. Whittington disappeared into the depths of the van as Shit'ead's voice came on the air.

"I've waited two weeks for this, I'm not stopping now!"

A police constable sidled up to me and removed a notebook from his uniform pocket. "What's the matter with those two gentlemen?" he pointed to where Batchy had wrestled Whittington out of the van and was now attempting to strangle him on the ground.

"I think they've probably had a few too many," I replied, picking up my suitcase and marching quickly into the station.

The Central Band of the Royal Air Force played the Dam Busters' March as Don Whittington and I ended our careers in the service of our country.

The End

Photograph Credits

Author Biography

Guy Clapshaw's passion for flying and writing is probably best described as a hobby that got out of hand.

He was educated at Charterhouse, where his ambition to become a pilot was condemned as 'No job for a gentleman', which didn't deter him from winning an RAF flying scholarship and going on to fly Vampire jet fighters during his RAF National Service, all of which is the subject of this book.

After demob, he joined the "If it's got two wings, an engine and a sharp end I'll fly it" brigade, the charter jocks, shunting cargo and hapless tourists around the world in aircraft that might even land on the same number of engines on which they took off.

After five years of this precarious existence, he joined Air New Zealand, a national airline where the staff were actually trained and paid, and the aircraft regularly maintained. The company was expanding into the jet age, and Guy flew for them for the next 28 years. His flying career took him all over the world – Europe, North America, the Pacific Islands, the Orient, Middle East and the North and South Poles. During that time he flew everything from diminutive de Havilland Moths, Rapide biplane airliners, DC-3s, through to Boeing 747 Jumbo jets. This experience enabled him to write several books and numerous magazine articles.

His only remaining ambition is to fly a Spitfire, "the most elegant fighter ever to be designed, that came along just when it was needed," he believes.He was a confirmed bachelor until he met Colleen, a young Air NZ stewardess. They married and now have two sons and live in Edinburgh, Auckland and Sydney, where Guy is approaching retirement from flying, as slowly as possible.